Plant Cell Organelles

Plant Cell Organelles

PROCEEDINGS OF THE
PHYTOCHEMICAL GROUP SYMPOSIUM
LONDON, APRIL, 1967

Edited by

J. B. PRIDHAM

Department of Biochemistry
Royal Holloway College, University of London
Englefield Green, Surrey, England

1968

ACADEMIC PRESS
LONDON AND NEW YORK

ACADEMIC PRESS INC. (LONDON) LTD.
Berkeley Square House
Berkeley Square
London, W.1

U.S. Edition published by
ACADEMIC PRESS INC.
111 Fifth Avenue
New York, New York 10003

Library of Congress Catalog Card Number: 68-9109

PRINTED IN GREAT BRITAIN BY
RICHARD CLAY (THE CHAUCER PRESS) LTD.
BUNGAY, SUFFOLK

List of Contributors

E. C. COCKING, *Department of Botany, University of Nottingham, Nottingham-shire, England.*

J. DAINTY, *School of Biological Sciences, University of East Anglia, Norwich, England.*

P. B. GAHAN, *Department of Biology and Cell Science, The Woolwich Polytechnic, London, England.*

M. HALLAWAY, *Department of Biochemistry, The University, Liverpool, England.*

A. C. HULME, *Agricultural Research Council, Food Research Institute, Norwich, England.*

A. T. JAMES, *Unilever Research Laboratory, Sharnbrook, Bedfordshire, England.*

R. M. LEECH, *Department of Biology, University of York, Heslington, England.*

U. E. LOENING, *Department of Botany, The University, Edinburgh, Scotland.*

R. F. LYNDON, *Department of Botany, The University, Edinburgh, Scotland.*

B. W. NICHOLS, *Unilever Research Laboratory, Sharnbrook, Bedfordshire, England.*

D. H. NORTHCOTE, *Department of Biochemistry, The University, Cambridge, England.*

H. ÖPIK, *Department of Botany, University College, Swansea, Glamorgan, Wales.*

J. M. PALMER, *Department of Botany, King's College, University of London, London, England.*

M. J. C. RHODES, *Agricultural Research Council, Food Research Institute, Norwich, England.*

D. Wilkie, *Department of Botany, University College, London, England.*

Foreword

This book is a record of the 1967 Annual General Meeting of the Phyto-chemical Group which was held in the Physics Department of the Imperial College of Science and Technology, London, during 10–12 April, 1967.

Existing works specializing in plant organelles are few. This book reviews most of the modern ideas concerning the structure, biochemistry and function of the nuclei, chloroplasts, mitochondria, vacuoles and other organelles. The detailed coverage is suitable for postgraduate workers although much of the material could be used in undergraduate courses.

Contributions to the Symposium by Professor F. R. Whatley (London: "The Chemistry of Cell Organelles") and Dr. H. E. Davenport (Norwich: "Energy Conversion by Chloroplasts") have not been included in this publication.

May, 1968   J. B. PRIDHAM

Contents

CHAPTER 1

The Enzymology of Cell Organelles

Mary Hallaway

CHAPTER 2

The Structure, Function and Development of the Nucleus

R. F. Lyndon

CHAPTER 3

The Structure and Possible Function of the Vacuole

CHAPTER 4

Structure, Function and Developmental Changes in Mitochondria of Higher Plant Cells

CHAPTER 5

Mitochondrial Biogenesis in Yeast

CHAPTER 6

Carbon Pathways in Mitochondria with Special Reference to Fruit Metabolism

CHAPTER 7

The Energy Transfer Function of Mitochondria

CHAPTER 8

The Chloroplast Inside and Outside the Cell

CHAPTER 9

The Function and Metabolism of Fatty Acids and Acyl Lipids in Chloroplasts

B. W. Nichols and A. T. James   163

CHAPTER 10

The Organization of the Endoplasmic Reticulum, the Golgi Bodies and Microtubules during Cell Division and Subsequent Growth

D. H. Northcote   179

CHAPTER 11

Protein Synthesis in Cell Organelles

E. C. Cocking   198

CHAPTER 12

The Occurrence and Properties of Polysomes in Plant Tissues

CHAPTER 13

Lysosomes

CHAPTER 1

The Enzymology of Cell Organelles

MARY HALLAWAY
Department of Biochemistry
The University, Liverpool, England

I. Introduction

Within the last two years studies of the distribution of enzymes among the different organelles of plant cells and of the activities of individual types of organelle have been extensively reviewed (Bonner, 1965a, b; Hallaway, 1965; Lieberman and Baker, 1965; Koblitz, 1966; Mollenhauer and Morré, 1966; Hall and Whatley, 1967). Since much of the recent information about the isolation and activities of particular organelles is summarized and assessed in the later chapters, this chapter will be restricted almost entirely to discussing some technical aspects of the separation and analysis of organelles, noting especially those points which may cause uncertainty in assigning a site to a particular enzyme and how this uncertainty may be reduced.

II. The Investigation of the Intracellular Locations of Enzymes

The most direct way to demonstrate unequivocally that an enzyme is present in a particular organelle is to isolate the organelle uncontaminated by other particles or fragments; to obtain a quantitative measure of the activity of enzyme, the organelle should be undamaged as well as uncontaminated. If, however, the organelles are isolated mixed with other subcellular particles then there will usually be some degree of doubt as to which of the enzymes

1

TABLE I

Distribution of nitrite reductase, nitrate reductase, fumarase and succinoxidase in preparations from leaves.

| | | *Zea mays** | | | | *Nicotiana tabacum*† | |
| | | Ratio of Activity | | | | Ratio of activity | |
Fraction No.	Chlorophyll µg/ml	NO_2 reductase/ Chlorophyll	NO_3 reductase/ Chlorophyll	Fraction No.	Chlorophyll µg/ml	Fumarase/ Chlorophyll	Fumarase/ Succinoxidase
I	37	0·07	0·4	1	160	0·04	0·60
II	13	0·07	0·8	2	180	0·07	0·50
III	8	0·08	1·3	3	130	0·13	0·27
				4	59	0·34	0·32
				5	36	0·33	0·29

* Taken from Ritenour *et al.* (1967).
† Calculated from Pierpoint (1962).

present in the fraction is located in each type of particle. This consideration is particularly important if the observed activity of the enzyme is low for low activity could be due to the enzyme being present either in trace amounts in a major component organelle or in larger amounts in a minor component organelle. Reducing the amount of damage which can occur to all types of organelle during homogenizing and fractionation reduces the degree of contamination of one type of particle with fragments of other types, as well as facilitating the study of the quantitative distribution of enzymes among the organelles. Therefore, any refinement of technique which leads to a reduction in damage to organelles, or to an increase in their purity, will be advantageous for localization studies (see de Duve, 1967).

It is also possible to assign an enzyme to a particular organelle if, in different subcellular fractions, the enzyme is present in constant proportion to an enzyme or other component which occurs exclusively in that organelle. For example, the consistency of the ratio of nitrite reductase to chlorophyll in three fractions prepared by a non-aqueous technique from leaves of *Zea mays* (Table I) shows that this enzyme is associated with the chloroplast (Ritenour *et al.*, 1967). Pierpoint (1962) found that the ratio of fumarase to succinoxidase varied little in fractions separated from a "mitochondrial" preparation from tobacco leaves by density gradient centrifugation (Table I). On the assumption that succinoxidase is a mitochondrial enzyme, he was able to conclude that fumarase was located in the mitochondria in the original preparation, even though it was heavily contaminated with chloroplast material. (Over 75% of the protein of the preparation was derived from chloroplasts.) This technique so far can be used only to identify enzymes localized in chloroplasts and mitochondria since these are the only organelles for which suitable reference compounds are known (chlorophyll and $NADP^+$ linked triosephosphate dehydrogenase for chloroplasts, cytochrome oxidase and succinic oxidase for mitochondria; see also p. 7).

If, however, the ratio of enzyme to reference compound is not constant, this does not necessarily mean that the enzyme is localized outside the particle *in vivo* since it could have been dissociated from the reference compound during fractionation (see Bucke *et al.* (1966) for an example of this type of problem). Taken by itself, the variation in the ratio of fumarase to chlorophyll (Table I) in the "mitochondrial" preparation is not definitive evidence for the absence of fumarase from chloroplasts. However, the variation combined with the other information provided by Pierpoint (1962), i.e. 95% of the fumarase was in the mitochondrial fraction and the small amount present in the "chloroplast" fraction separated from the bulk of the chlorophyll on density gradient centrifugation, does indicate a non-chloroplast site for the enzyme. Nitrate reductase, also, appears to be located outside the chloroplast (see discussion by Ritenour *et al.*, 1967). In investigating

B

intracellular location of enzymes by this use of reference compounds, the possibility of adsorption of the enzyme on to the particle containing the "marker" may have to be considered (Siebert and Smillie, 1957; Jansen *et al.*, 1960).

A. PREPARATION OF HOMOGENATES AND SEPARATION OF PARTICLES

The only new technique for separating particles which has been developed in the last few years is stable-flow free boundary sedimentation electrophoresis (Mel, 1964a, b, c) which separates organelles or whole cells by a combination of sedimentation and electric field. In the first application of this technique to organelles, Packer *et al.* (1966) were able to fractionate a chloroplast preparation within 30 min in a gradient of 0·2M to 0·3M sucrose into particles differing in size and activity. Earlier, Gross *et al.* (1964) had subjected chloroplast fragments to electrophoresis in a pH gradient and obtained particles differing in Hill reaction activity and Hannig *et al.* (1964) had succeeded in separating chloroplasts almost completely from mitochondria by electrophoresis. Of other techniques proposed for separating organelles, gel filtration (Tiselius *et al.*, 1963) cannot yet be employed since suitable gels are not available and counter current distribution does not appear to have been extended beyond the initial study by Albertsson and Baltscheffsky (1963). Zonal centrifugation, which permits the processing of relatively large amounts of tissue and which can separate particles on the basis of both sedimentation coefficient and equilibrium density, has not been used widely as yet for isolating plant organelles (Price and Hirvonen, 1966; Still and Price, 1966; Quigley and Price, 1966).

Recent refinements in the techniques for fractionating cells have yielded organelles much less damaged than those prepared by earlier procedures (as assessed using biochemical activity as the criterion for structural integrity) In most instances the degree of contamination is still considerable. Both Jensen and Bassham (1966) and Walker (1967) describe the isolation of highly active chloroplasts and Leech (1964) gives details of how to prepare intact and almost uncontaminated chloroplasts. Active mitochondria showing respiratory control have been isolated from a number of tissues; e.g. from sweet potatoes (Wiskich and Bonner, 1963), potato tubers (Verleur, 1965) and etiolated mung bean hypocotyls (Ikuma and Bonner, 1967). However, any alteration in the tissue, type of plant or growth conditions from those for which a particular procedure was developed may necessitate an alteration in the isolation technique in order to achieve the required type of preparation. Jagendorf (1955) found that chloroplasts from different species, or from leaves of the same species but of different ages, did not behave identically on density gradients so gradients which will separate one type of chloroplast may not separate another. Smillie (1956) showed it was possible to prepare mitochondria from etiolated pea leaves only slightly contaminated with plastids but the same procedure applied to green leaves yielded mitochondria heavily contaminated with chloroplast material. The amount of lipid lost from chloroplast fractions during isolation varied with the tissue, the media and the method by which the leaves were homogenized (Jervis and Hallaway, see page 154).

Honda *et al.* (1966) have developed a medium containing sucrose, dextran, albumin and Ficoll, buffered with Tris. Mitochondria and chloroplasts isolated in this medium by their procedure retain the pleomorphic character they have *in vivo* and damage to nuclei is also reduced. Many of the procedures available for isolating relatively intact mitochondria, chloroplasts, nuclei and Golgi apparatus (Morré and Mollenhauer, 1964; Morré *et al.*, 1965) have in common the use of gentle methods for disrupting the cells, e.g. slicing the tissue up with razor blades and then floating out the organelles by stirring the finely sliced tissue in a suitable medium. Close control of pH is often critical, particularly during isolation of mitochondria (Wiskich and Bonner, 1963). Polyvinylpyrrolidone (PVP) in either water soluble form or as the highly cross-linked insoluble "Polyclar" or polyethylene-glycol (PEG) may be added to the isolation media to precipitate tannins (Loomis and Battaile, 1964; Hulme *et al.*, 1964; Badran and Jones, 1965) which otherwise can precipitate and partially inactivate enzymes (Goldstein and Swain, 1965).

The use of PVP or PEG while maintaining the activity of enzymes can give rise to difficulty in determining the intracellular site for enzymes. Lin and Hassid (1966), for example, found that the presence of PVP (at a final concentration of 5–10%) in the isolation media was essential to obtain preparations from *Fucus gardneri* which were active in forming GDP-mannose from mannose-l-phosphate and in oxidizing GDP-mannose to GDP-mannuronic acid. In the presence of PVP the activities were partially sedimented by centrifugation at $40,000 \times g$ for 150 min and much of the sedimented activity could be removed by one wash in 0.1M Tris buffer. If the PVP were replaced by Polyclar then the activities remained in the supernatant after centrifugation at $2000 \times g$ for 120 min. Sanderson (1964), in a study of the localization of catechol oxidase in tea shoots, observed that adding an insoluble polyamide to the isolation media increased the total activity of the homogenate. In the absence of polyamide all the activity was sedimented in 2 min at $2000 \times g$ (Table II) and this activity was not removed by washing. On grinding the tea shoots in the presence of increasing amounts of polyamide, the activity was progressively shifted to the low speed supernatant but, at ratios of amide to tissue above 0.75, the activity in the sediment began to increase again. This sedimented activity was removed by one wash with buffer in the absence of polyamide. An explanation for these observations may lie in the fact that both PVP and PEG can precipitate proteins as a rule at concentrations higher

B 2

than the 1–2% normally used to precipitate tannins. The amount of protein precipitated is affected by pH and by the nature and concentration of the ions, proteins and PVP or PEG present in the solution (Zeppezauer and Brishammer, 1965). The precipitated proteins are readily re-dissolved after removing the polymer. In the case of the catechol oxidase of tea shoots, at low concentrations the polymer appeared to be preventing the inactivation

TABLE II

Effect of polycaprolaktam (polyamide) powder on the activity, distribution and recovery of catechol oxidase from tea shoots (calculated from Sanderson, 1964).

Experiment No.	Level of polyamide in extraction media (g/g fresh wt tissue)	Relative catechol oxidase activity (activity in homogenate without polyamide = 100)		
		Homogenate	Fractions Precipitate (2000 × g; 2 min)	Supernatant
1	0	100 (61·5)*	66	0
2	0	100 (71·5)*	78	0
3	0	100 (65·1)*	83	0
1	0·25	113	81	0
2	0·5	122	60	23
3	0·75	141	6	80
1	1·0	160	8	84
3	1·5	161	11	90

* μMoles of catechol oxidized per g fresh wt tissue min^{-1}.

and irreversible precipitation of the enzyme caused by tannins but at high levels the polymer itself brought about a reversible precipitation of the activity. Similarly the high levels of PVP necessary to give maximum activity in Lin and Hassid's (1966) preparations may have precipitated the enzymes but the insoluble "Polyclar" seemed to have a predominantly protective effect. From the point of view of determining intracellular localization, it would seem useful if, when PVP or PEG are included in isolation media, the effect on enzyme distribution of varying their concentration and of replacing them with "Polyclar" were determined.

B. ASSESSMENT OF CONTAMINATION AND DAMAGE

The usual methods for assessing the degree of contamination or damage to subcellular particles are examination in the light or electron microscope and chemical or enzyme analysis. The presence of some component which is restricted to one organelle or part of the cell can be used as an index of the degree of contamination of a preparation by that organelle. For example, the determination of pyruvic kinase in chloroplast preparations will give a measure of cytoplasmic contamination (Heber, 1960) and chlorophyll can be used as a measure of the amount of chloroplast material. Similarly, in a preparation of some organelle, the level of a component or activity which is readily lost from it during its separation can indicate the integrity of the organelle; e.g. mitochondria in which phosphorylation and oxidation are tightly coupled are regarded as relatively undamaged.

The number of reference compounds and activities suitable for assessing damage and contamination is rather limited. Reference compounds for mitochondria and chloroplasts are mentioned earlier (p. 3). DNA is concentrated in the nucleus but it is also present in minor amounts in both chloroplasts and mitochondria; however, the presence of more than a small amount of DNA in a preparation is indicative of nuclear contamination. RNA is present in so many organelles (nuclei, mitochondria, chloroplasts and cell wall) as well as in cytoplasmic ribosomes that it can be used only as a measure of gross contamination with ribosomal material. Although cellulose is restricted to the cell wall, it is not simple to assay and does not appear to have been used as a reference compound for cell walls.

Even in those cases where a component is restricted to the one type of organelle the measurement of the level of the reference compound can give only an indication of the range of contamination, not of its precise degree. This follows from the fact that enzymes or other components associated with the marker *in vivo* may become dissociated from it to differing degrees *in vitro*. In chloroplasts, for example, the enzymes catalysing CO_2 fixation are much more readily lost than are the enzymes catalysing the Hill reaction (Smillie, 1963) so the amount of chlorophyll in a preparation provides only an approximate guide to the amount of protein of chloroplast origin in the preparation. If the protein/chlorophyll ratio for intact chloroplasts and for washed chloroplast fragments are known for the species concerned (see Leech (1966) for values for *Vicia faba*) then the maximum and minimum values for chloroplast protein can be calculated from the chlorophyll levels. In many cases this refinement may not be necessary but, for those enzymes which occur in more than one sub-cellular location, such quantitative assessment of degree of contamination may be useful for determining the precise distribution of activity within the cell.

C. THE PRESENCE OF BACTERIA

Sub-cellular fractions from plant tissues frequently contain relatively large numbers of bacteria. Table III lists the total colonies grown from four sub-cellular fractions from three types of leaf after homogenizing in different buffers. The number of colonies is large and very variable; there were 3 to 6

TABLE III

Number of bacterial colonies grown from leaf preparations. The washed leaves were ground in 4 vols of buffer, the homogenate was strained through muslin and centrifuged to give 3 fractions and a final supernatant. Samples of each fraction, the supernatant and the buffer were plated on nutrient broth plates and counted after 72 hr at 34°C.

Species	Weight g	Buffer*,†	Total colonies × 10⁻⁶				Supernatant
			Material sedimented at				
			200 × g 5 min	1000 × g 10 min	20000 × g 30 min		
Beta vulgaris	8	Tris-sucrose	72	37	6		6
Beta vulgaris	11	Sucrose-phosphate	67	190	30		45
Beta vulgaris	10	Sucrose-phosphate (sterile)	627	260	459		180
Beta vulgaris	4	Honda	125	133	47		49
Phaseolus vulgaris	9	Sucrose-phosphate (sterile)	1146	1050	305		52
Phaseolus vulgaris	5	Tris-sucrose (sterile)	220	11	29		1
Phaseolus vulgaris	4	Honda	9	2	27		3
Vicia faba	15	Sucrose-Phosphate (sterile)	10	210	100		207

* Buffers: Honda *et al.* (1966) pH 7·0;
Tris-sucrose, 0·025 MTris-HCl and 0·25 M sucrose, pH 7·8;
Sucrose-phosphate, 0·01M phosphate and 0·2M-sucrose pH 7·1.
† Maximum number of colonies derived from non-sterile buffers was 10⁵.

distinct types of colony and the proportion of the types varied from fraction to fraction and from day to day. Freshly prepared but non-sterile buffers did not contribute significantly to the bacterial contamination, the maximum number of colonies derived from the buffer being about 10^5.

The levels of bacterial infection recorded in literature are the same order, i.e. 10^8 per mg chlorophyll in chloroplast preparations (App and Jagendorf, 1964), 2×10^6 per mg protein bodies (Wilson, 1966), 30×10^6 per disc of sugar beet (Leaver and Edelman, 1965). A rat liver mitochondrial preparation (Roodyn et al., 1961), however, contained fewer—about 10^5 ml. B. Gyldenholm (private communication) has also found considerable bacteria contamination of chloroplast preparations ranging from 75 to 600 chloroplasts per bacterium.

The significance of bacterial infection in the study of protein synthesis by subcellular fractions is discussed by Cocking (page 198) and by App and Jagendorf (1964) and Wilson (1966). It is relevant to note that Wheeldon (1966), using a rat liver mitochondrial preparation containing 10^6 bacteria, found that 90% of the amino acid incorporation observed was attributable to the bacteria which had pre-empted the amino acids. The presence of bacteria in large numbers may also interfere with the study of processes other than protein synthesis. The QO_2 (dry wt) of bacteria is 10 to 100 times greater than that of plant tissues so infection by bacteria could contribute significantly to the oxygen uptake of tissue slices or of subcellular fractions. Heavy bacterial infection (10^{10} bacteria) would add about 500 μg RNA (including ribosomal and transfer RNA) and 100 μg DNA to a subcellular fraction (McQuillen, 1965). Finally, as noted earlier, low enzyme activities exhibited by a fraction containing a mixture of organelles cannot easily be assigned to one or other of the components and the possibility that bacteria may contribute to some of the activities may have to be considered.

Ways to reduce or eliminate bacterial infection of preparations have been investigated repeatedly. In Wilson's (1966) experiments, the use of sterile media reduced the number of bacteria 100-fold but in the experiments summarized in Table III the infection did not come from the media but from the plants themselves. App and Jagendorf (1964) also considered that the plant material was a major source of infection, particularly if the tissues were bought, and they contrasted the bacterial count in their preparations with the much lower levels of Stephenson et al. (1956). Leaver and Edelman (1965) surveyed a range of antibiotics for use in controlling bacterial infection of beet discs; chloramphenicol (at 50 μg/ml) in the media in which the discs were aerated almost entirely eliminated bacteria without altering the metabolic processes they examined. None of the other antibiotics, which included penicillins, tetracycline, neomycin, terramycin and polymixin, were satisfactory.

Chloramphenicol (at 50 $\mu g/ml$) inhibited amino acid incorporation by contaminated protein bodies but did not reduce the bacterial count (Wilson, 1966). In Wheeldon's (1966) experiments with rat liver mitochondria, chloramphenicol at this concentration inhibited amino acid incorporation by the mitochondria themselves. Although antibiotics are useful in preventing extensive growth of bacteria in prolonged experiments, taking into account the number of types of bacteria which may be present and their probable differences in sensitivity to antibiotics as well as the multiple effects of many antibiotics on biological systems, the use of sterile tissue as recommended by Cocking (p. 198) and Boulter (1965) seems the ideal.

Bacteria stick firmly on to subcellular particles and cannot be removed completely by washing or by differential or density gradient centrifugation (App and Jagendorf, 1964; Boulter, 1965; B. Gyldenholm, personal communication; L. Jervis and M. Hallaway, unpublished work).

If non-sterile tissues are used, the degree of bacterial contamination is readily measured and, if necessary, suitable tests can be carried out to exclude the possibility that an observed activity or component is bacterial in origin (see Van Huyster and Cherry, 1966; Wheeldon, 1966; Phethean et al., 1968). If subcellular fractions are prepared by non-aqueous techniques most of any bacteria present will be rendered non-viable and to measure the degree of contamination it would be necessary to estimate some bacterial component, possibly α, ε-diaminopimelic acid (Holm-Hanson et al., 1965).

D. ASSAY OF THE ENZYMES

1. Latent Enzymes

The determination of the quantitative distribution of enzyme activity among subcellular organelles can be complicated by the existence of latent activity and by the related phenomenon of the changes in enzyme activity which may occur when an enzyme is bound to (or released from) subcellular particles. The question of latent enzymes in connection with the occurrence of lysosomes in plants is discussed fully by Gahan in a later chapter (p. 228). Siekevitz (1962) has summarized the effects of siting enzymes in membrane systems but there have been so far only a few studies on the changes in enzyme activity consequent on binding or release from particles, although the degree of change is often striking (Table IV).

Arnold (1965) has shown that about 25% of the β-fructofuranosidase of grape berries is recovered in the cell wall fraction; if the walls were treated with 0·2M borate at pH 8·5, β-fructofuranosidase was dissolved from the wall and the total activity (i.e. dissolved plus a trace remaining in the wall) was 90% higher than the original activity in the wall fraction (Arnold, 1966a). The increase in activity was not due to a fall in Km of the enzyme on changing from a bound to a free state, since both bound and solubilized activities have approximately the same Km and Vmax (Arnold, 1966b) and both were assayed at saturating levels of sucrose. Like β-fructofuranosidase, some of ascorbic oxidase activity of cell walls is masked and has been released by treating the cell walls with purified cellulase (J. Taggart and M. Hallaway, unpublished results) and with a consequent increase in total activity.

Cell walls and other subcellular particles can bind soluble enzymes and this may be accompanied by a change in activity. When soluble ascorbic oxidase is bound to cell walls, we have found a small but reproducible drop

TABLE IV

Enzyme	Treatment	Activity change
β-Fructofuranosidase (Arnold, 1966)	release of cell-wall enzyme by 0·2M borate	+90%
ADPG-starch transglucosylase (Akazawa and Murata, 1965)	adsorption of soluble enzyme on to starch grains	−15%
Ascorbic oxidase	release of cell-wall enzyme by cellulase	+60%
Ascorbic oxidase	adsorption of soluble enzyme on to cell walls	−15%
Adenosine triphosphatase (Brown et al., 1966)	binding of soluble enzyme on to cellulose matrix	−50%
Hexokinase (Siekevitz, 1962)	adsorption of soluble enzyme on to mitochondria	+100%

in activity which is not attributable to denaturation or change in Km and a similar fall in activity was noted by Akazawa and Murata (1965) when the soluble ADPG-starch transglucosylase was adsorbed on to starch grains. Potato adenosine triphosphatase showed a drop in activity and a change in pH optimum on binding to a cellulose matrix (Brown et al., 1966). Adsorbing enzymes on to particles does not always produce a reduction in activity since the activity of hexokinase was increased by up to 100% by adsorption on to mitochondria (Siekevitz, 1962, Ruchti and McLaren, 1965). The explanation for the change in activity in these experiments is not known.

2. Effects of Ions

An effect of ions on the localization of enzymes has occasionally been noted. Lipetz and Garro (1965), for example, observed that the cell walls of crown gall contained a peroxidase which was released by ions (in order of effectiveness $Ca^{2+} > Ba^{2+} > Mg^{2+}$) and they suggested that the concentration of ions could control lignin formation by controlling peroxidase location. The adsorption of phosphorylase on to starch grains *in vitro* is promoted by a number of ions including Na^+ Cl^-, NH_4^+ and Na^+ $EDTA^-$ and is inhibited by sucrose. It is possible that the location of phosphorylase *in vivo* is regulated by the relative concentrations of ions and sucrose (de Fekete, 1966). The localization of phosphorylase is uncertain; most of the phosphorylase of leaf homogenates remains in the supernatant after centrifuging down the plastids but, if non-aqueous techniques are used, about half the phosphorylase is recovered with the chloroplasts (Stocking, 1959). The phosphorylase activity of starch grains was not investigated in these experiments.

III. Localization of Enzymes by Cytochemical Techniques

Although there have been a few studies of the intracellular localization of enzymes in plants using cytochemical techniques, the results obtained from such studies can remove much of the uncertainty about the subcellular location of enzymes studied in cell free preparations (see Chapter 13 for a review of investigations on lysosomal enzymes using cytochemical techniques). Recent work on the localization of the pectin synthesizing enzymes illustrates this point well. Many of the enzymes involved in pectin synthesis are present in a fraction sedimented from homogenates of mung bean seedlings in 10–20 min by forces between $10,000 \times g$ and $35,000 \times g$. These enzymes include those catalysing (*a*) the conversion of UDP-glucuronic acid to UDP-galacturonic acid (Feingold *et al.*, 1961); (*b*) the incorporation of UDP-galacturonic acid into pectin (Villemez *et al.*, 1965) and (*c*) the methylation of pectin (Kauss *et al.*, 1967). The same fractions also catalyse the incorporation of GDP-glucose into cellulose and GDP-mannose into glucomannan (Barber *et al.*, 1964; Elbein and Hassid, 1966). This fraction is likely to contain fragments of membrane systems and nuclei, mitochondria and plastids as well as some cell wall material (Bailey *et al.*, 1967). In 1961 Mollenhauer *et al.* suggested that the Golgi apparatus was implicated in the synthesis of some cell wall components and in 1966 Northcote and Pickett-Heaps demonstrated by radioautography that tritiated glucose, fed to root tips of wheat, is rapidly incorporated into a high molecular weight material in the Golgi apparatus. Much of the activity is in galactosyl residues and this is incorporated into the cell wall and slime layer. This cytochemical study both compliments and extends the work on isolated cell free preparations and suggests that in the mung bean preparation it may be the fragments of Golgi apparatus that carry the pectin synthesizing enzymes. In a preliminary study of isolated dictyosomes from the Golgi bodies of mung bean and onion,

Morré (1966) noted that they accumulated lipids, apparently in the membranes, and glucose, apparently in the cisternal lumen.

IV. CONCLUSIONS

The precise intracellular distribution of many enzymes is unknown and difficulties in determining distribution may arise partly from the techniques used to isolate and assay the organelles and partly from features of the binding of the enzyme to particular sites *in vivo*. Ideally, the study of the enzymology of organelles requires the use of cytochemical techniques as well as the analysis of subcellular particles.

REFERENCES

Akazawa, T. and Murata, T. (1965). *Biochem. biophys. Res. Commun.* **19**, 21.
Albertsson, P. A. and Baltscheffsky, H. (1963). *Biochem. biophys. Res. Commun.* **12**, 14.
Arnold, W. N. (1965). *Biochim. biophys. Acta* **110**, 134.
Arnold, W. N. (1966a). *Biochim. biophys. Acta* **128**, 124.
Arnold, W. W. (1966b). *Biochim. biophys. Acta* **128**, 196.
App, A. A. and Jagendorf, A. T. (1964). *Pl. Physiol., Lancaster* **39**, 772.
Badran, A. M. and Jones, D. E. (1965). *Nature, Lond.* **206**, 622.
Bailey, R. W., Haq, S. and Hassid, W. Z. (1967). *Phytochem.* **6**, 293.
Barber, S. A., Elbein, A. D. and Hassid, W. Z. (1964). *J. biol. Chem.* **239**, 4056.
Bonner, J. (1965a). *In* "Plant Biochemistry". (J. Bonner and J. E. Varner, eds), p. 3. Academic Press, London and New York.
Bonner, J. (1965b). *In* "Plant Biochemistry". (J. Bonner and J. E. Varner, eds), p. 38. Academic Press, London and New York.
Boulter, D. (1965) *In* "Biosynthetic Pathways in Higher Plants". (J. B. Pridham and T. Swain, eds), p. 101. Academic Press, London and New York.
Brown, H. D., Patel, A. and Chattopadhyay, S. K. (1966). *Plant Physiol.* **41**, lxvi.
Bucke, C., Leech, R. M., Hallaway, M. and Morton, R. A. (1966). *Biochim. biophys. Acta.* **112**, 19.
de Duve, C. (1967). *In* "Enzyme Cytology". (D. B. Roodyn, ed.), p. 1. Academic Press, London and New York.
de Fekete, M. A. R. (1966). *Arch. S. Biochem. Biophys.* **116**, 368.
Elbein, A. D. and Hassid, W. Z. (1966). *Biochem. biophys. Res. Commun.* **23**, 313.
Feingold, D. S., Neufeld, E. F. and Hassid, W. Z. (1961). *J. biol. Chem.* **235**, 910.
Goldstein, J. L. and Swain, T. (1965). *Phytochem.* **4**, 185.
Gross, J. A., Becker, M. J. and Shefner, A. M. (1964). *Experientia* **20**, 261.
Hall, D. O. and Whatley, F. R. (1967). *In* "Enzyme Cytology". (D. B. Roodyn, ed.), p. 181. Academic Press, London and New York.
Hallaway, M. (1965). *Biol. Rev.* **40**, 188.
Hannig, K., Klofat, W. and Endres, H. (1964). *Z. Naturf.* **19b**, 1072.
Heber, U. (1960). *Z. Naturf.* **15b**, 100.
Holm-Hansen, O., Prasad, R. and Lewin, R. A. (1965). *Phycologia* **5**, 1.
Honda, S. I., Hongladorom, T. and Laties, G. G. (1966). *New Phytol.* **17**, 460.

Hulme, A. C., Jones, J. D. and Wooltorton, L. S. C. (1964). *Phytochem.* 3, 173.
Ikuma, H. and Bonner, W. D. (1967). *Pl. Physiol.*, *Lancaster* 42, 67.
Jagendorf, A. T. (1955). *Pl. Physiol.*, *Lancaster* 30, 138.
Jansen, E. F., Jang, R. and Bonner, J. (1960). *Pl. Physiol.*, *Lancaster* 35, 567.
Jensen, R. G. and Bassham, J. A. (1966). *Proc. natn. Acad. Sci.*, *U.S.A.* 56, 1095.
Kauss, H., Swanson, A. L. and Hassid, W. Z. (1967). *Biochem. biophys. Res. Commun.* 26, 234.
Koblitz, H. (1966). *Ber. dt. bot. Ges.* 79, 101.
Leaver, C. J. and Edelman, J. (1965). *Nature, Lond.* 207, 1000.
Leech, R. M. (1964). *Biochim. biophys. Acta* 79, 637.
Leech, R. M. (1966). *In* "Biochemistry of Chloroplasts". (T. W. Goodwin, ed.), Vol. 1. p. 65. Academic Press, London and New York.
Lieberman, M. and Baker, J. E. (1965). *A. Rev. Pl. Physiol.* 16, 343.
Lin, T-Y. and Hassid, W. Z. (1966). *J. biol. Chem.* 241, 5284.
Lipetz, J. and Garro, A. J. (1965). *J. Cell Biol.* 25, 109.
Loomis, W. D. and Battaile, J. (1964). *Pl. Physiol.*, *Lancaster* 39, xxi.
Mel, H. D. (1964a). *J. Theoret. Biol.* 6, 159, 181, 307.
Mel, H. D. (1964b). *J. Theoret. Biol.* 6, 181.
Mel, H. D. (1964c). *J. Theoret. Biol.* 6, 307.
McQuillen, K. (1965). *In* "Function and Structure in Micro-organisms". (M. R. Pollock and M. H. Richmond, eds), p. 134. Cambridge University Press.
Mollenhauer, H. H. and Morré, D. J. (1966). *A. Rev. Pl. Physiol.* 17, 27.
Mollenhauer, H. H., Whaley, W. G. and Leech, J. H. (1961). *J. Ultrastruct. Res.* 5, 193.
Morré, D. J. (1966). *Pl. Physiol.*, *Lancaster* 41, lxviii.
Morré, D. J. and Mollenhauer, H. H. (1964). *J. Cell Biol.* 23, 295.
Morré, D. J. Mollenhauer, H. H. and Chambers, J. E. (1965). *Expl. Cell. Res.* 38, 672.
Northcote, D. H. and Pickett-Heaps, J. D. (1966). *Biochem. J.* 98, 159.
Packer, L., Nobel, P. S., Gross, E. L. and Mel, H. C. (1966). *J. Cell Biol.* 28, 443.
Phethean, P. D., Hallaway, M. and Jervis, L. (1968). *Biochem. J.* (in press).
Pierpoint, W. S. (1962). *Biochem. J.* 82, 143.
Price, C. A. and Hirvonen, A. P. (1966). *Pl. Physiol.*, *Lancaster* 41, ix.
Quigley, J. W. and Price, C. A. (1966). *Pl. Physiol.*, *Lancaster* 41, xxv.
Ritenour, G. L., Joy, K. W., Bunning, J. and Hageman, R. H. (1967). *Pl. Physiol.*, *Lancaster* 42, 233.
Roodyn, D. B., Reis, P. J. and Work, T. S. (1961). *Biochem. J.* 80, 9.
Ruchti, J. and McLaren, A. D. (1965). *Enzymologia* 28, 201.
Sanderson, G. W. (1964). *Biochim. biophys. Acta* 92, 622.
Siebert, G. and Smillie, R. M. S. (1957). *Int. Rev. Cytol.* 6, 383.
Siekevitz, P. (1962). *In* "The Molecular Control of Cellular Activity". (J. M. Allen, ed.), p. 143. McGraw-Hill Inc., New York, Toronto and London.
Smillie, R. M. S. (1956). *Aust. J. biol. Sci.* 9, 347.
Smillie, R. M. S. (1963). *Can. J. Bot.* 41, 123.
Stephenson, M. L., Thimann, K. V. and Zamecnik, P. C. (1956). *Archs. Biochem. Biophys.* 65, 194.
Still, C. C. and Price, C. A. (1966). *Pl. Physiol.*, *Lancaster* 41, ix.
Stocking, C. R. (1959). *Pl. Physiol.*, *Lancaster* 34, 56.
Tiselius, A., Porath, J. and Albertsson, P. A. (1963). *Science, N.Y.* 141, 13.

van Huyster, R. B. and Cherry, J. (1966). *Biochim. biophys. Res. Commun.* **23**, 835.
Verleur, J. D. (1965). *Pl. Physiol., Lancaster* **40**, 1003.
Villemez, C. L., Lin, T-Y. and Hassid, W. Z. (1965). *Proc. natn. Acad. Sci., U.S.A.*
    54, 1626.
Walker, D. A. (1967). *In* "Biochemistry of Chloroplasts". (T. W. Goodwin, ed.),
    Vol. II, p. 53. Academic Press, London and New York.
Wheeldon, L. (1966). *Biochem. biophys. Res. Commun.* **24**, 407.
Wilson, C. M. (1966). *Pl. Physiol., Lancaster* **41**, 325.
Wiskich, J. T. and Bonner, W. D. (1963). *Pl. Physiol., Lancaster* **38**, 594.
Zeppezauer, M. and Brishammar, S. (1965). *Biochim. biophys. Acta* **94**, 581.

CHAPTER 2

The Structure, Function and Development of the Nucleus

R. F. LYNDON

Department of Botany, The University, Edinburgh, Scotland

I. INTRODUCTION

The nucleus is the largest cell organelle and it is therefore hardly surprising to find that its structure is complex and that it performs many different functions. The very size of the nucleus has proved an obstacle to understanding its ultrastructure and to isolating it without damage from the cell for analysis and experimentation. The nuclei of both plants and animals appear to have the same structure and functions and in many cases much more work has been done using animal nuclei. Although it is therefore inappropriate to consider the plant nucleus alone, in this chapter the emphasis will be on work which has been done on plant nuclei.

II. STRUCTURE

A. NUCLEAR ENVELOPE

The most characteristic feature of the ultrastructure of the nucleus is the limiting envelope which is a double membrane consisting of two unit membranes each 80 Å thick separated by a space, the perinuclear space, about 150 Å wide and perforated by pores of about 800 Å in diameter. The pores are places in the nuclear envelope where the inner and outer membranes are fused together at their edges (Fig. 1). The structure of the pores has been seen in more detail in nuclear envelopes isolated from cells of the onion Franke, 1966). The border of the pore is an annulus showing 8-fold sym-

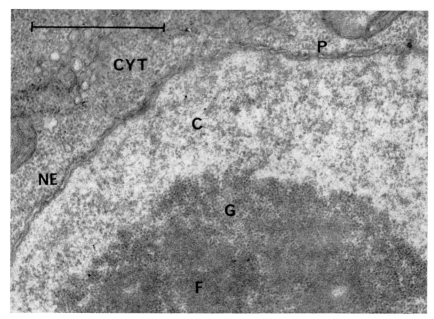

FIG. 1 Electron micrograph of part of a cell of the root meristem of a seedling of *Sinapis alba* showing the structure of the nucleus. NE, nuclear envelope with pore, P; C, chromatin, consisting of the extended chromosomes; G, granular and F, fibrillar regions of the nucleolus; CYT, cytoplasm. The line represents 1μ. Fixed in glutaraldehyde followed by osmium tetroxide. The section was stained with uranyl acetate followed by lead citrate. Photograph by courtesy of Mr. A. J. Tulett, Department of Botany, University of Edinburgh.

metry, similar to the octagonal pores in the nuclear envelope of the amphibian egg (Gall, 1967). The technique of freeze etching has also been used to obtain surface views of the nuclear envelope in yeast (Moor and Muhlethaler, 1963) and in onion roots (Branton and Moor, 1964) so that the number and distribution of pores can be seen. Approximately 8 % or more of the area of the nuclear envelope may be occupied by pores. This means there are about 200 pores per nucleus for a small nucleus (diameter 2μ), such as in yeast, or about 3000 pores per nucleus in a higher plant, such as the onion, having nuclei about 8μ in diameter.

In many lower plants, especially in the fungi, the nuclear envelope remains intact during nuclear division but it divides and is partitioned equally to the daughter nuclei (Hawker, 1965). In higher plants the nuclear envelope is ruptured at the end of prophase and disintegrates into pieces which become indistinguishable from the endoplasmic reticulum which is distributed more or less equally to the two poles (Porter and Machado, 1960). The nuclear envelope is reformed in telophase from pieces of the endoplasmic reticulum which come to lie close to the chromosomes. These pieces of membrane join up in some way and eventually become continuous to form the new nuclear envelope around the telephase chromosomes (Porter and Machado, 1960; Lafontaine and Chouinard, 1963). Whether or not the new nuclear envelope is formed from pieces of the old envelope which have retained their identity through division is perhaps a meaningless question, for the outer membrane of the nuclear envelope is continuous with the endoplasmic reticulum and they are, therefore, really a single system of membranes (Marinos, 1960). The envelope of fusion nuclei in the embryo sac is derived equally from the two nuclei which fuse together (Jensen, 1964).

Since the endoplasmic reticulum is continuous through the plasmodesmata from one cell to the next, it is very probable that the perinuclear spaces of nuclei in adjacent cells are in direct continuity and that substances could therefore pass through the lumen of the endoplasmic reticulum from one nucleus to another without having contact with any other cytoplasmic components. It is often believed that the endoplasmic reticulum is also continuous with the plasma membrane. Were this so, there could be direct continuity between the perinuclear space and the external environment of the cell. However, this belief has only the most slender evidence to support it. To the writer's knowledge there is only one instance of an electron micrograph showing continuity of the plasma membrane and the endoplasmic reticulum in plant cells (Buvat, 1963) and two examples in animal cells (see Fawcett, 1964). We must surely agree that ". . . if communication between the lumen of the reticulum and the extracellular space does exist, it is relatively rare and probably quite transient" (Fawcett, 1964).

B. CHROMOSOMES

Chromosomes appear in electron micrographs as a tangle of fine threads 100–140 Å in diameter which are sometimes resolvable into two or four separate strands each 20–50 Å in diameter. Such fibrils form the fundamental structure of the chromosomes of plants (as of animals) during both division and interphase (Bopp-Hassenkamp, 1959; Peveling, 1961; Rossner, 1961; Setterfield, 1961; Ris, 1961, 1966; Chadard, 1962; Albersheim and Killias. 1963; Resch and Peveling, 1964; Hyde, 1964; Brandham and Godward, 1965). Since the diameter of the deoxyribonucleohistone helix is about 30 Å (Zubay and Doty, 1959), the fine strands are probably nucleohistone helices. The 100 Å strands may in turn make up fibres about 200 Å thick (Ris, 1961) which in turn may make up thicker strands. The sensitivity of the fibres to deoxyribonuclease and proteinases shows them to be deoxyribonucleoprotein (Setterfield, 1961; Callan, 1963; Wolfe, 1965).

How is this hierarchy of fibres related to the structure of the chromosome? The 30 Å fibrils have been interpreted as the individual chromatids, coiled on themselves to form the 100 Å fibrils and these being themselves coiled and so on until the coiled coil is the dimensions of the chromosome (Hyde, 1964). In this view the anaphase chromosome consists basically of a single, extremely long, strand of nucleohistone. An alternative view is that the chromosome consists of many strands coiled together like a rope, so that the 100 Å fibre consists of two 30 Å fibrils twisted around each other and the 200 Å fibre is two 100 Å fibres twisted together (Ris, 1961, 1966).

The discovery that plant chromosomes (Taylor et al., 1957) and DNA (Filner, 1965) replicated in a semi-conservative fashion as expected of the DNA helix, suggested that the basis of the anaphase chromosome was one long double helix of DNA, coiled in a complex manner. This is consistent with the genetic and mutational evidence that the functional unit is the chromatid. On the other hand, there is considerable evidence from classical cytology (see Sharp, 1943; Swanson, 1958; Mazia, 1961) and from X-ray and other evidence (Ris, 1961; Peacock, 1965) that the anaphase and telephase chromosomes are multistranded. Most electron micrographs can be interpreted on either hypothesis. However, in electron micrographs of prophase nuclei of *Tradescantia* the ends of the chromosomes were often found abutting on the nuclear membrane and at this point each chromatid could sometimes be seen to consist of several distinct strands about 3000 Å thick (Sparvoli et al., 1965). Models reconstructed from serial sections showed that there were at least five, and probably about eight, strands in each prophase chromatid. These strands are an order of magnitude larger than the 100 Å and 200 Å fibres and what the relation is of one to the other is not known. The number of such strands per chromatid has been estimated, by different procedures, to be 4 in *Vicia* (Trosko and Wolff, 1965) and 8 in *Tradescantia* (Ris, 1961).

The linear continuity of either a single stranded (unieme) or a multistranded (polyneme) chromosome would presumably be due to the DNA molecules stretching from one end of the chromosome to the other but there is evidence that the linear continuity of the chromosome may not be due entirely to DNA. Mirsky and Ris (1951) first showed that the continuity of isolated chromatin was not affected by the removal, by enzyme action, of histone but that the chromatin fell apart as soon as the DNA or the non-histone proteins were attacked. Wolff (1965) has recently made very similar observations on *Vicia* chromosomes. He has also found that when chromosomes were broken by radiation they could rejoin and that the rejoining was prevented by puromycin (an inhibitor of protein synthesis) but not by fluorodeoxyuridine (an inhibitor of DNA synthesis). A model, proposed by Uhl (1965), for the structure of the chromosome demonstrates that both multistrandedness and the participation of proteins in the linear continuity could be compatible with the observed behaviour of the chromosomes in mitosis, meiosis and crossing over. The essential point is that multiple strands of DNA must behave as a unit. It is equally difficult to understand how a mutation would occur in all the copies of a gene which undoubtedly exist (Birnstiel *et al.*, 1967), whether they are arranged linearly, in a unieme chromosome, or side by side, in a polyneme chromosome.

Apart from the demonstration that plant chromosomes, like those of animals, consist partly of RNA (Kaufmann *et al.*, 1948; La Cour, 1963) and proteins other than histones (Wolff, 1965) and may contain calcium (Steffensen and Bergeron, 1959), little is known of their chemical structure. The only components of which we have a little more than passing knowledge are the DNA and the histones. The DNAs of plants are characterized by having a relatively high content of 5-methylcytosine (Thomas and Sherratt, 1956). Histones isolated from plant sources have an amino acid composition similar to comparable fractions from calf thymus, the classical animal source. The histones of wheat embryos, pea buds and *Chlorella* cells, in contrast to those of most animal cells examined, consist predominantly of the lysine-rich fractions (Johns and Butler, 1962; Iwai, 1964) which in pea buds comprise three quarters of the histone of the nucleus (Huang and Bonner, 1965). The histone fractions of rice embryos are, however, very similar to those of calf thymus (Iwai, 1964). As would be expected of lysine-rich histones, the major fraction from wheat embryos does not aggregate above pH5 as arginine-rich histone does (Cruft *et al.*, 1957). An interesting qualitative difference between the lysine-rich histones of animals and wheat embryos (the only plant source for which data are available) is that in the plant these histones have alanine as the principal N-terminal amino acid rather than proline. This is usually a characteristic of arginine-rich histones (Johns and Butler, 1962). Not all the DNA of the chromosome may be complexed with histone; probably only about 80% of it is complexed at any one time (Bonner, 1965).

In meiotic chromosomes of both plants and animals a consistent feature is the occurrence of paired strands of dense material, about 300 Å wide and about 1500 Å apart, which have been called the synaptimemal complex because they are found only during zygotene and pachytene, i.e. during synapsis. Since the complex is not found in organisms in which the chromosomes pair but crossing over does not take place, it is almost certainly of some special significance in the formation of chiasmata (Moses, 1964). The synaptinemal complex has been observed in plants during both micro- and mega-sporogenesis (Israel and Sagawa, 1965; Menzel and Price, 1966; Lu, 1966; other references in Moses, 1964). It is thought that the dense strands represent the axes of the meiotic chromosomes and that the thin line sometimes seen midway between the paired strands represents the junction of the two chromosomes forming the bivalent.

Giant chromosomes, like those of Dipteran salivary glands, are also found in some specialized plant cells (references in Stange, 1965) and emphasize the similarity of the chromosomes of animals and plants. We are still some way from being able to say what is the fundamental organization which is common to interphase, mitotic, meiotic, lampbrush and giant chromosomes. The numbers of different models for chromosome structure which have been proposed are really only cloaks for our ignorance. The difficulties in the electron microscopy may be simply that the chromosome is a relatively large body made up of very fine fibrils coiled in three dimensions. If this is so then the structure of the chromosome at this level may yet be resolved by someone with a sufficient fund of patience to obtain sufficient serial sections.

C. NUCLEOLUS

The nucleolus has no membrane and is therefore in direct continuity with the rest of the nucleus. It consists of a network of fibres about 100 Å in diameter which in turn consist of fibrils about 20 Å in diameter. The fibres stain for protein but unlike the chromosomes are destroyed by RNase and not by DNase, so that they are ribonucleoprotein (Hyde *et al.*, 1965; La Cour, 1966). In parts of the nucleolus there are also granules about 150 Å in diameter which probably represent tightly packed fibres (Hyde *et al.*, 1965; Lafontaine and Chouinard, 1963). The granules, which are almost certainly the precursors of ribosomes, are often found around the periphery of the nucleolus so that the centre is virtually free of them and consists of fibrils in an amorphous protein matrix (Fig. 1). These two parts of the nucleolus, the fibrillar and granular regions, can with the appropriate stains be made visible in the light microscope (Chouinard, 1966). The granular region often appears to be organized into strands about 1000 Å thick which have been called the nucleolonema. Structures probably representing the chromatin of the nucleolar organizer can be derived from the central part of the nucleolus by treatment with detergent (La Cour, 1966) and seem to be analogous to nucleoli of amphibian eggs which can be made to form ring nucleoli in the same way (Callan, 1966). The association of the chromatin of the nucleolar organizer with the nucleolus has been most clearly seen in electron micrographs of *Spirogyra* (Godward and Jordan, 1965).

The nucleolus may therefore be regarded as a collection of gene products having sufficient morphological structure to remain associated with the loci at which they were produced. This implies of course that the nucleolus has DNA associated with it. Plant nucleoli in fact contain about 10–20% of the DNA of the nucleus (Birnstiel *et al.*, 1964; McLeish, 1964) but this DNA does not stain with Feulgen (McLeish, 1964). In *Blastocladiella* the DNA of the nucleus could be fractionated into two components α and β which were found in the ratio of $3\alpha : 2\beta$ in the chromosomes but only the α component was present in the nucleoli (Comb *et al.*, 1964). The DNA in the pea nucleolus is perhaps localized in the knots which were seen in the fibrous network, for some unknotting occurred when the nucleoli were treated with DNase (Hyde *et al.*, 1965).

In dividing cells the nucleolus typically disappears at the end of prophase and is reformed at telophase. Electron microscopy has shown that in late prophase the nucleolus becomes more loosely organized until the 100 Å fibrils merge with the surrounding nucleoplasm and the 150 Å granules become dispersed throughout the nucleoplasm (Lafontaine and Chouinard, 1963). The formation of new nucleoli in telophase has long been recognized to be a function of specific parts of certain chromosomes (the nucleolar organizers) so that initially the number of new nucleoli is the same as the number of organizers although later the nucleoli may fuse to form a single nucleolus. In telophase when the new nucleoli are first observed the chromosomes are seen to be coated with a material that is fibrillar-granular in texture (Albersheim and Killias, 1963; Lafontaine and Chouinard, 1963; Sparvoli *et al.*, 1965). This material disappears in late telophase and some have considered that it represented nucleolar material synthesized at various sites on the chromosomes and then assembled by the nucleolar organizer into a nucleolus. Further work is necessary before the significance of the material coating the chromosomes is known. The nucleolus may well be formed where it is assembled, i.e. at the nucleolar organizer.

D. MACROMOLECULAR COMPOSITION OF THE NUCLEUS

The structural and staining evidence indicates that the chromatin consists primarily of deoxyribonucleohistone and the nucleolus of ribonucleoprotein which includes particles looking like ribosomes. To what extent can chemical analyses of isolated and fractionated nuclei clarify this picture? The DNA content of the nucleus can vary widely (Martin, 1966) from 0·48 $\mu\mu$g in *Marchantia* (Ishida, 1961) to more than 300 $\mu\mu$g in tetraploid *Lilium* (Sunderland and McLeish, 1961). This variation is related to chromosome size rather than chromosome number for closely related species within the same family and having the same number of chromosomes can have widely different amounts of DNA per chromosome (Rothfels *et al.*, 1966).

Measurements on isolated nuclei have shown that DNA may represent anything from 8–40% of the dry mass of the nucleus. The amount of RNA

(6–21 %) is usually somewhat less than that of DNA and the bulk of the nucleus (50–80 %) consists of protein (Table I). The nucleus also presumably contains small amounts of lipids. The techniques used for isolation of the nuclei would allow the loss of soluble constituents which are small molecules

TABLE I

Amounts of DNA, RNA and protein in the nucleus.

Dry mass μμg	DNA μμg	% DNA	RNA	Protein	Plant	Author†
—	—	3	9	88	Yeast	1
150*	13	8	17	75	Tobacco cell culture	2
70*	10	14	12	74	Pea seedling	3
—	—	16	8	76	Pea stem	4
84	21	25	21	54*	Pea root tip	5
81	16	20	19	61*	Pea root tip	6
76	31	41	12	47*	Pea epicotyl	6
—	—	7	3	90	Pea embryos	7
129*	33	25	11	63	Pea embryos	8
—	—	17	4	79	Wheat embryos	9
—	—	5	4	53	Wheat embryos‡	10
152	60	39	9	52*	Broat bean root tip	5
230	77	33	6	61*	Onion root tip	5

* Determined indirectly.
† 1, Rozijn and Tonino, 1964; 2, Flamm and Birnstiel, 1964b; 3, Birnstiel et al., 1964; 4, Birnstiel et al., 1962b; 5, McLeish, 1963; 6, Lyndon, 1963; 7, Johnston et al., 1959; 8, R. F. Lyndon, unpublished; 9, Johnston et al., 1957; 10, Stern and Mirsky, 1952; 11, McLeish, 1964.
‡ Isolated by a non-aqueous procedure.

but macromolecules such as protein are not lost during these isolation procedures. The dry mass of isolated pea root nuclei was the same as that before isolation (Lyndon, 1963) and the same as nuclei isolated from fixed pea roots (McLeish, 1963).

Measurements on isolated nucleoli (Tables II and III) show that 20–40 % of the nuclear dry matter is in the nucleolus. The volume of the nucleolus is usually less than 10 % of that of the nucleus so that the concentration of material in the nucleolus is two or three times as great as in the rest of the nucleus. From 10 to 20 % of the DNA of the nucleus is found associated with the nucleolus and about a third of the RNA.

A more detailed analysis of the composition of pea nuclei and nucleoli has been made by Birnstiel et al. (1964). Probably something like half of the ribosomal type of particles, and of the ribosomal RNA and also half of the transfer RNA of the nucleus, is located in the nucleolus. Their data make possible a comparison of the relative concentrations of ribosomal particles in the nucleus and the cytoplasm. The nucleoli of their preparations were about 6% of the volume of the nucleus and in cells of the pea root tip the cytoplasm is about four times the volume of the nucleus (Lyndon, 1967) so that the relative volumes of nucleolus : rest of nucleus : cytoplasm are approximately 1 : 16 : 64. The cytoplasm contains about 10 times as much RNA as the nucleus (Lyndon, 1963). Since 80% of cytoplasmic RNA and

TABLE II

Amounts of DNA, RNA and protein in the nucleolus.

Dry mass μμg	DNA μμg	% DNA	RNA	Protein	Plant	Author[†]
25*	1·5	6	11	83	Pea seedlings	3
—	—	≪ 1	9	91	Pea embryos	7
28	10·5	37	19	44*	Broad bean root tips	11

* Determined indirectly.
† See Table I.

TABLE III

Proportion of nuclear material in the nucleolus.

$$\text{Ratio } \frac{\mu\mu\text{g in Nucleolus}}{\mu\mu\text{g in Nucleus}} \times 100$$

Dry mass	DNA	RNA	Protein	Plant	Author*
36	15	33	40	Pea seedlings	3
8	1	20	6	Pea embryos	7
19	18	41	16	Broad bean root tips	11

* See Table I.

50% of the nuclear RNA is ribosomal, half of this being in the nucleolus (Chipchase and Birnstiel, 1963b), the ratio of the number of ribosomes in the nucleolus: rest of nucleus : cytoplasm is about 1 : 1 : 32. The relative concentrations of ribosomes in nucleolus : rest of nucleus : cytoplasm are therefore approximately 16 : 1 : 8. This compares with what is seen in electron micrographs (Fig. 1) where the concentration of granules in the nucleolus is about twice that found in the cytoplasm and there is a much lower concentration in the rest of the nucleus.

There are not sufficient data available to be able to say how the variations in the composition of the nucleus may be related to the developmental and metabolic status of the cell. Such overall data are in any case of limited value. It will be necessary to find out what changes may occur in the different parts of the nucleus and to correlate this with the ultrastructural changes which they reflect.

III. Function

A. SEQUESTRATION OF THE CHROMOSOMES

In a meristematic cell the nuclear envelope serves as a bag to keep the chromosomes together from one division to the next. This may be particularly important in large dividing cells such as those of the cambium. In addition we like to think that the nuclear envelope can in some way regulate the passage of molecules between nucleus and cytoplasm so that these two parts of the cell could interact with each other during development in a way which would be impossible if they were a continuum. This idea implies that the pores in the nuclear envelope may sometimes be open and sometimes occluded. Electron micrographs usually show the pores as being open but it can always be argued that the occluding substances when present are not electron-dense with the procedures used. Attempts have been made with animal cells to relate the electrical resistance across the nuclear envelope to the structure and metabolic properties of the envelope but without any real success. In salivary gland nuclei there was a high resistance across the envelope but this had the same structure as that of the envelope of the nucleus of the frog oocyte which showed no resistance (Loewenstein et al., 1966) despite being semi-permeable (Harding and Feldherr, 1959). However, it is tantalizing to find that in salivary glands the resistance of the envelope changed in a regular fashion during development and could be altered in a predictable way when the cells were treated with hormones which affected development (Loewenstein et al., 1966).

Another suggested function of the nuclear envelope is that mitochondria and plastids originate from it by evagination during oogenesis (Bell and Muhlethaler, 1964; Bell et al., 1966). It is difficult to be sure since evaginations from the nuclear envelope cannot be classed as mitochondria and free organelles have not been shown with certainty to have been continuous with the nucleus. Although evaginations from the nuclear envelope have often been seen during oogenesis, in animals as well as plants, it can be argued even more convincingly that the organelles show continuity throughout oogenesis and do not arise from the nuclear envelope (Diers, 1966). Studies of oogenesis in other plants have likewise provided no evidence for a nuclear origin of cytoplasmic organelles (Jensen, 1965; Israel and Sagawa, 1964).

B. REPLICATION OF THE CHROMOSOMES

The synthesis of the DNA of the chromosomes takes place usually about the middle of interphase and may be initiated simultaneously at several sites

C

on a chromosome (Evans, 1964). Synthesis is completed sooner at some loci than at others (Wimber, 1961; Evans and Rees, 1966). The last parts of the chromosomes to finish DNA replication are the heterochromatin (Evans, 1964) and those parts which show the greatest frequency of chiasmata (Rees and Evans, 1966). The rate of synthesis of DNA may not be constant but may change, being less in the middle of the S-period than at the beginning and end (Howard and Dewey, 1961; Kusanagi, 1966). The maturation of the seed apparently results in an abrupt suspension of metabolism, including DNA synthesis, for nuclei could be found in dry wheat embryos which had amounts of DNA intermediate between telophase and prophase values, suggesting that chromosomes could be suspended in the process of replicating their DNA while the embryo was in the dry fruit and could resume synthesis on germination (Avanzi et al., 1963). The histones are probably replicated at the same time as the DNA (McLeish, 1959; Rasch and Woodard, 1959; Woodard et al., 1961; De, 1961). Some of the chromosomal protein may be renewed completely after each division of the nucleus. ³H-arginine incorporated into chromosomes of Vicia faba roots during or just after DNA synthesis was found, by radioautography, to be present on the chromosomes when they reached metaphase but by the next division most chromosomes had lost this protein for they were unlabelled (Prensky and Smith, 1964).

In meiosis, after the main period of DNA synthesis is completed in the microspore mother cell, there is a later synthesis of DNA during the zygotene and pachytene stages of prophase (Hotta et al., 1966). The amount of DNA synthesized at this time is very small, being only 0·3 % of the total. This late synthesis has also been found in animal cells (Wimber and Prensky, 1963) and may be concerned with the reformation of DNA molecules that are broken during crossing over which occurs at this time. Before the chromosomes enter the meiotic prophase, there is synthesized a characteristic histone component which is not found in any of the somatic cells of the plant (Sheridan and Stern, 1967). This histone has been found in both lily and tulip but its significance is unknown. When the microspores have been formed and are maturing there may be changes in the relative amounts of the different histone fractions. This is long after DNA synthesis has ceased but it is consistent with the finding that synthesis of histones can continue when DNA synthesis is inhibited (Flamm and Birnstiel, 1964a).

In plant cells the replication of the chromosomes occurs not only prior to division but also in cells which have completed division. As the cells of the root pass out of the meristem into the more basal regions where they do not divide, they nevertheless synthesize DNA (Jensen et al., 1960) so that the proportion of nuclei with the 4C amount of DNA increases (McLeish and Sunderland, 1961). In addition some of these cells undergo endomitosis and further DNA synthesis so that they become polyploid. This may be looked upon as a type of cellular differentiation (Partanen, 1965) and it is more often found in dicotyledons than in monocotyledons (Deeley *et al.*, 1957; McLeish and Sunderland, 1961).

C. DIVISION OF THE CHROMOSOMES:
FORMATION OF THE SPINDLE

The formation of spindle material by the nucleus has been followed in a series of elegant experiments by Bajer and his colleagues using the cells of endosperm. During prophase the mass of the chromosomes increased. Then in late prophase the nuclear volume decreased slightly and, while the nuclear envelope was still intact, the dry mass of the nucleus began to fall (Ambrose and Bajer, 1961). The loss of nuclear dry matter coincided with the formation just outside the nucleus of the clear zone which contained birefringent material and microtubules and which later formed the spindle (Inoue and Bajer, 1959; Pickett-Heaps and Northcote, 1966). While the clear zone was being formed, and the mass of the chromosomes was falling, the mass of the nucleoplasm remained constant. The inference was that the material which had accumulated earlier on the chromosomes was now being secreted from them to pass out of the nucleus into the clear zone. Material continued to be lost through the nuclear membrane until this broke down, marking the end of prophase. At this point the nuclear sap became birefringent, like the clear zone with which it became mixed, and formed the spindle (Ambrose and Bajer, 1961). Each spindle fibre consists of a bundle of fine filaments (Bajer and Allen, 1966). These are probably the microtubules each about 200 Å in diameter which are seen in electron micrographs (Ledbetter and Porter, 1963; Manton, 1964; Harris and Bajer, 1965; Pickett-Heaps and Northcote, 1966).

D. TRANSCRIPTION OF THE GENES: RNA SYNTHESIS

A vast amount of work has made it clear that the nucleus is the main site of RNA synthesis in the cell although some of the cytoplasmic organelles can synthesize RNA in their own right. Most, if not all, RNA synthesis is DNA-dependent and hence the nucleus, as the main site of localization of DNA in the cell, is the main site of RNA synthesis (Zalokar, 1960; Mitchison, 1966; Perry, 1965). Although RNA synthesis is not restricted to any one part of the nucleus, it is perhaps a reflection of the fact that 85% of the DNA is in the extranucleolar chromatin that this is where most of the RNA is synthesized.

Isolated plant nuclei will synthesize RNA to a limited extent (Rho and Chipchase, 1962; Bandurski and Maheshwari, 1962). In intact cells (Woods, 1960), as in nuclei, RNA may be synthesized by the chromatin and the nucleolus but the RNA synthesized by the chromatin may move to the nucleolus and accumulate there (Rho and Bonner, 1961). The RNA appears to be synthesized on the chromatin while this is in an expanded state, although it may later contract (Kemp, 1966). In the nucleolus newly synthesized RNA is first detected in the central, fibrillar region (La Cour and Crawley, 1965) and only later in the outer granular region (Karasaki, 1965).

1. Ribsomal RNA

A ribosome contains three molecules of RNA, one each of the 28S, 18S and 5S components. The sedimentation coefficients of ribosomal RNAs from plants may in fact be slightly lower. There is lots of evidence, nearly all from animal cells, that the 28S and 18S RNAs are synthesized in the nucleolus (Perry, 1965; Birnstiel, 1967). The clearest evidence that the nucleolus is the site of synthesis is that the mutant of the toad *Xenopus*, which lacks a nucleolus, cannot synthesize ribosomal RNA (Brown and Gurdon, 1964). The nucleus of the anucleolate mutant also lacks the 150 Å particles which resemble cytoplasmic ribosomes and which are found in the nucleus of the wild type (Jones, 1965).

The nucleolus of the pea has been shown to contain RNA having the same sedimentation coefficients, 28S and 18S, as the RNA of cytoplasmic ribosomes (Birnstiel *et al.*, 1963a). This RNA was extracted from isolated pea nucleoli and was annealed with pea DNA to form a hybrid RNA–DNA complex. RNA extracted from cytoplasmic ribosomes also annealed with DNA and competed with the nucleolar RNA for the same sites on the DNA, showing that the nucleolar RNAs were identical in base sequence with the ribosomal RNAs (Chipchase and Birnstiel, 1963b). The 5S RNA, which is thought to link the two subunits of the ribosome, has also recently been shown to be synthesized in the nucleolus in *Blastocladiella* (Comb and Katz, 1964; Comb and Zehavi-Willner, 1967).

2. Transfer RNA

Transfer RNA is synthesized in the nucleus but it is not yet clear in what part of the nucleus. The transfer RNA is distinguished experimentally from other RNA by its ability to combine with amino acids in the presence of activating enzymes. About 30% of the RNA of the pea nucleus is transfer RNA and it can be synthesized by isolated nuclei (Chipchase and Birnstiel, 1963a). In the pea about 50% of the nuclear transfer RNA is found in the nucleolus (Chipchase and Birnstiel, 1963b). The nucleolus of *Blastocladiella* also contains transfer RNA (Comb and Katz, 1964). This is consistent with the synthesis of transfer RNA occurring in the nucleolus, as it apparently does in Dipteran salivary glands (Sirlin *et al.*, 1965). On the other hand, in *Vicia faba* roots the nucleoli seem to contain no transfer RNA and experimental evidence points to the extranucleolar chromatin as the exclusive site of transfer RNA synthesis (Woods and Zubay, 1965). The incorporation of nucleotides into transfer RNA in the cytoplasm was thought to represent the addition there of the cytidine-cytidine-adenine end of the molecule. The concentration of methylating enzymes in the nucleolus of the pea (Birnstiel *et al.*, 1963b) does not necessarily point to the nucleolus as the site of synthesis of transfer RNA; it could be other RNAs, including ribosomal RNA, which are methylated there (Greenberg and Penman, 1966).

3. *Messenger RNA*

The DNA-like RNA which has been isolated from root tissues has been found in association with ribosomes (Loening, 1965) and polyribosomes (Lin *et al.*, 1966) and therefore possesses one of the qualifications of messenger RNA. This RNA is also rapidly labelled and in excised soybean hypocotyl has a half life of only 2 hr (Ingle *et al.*, 1965). Since only 20% of the DNA-like RNA was associated with 75% of the ribosomes of the tissue, one might guess that most of the other 80% of this RNA would be found in the nucleus where it is presumably synthesized (Lin *et al.*, 1966). Much of this RNA may indeed never leave the nucleus (see Mitchison, 1966) and some of it could be involved in protein synthesis within the nucleus.

E. TRANSLATION OF THE GENIC INFORMATION: PROTEIN SYNTHESIS

When cells are supplied with radioactive amino acids the nucleus is labelled quickly (Mattingly, 1963) but, at least in some cases, this could represent accumulation rather than synthesis of protein for it is now known that there are proteins which can shuttle to and fro between the cytoplasm and the nucleus (Prescott, 1964). Unequivocal evidence that nuclei can synthesize protein can be obtained by the use of nuclei *in vitro*. Nuclei isolated from pea and tobacco cells have been shown to incorporate amino acids into their protein (Birnstiel *et al.*, 1962a; Flamm *et al.*, 1963). Labelling kinetics pointed to the nucleolus as the principal site of protein synthesis in the nucleus (Birnstiel *et al.*, 1961; Flamm and Birnstiel, 1964b). When nuclei were fractionated and the ability of the isolated fractions to incorporate amino acids was examined, the isolated nucleoli were found to be more active than the chromatin. The nucleolar proteins which eventually became most highly labelled were the residual proteins, the amino acid composition of which was similar to that of ribosomes (Birnstiel and Hyde, 1963). It was not clear whether these were ribosomal proteins which had been synthesized in the nucleolus or whether the newly synthesized protein was still associated with ribosomes on which it had been synthesized. There is, however, considerable evidence that the nucleolus is in fact the site of synthesis of ribosomes (Birnstiel, 1967). Ribonucleoprotein particles, which look like ribosomes, are very similar in size (Hyde *et al.*, 1965) and have a composition and sedimentation characteristics like those of ribosomes (Birnstiel *et al.*, 1963a) are concentrated in the nucleolus in pea cells. These ribosome-like particles differed from cytoplasmic ribosomes in their labelling kinetics and their proteins also became labelled more slowly than the other proteins of the nucleus (Flamm and Birnstiel, 1964b). The relative inactivity of these particles in protein synthesis, together with the observation that sometimes they occurred mainly as 60S (rather than 78S) particles, makes it probable that they are in fact precursors of the cytoplasmic ribosomes and that they are synthesized in the nucleolus (Birnstiel *et al.*, 1963a). The preponderance of 60S particles in the plant nucleus also suggests that, as in animal cells (Penman, 1966), the 39S subunit of the ribosomes is released from the nucleus into the cytoplasm before the 60S subunit.

F. FORMATION AND RELEASE OF MORPHOGENETIC SUBSTANCES

The unicellular alga *Acetabularia* can be grown for long periods after removal of the single nucleus. This has made possible the direct study of nuclear function by observing the effects of enucleation. Such experiments, and also those in which nuclei have been transferred from one strain to another, have shown that the nucleus is responsible for the formation of morphogenetic substances, almost certainly RNA, which are released into the cytoplasm and there determine the structure of the cap which is formed (Haemmerling, 1963; Werz, 1965; Brachet, 1967). The chloroplasts too are in some way dependent on the nucleus for the rate of division of the chloroplasts is less when the nucleus is absent (Shephard, 1965).

Experiments with *Micrasterias* have shown that the nucleus synthesizes material which is necessary for the ordered growth of the cell. This material again is almost certainly RNA (Kallio, 1963; Selman, 1966). By inactivating the nucleus at particular points in the cell cycle, specific blockages or changes at specific points in the subsequent growth of the cell can be induced. In this way the time at which the message, determining the growth of a particular arm or lobe of the cytoplasm, is formed in the nucleus can be measured quite precisely (Selman, 1966).

IV. DEVELOPMENT

A. DEVELOPMENT OF THE NUCLEUS

The obvious development of the nucleus is during the mitotic cycle. The nucleus and nucleolus grow throughout interphase by accumulation of protein and nucleic acid until they reach maximum size at the end of prophase. Accumulation of most nuclear protein and RNA occurs more or less linearly throughout interphase (Woodard *et al.*, 1961; Lyndon, 1967) although there is some evidence that RNA synthesis is twice as fast in G2 as in G1 (Van't

Hof, 1967). If so this might imply that the rate of RNA synthesis is a function of the amount of DNA present. The synthesis of histones occurs at the same time as DNA synthesis, about the middle of interphase (Rasch and Woodard, 1959), and the spindle proteins seem to be synthesized in prophase (Ambrose and Bajer, 1961). While the chromosomes in mitosis are attached to the spindle, synthesis of RNA drops to a low level or stops (Taylor, 1953; Harris and La Cour, 1963; Van't Hof, 1963; Davidson, 1964; Das, 1963; Das et al., 1965). In meiosis the rate of RNA synthesis fluctuates and is inversely related to the degree of contraction of the chromosomes (Taylor, 1958; Hotta and Stern, 1963).

Much of the RNA and protein which is synthesized in the nucleus during interphase and about half of what accumulates in the nucleus will be in the

TABLE IV

Changes in the composition of nucleus and cytoplasm during cellular development in roots of *Pisum*.

	μμg per cell					
	Nucleus			Cytoplasm		
	mm from root apex			mm from root apex		
	0–2	2–4	4–9	0–2	2–4	4–9
DNA	16	18	21	—	—	—
RNA	15	9	7	64	101	177
Protein	45	56	65	242	413	697
Sum	76	83	93			
Dry mass (measured by inter- ferometry)	82	86	87			

form of ribosome precursors and accumulation of these will contribute to the rapid growth of the nucleolus. At prophase, when the nuclear membrane breaks down and the nucleolus disintegrates, ribosomal precursors flood out into the cytoplasm (Lafontaine and Chouinard, 1963). We do not yet know to what extent the growth of the nucleolus during interphase is due to a retention of the ribosomes which are synthesized there. In development after division has ceased in the root the nucleolus no longer grows (R. F. Lyndon, unpublished) presumably because ribosomes are released into the cytoplasm as fast as they are formed. The nuclei of embryos which are still dormant contain very few or no ribosomes (Setterfield, 1961).

The increase of all the nuclear components slows down considerably as cells in the root mature (Table IV). In enlarging cells of the root, cytoplasmic protein and RNA continue to increase rapidly but nuclear protein and RNA increase little if at all. This may be either because synthesis in the nucleus stops or because it continues but the products are broken down or exported to the cytoplasm. The continued accumulation of RNA in the cytoplasm during cell enlargement suggests that synthesis in the nucleus in fact continues but that RNA (and perhaps protein, too) passes into the cytoplasm and does not contribute to the growth of the nucleus. The increased incorporation of protein and RNA precursors into the cytoplasm but not into the nucleus of enlarging cells is consistent with this view (Jensen, 1957). The formation of large cells by endopolyploidy, especially those of the developing vascular elements (List, 1963), is probably related to the increase in ribosome content which accompanies doubling of the chromosomes (Li and Anderson, 1967; Painter and Biesele, 1966). In microsporogenesis synthesis of RNA in the nucleolus and on the chromosomes falls off during meiotic prophase but the decrease in nucleolar synthesis is much more rapid (Das, 1965). When the pollen has been released and germinated, the nuclei of the pollen tube of *Zea* possess no nucleoli. Synthesis of RNA is resumed but it is not ribosomal RNA which is made (Steffensen, 1966). The ribosomes in the pollen tube are apparently made earlier during the formation of the pollen. It would be interesting to know to what extent the limited growth of the pollen tube is a result of the apparent inability of its nuclei to synthesize ribosomes.

Another case which may prove of interest in this respect is the difference which may be found between the nuclei of the root and shoot meristems of the same plant. The cells of the shoot meristem divide more slowly than those in the root. Prophase nuclei in the shoot meristem are only about half the size of those in the root and their dry mass is correspondingly smaller. Their DNA content, as expected, is the same (Table V). The increases of nuclear

TABLE V

Comparison of early prophase nuclei in root and short meristems of *Pisum*.

	Root	Shoot
Nuclear volume μ^3	460	310
Nuclear dry mass $\mu\mu$g	100	70
DNA per nucleus $\mu\mu$g	20	20
Nucleolar volume μ^3	25	8

protein and RNA during interphase are therefore only about half the corresponding increases during interphase in the root. The growth of the nucleolus is also very much less during interphase in the shoot, which might point to a synthesis of fewer ribosomes than during interphase in the root.

The growth of the nucleus during interphase is also due to intake of water. The dry mass of the nucleus approximately doubles but the volume increases

5-fold (Lyndon, 1967) and the nuclear envelope therefore doubles in area. This may be by stretching for the diameter of the pores may increase as the nucleus enlarges (Tamiya, 1964; Branton and Moor, 1964). Alternatively, the nuclear envelope might grow at least partly by addition of new material and the pores could become redistributed by closure of old pores and opening of new ones as was found in aged yeast cells (Moor and Muhlethaler, 1963). The number of pores in the envelope may also change during development. Large discontinuities in the envelope are characteristic of nuclei in the meristem but as the cells mature these holes are no longer found and the envelope also has fewer connections with the endoplasmic reticulum (Whaley *et al.*, 1960). When formed in telophase, the nuclear envelope at first has no pores (Porter and Machado, 1960; Chadard, 1962). They must be formed soon afterwards. At the end of interphase, the pores close up for just before the envelope is ruptured at the end of prophase it is once more devoid of pores (Porter and Machado, 1960; Israel and Sagawa, 1965). An uneven distribution of the pores could possibly result in a concentration difference, between one end of the cell and the other, of nuclear products such as RNA which pass out into the cytoplasm and might thus contribute to polarity within the cell.

B. REGULATION OF GENE ACTION

In whatever ways the activity of the nucleus changes, this must ultimately be by the repression or derepression of the activity of the genes. Histones have been the obvious candidates as the actual gene repressors. Huang and Bonner (1962) first showed that histones could act as inhibitors of DNA-primed synthesis of RNA. It was later shown that deoxyribonucleoprotein (DNP) isolated from dormant potato buds was much less effective in supporting RNA synthesis than DNP from buds released from dormancy (Tuan and Bonner, 1964). These and similar experiments were criticized on several scores. It was pointed out that the reconstituted DNP was likely to be inactive simply because of the electrostatic aggregation of the DNA with a polycation. This is probably why histones can inhibit the growth of plant tissues (Kaufmann and Das, 1955; Fellenberg, 1965; Fellenberg and Bopp, 1966; McLaren and Bradfute, 1966). The observation that the recombination of histone with DNA in reconstituted DNP was nonspecific confirmed this view (Barr and Butler, 1963). Another criticism was that although DNP was a poor primer for RNA synthesis its priming ability could be increased when it was broken into small fragments by sonication without altering the ratio of histone to DNA. The lesser ability of DNP than DNA to act as a primer for RNA synthesis could therefore be due to the precipitation and aggregation of the DNA when the histone was added (Sonneberg and Zubay, 1965).

A difficulty with all these experiments was that they concerned only quantitative effects of histone on the priming ability of DNA. If the histones really are the agents of genetic repression then it needs to be demonstrated that in native DNP some genes are repressed and others are not and that the genes which are repressed are specific to a particular type of cell or tissue. This problem was anticipated by Bonner et al. (1963) who got some evidence to show that the DNP from pea cotyledons could direct the synthesis of globulin but that the DNP from buds and roots (in which globulin does not occur in any quantity) could not, although the DNA from all sources was effective. Recently experiments have been carried out which have vindicated the idea that specific stretches of the DNA are free of histone in native DNP. Paul and Gilmour (1966) used sonicated and unsonicated DNP from calf thymus as templates for the synthesis of RNA. They then took the RNA which was synthesized and annealed it with calf thymus DNA. The RNA could anneal with only 5–10% of the sites on the DNA showing that in the DNP it was specific sites on the DNA which were not complexed with histone. Had the histone been removed unspecifically from the DNP, the RNA which was synthesized on the DNP would have been expected to correspond to all the sites on the DNA, since different parts of the DNP would have had different stretches of DNA exposed. Similar results have also been obtained by Georgiev et al. (1966). It is important to note that these experiments demonstrate that histone complexed with DNA reduces the ability of the DNA to prime RNA synthesis but they do not demonstrate that the histone complexes in a specific way with the DNA. What they do show is that the *removal* of histone from DNP may be specific.

If the histones are the gene repressors and act specifically, one would expect that there ought to be as many species of histones as there are genes to be repressed. This is almost certainly not the case, for whereas there are probably many thousands of genes in an organism, it is doubtful if there will prove to be, at the most, more than a hundred or so histones. Indeed in bacteria, for which the concepts of gene repression and activation were formulated, almost all the DNA is free of histone (Wilkins and Zubay, 1959; Leaver and Cruft, 1966). Also, in the ctenophores (simple, multicellular, differentiated animals) more than 99% of the DNA is free of histone (Cruft, 1966). It has been suggested that the specificity of the histones would be increased if they were combined with molecules which did show specificity such as RNA. Huang and Bonner (1965) have been able to isolate from pea buds a complex of histone and an RNA characterized by a high dihydrouridylic content. A similar RNA-histone complex has been isolated from mammalian cells (Benjamin et al., 1966) but its existence in mouse cells is denied (Commerford and Delihas, 1966).

The evidence which we have so far does not allow us to say with certainty what the role of the histones is. It may be purely structural, it may be as the repressor of gene activity. Some histones may perform one function, some the other. Whatever it is which does repress the genes it must ultimately be governed by substances from elsewhere in the cell. The nucleus by its products regulates the activity of the cytoplasm but in turn the cytoplasm regulates the activity of the nucleus. Nuclear transplantation experiments with amphibia have shown that the synthetic activity of the nucleus depends on the cytoplasmic *milieu* in which it finds itself (Gurdon, 1966). Whether or not the nucleus synthesizes DNA and RNA depends on the developmental stage not of the nucleus but of the cytoplasm which surrounds it (Gurdon and Brown, 1965; Graham *et al.*, 1966).

In plants the activity of the nucleus is presumably affected by the growth substances which are produced in the apices of the axis. When kinetin is applied to onion roots, within less than 30 minutes there is a very rapid and marked increase of RNA in the cells (Jensen *et al.*, 1964). The RNA content of the nuclei, especially the chromatin, is very much increased (Guttman, 1957) and it is probably due to an increased rate of synthesis of RNA in the nucleus (Olszewska, 1959). We may anticipate that work now in progress in several laboratories will point to a direct effect of growth substances on the rate of RNA synthesis by the nucleus and we may hope that this will provide a pointer to the mechanism of the regulation of gene action.

REFERENCES

Albersheim, P. and Killias, U. (1963). *J. Cell Biol.* **17**, 93.

Ambrose, E. J. and Bajer, A. (1961). *Proc. R. Soc.* B. **153**, 357.

Avanzi, S., Brunori, A., D'Amato, F., Nutti Ronchi, V. and Scarascia Mugonzza, G. T. (1963). *Caryologia*, **16**, 553.

Bajer, A. and Allen, R. D. (1966). *Science, N.Y.* **151**, 572.

Bandurski, R. S. and Maheshwari, S. C. (1962). *Pl. Physiol., Lancaster* **37**, 556.

Barr, G. C. and Butler, J. A. V. (1963). *Nature, Lond.* **199**, 1170.

Bell, P. R., Frey-Wyssling, A. and Muhlethaler, K. (1966). *J. Ultrastruct. Res.* **15**, 108.

Bell, P. R. and Muhlethaler, K. (1964). *J. Cell Biol.* **20**, 235.

Benjamin, W., Levander, O. A., Gellhorn, A. and Debellus, R. H. (1966). *Proc. natn. Acad. Sci., U.S.A.* **55**, 858.

Birnstiel, M. (1967). *A. Rev. Pl. Physiol.* **18**, 25.

Birnstiel, M. L. and Hyde, B. B. (1963). *J. Cell Biol.* **18**, 41.

Birnstiel, M. L., Chipchase, M. I. H. and Bonner, J. (1961). *Biochem. biophys. Res. Commun.* **6**, 161.

Birnstiel, M. L., Chipchase, M. I. H. and Hayes, R. J. (1962a). *Biochim. biophys. Acta* **55**, 728.

Birnstiel, M. L., Rho, J. H. and Chipchase, M. I. H. (1962b). *Biochim. biophys. Acta* **55**, 734.

Birnstiel, M. L., Chipchase, M. I. H. and Hyde, B. B. (1963a). *Biochim. biophys. Acta* **76**, 454.

Birnstiel, M. L., Fleissner, E. and Borek, E. (1963b). *Science, N.Y.* **142**, 1577.

Birnstiel, M. L., Chipchase, M. I. H. and Flamm, W. G. (1964). *Biochim. biophys. Acta* **87**, 111.

Birnstiel, M. L., Wallace, H., Sirlin, J. L. and Fischberg, M. (1967). *Natn. Cancer Inst. Monog.* **23**, 431.

Bonner, J. (1965). "The Molecular Biology of Development". Clarendon Press, Oxford.

Bonner, J., Huang, R. C. and Gilden, R. V. (1963). *Proc. natn. Acad. Sci., U.S.A.* **50**, 893.

Brandham, P. E. and Godward, M. B. E. (1965). *Jl. R. microsc. Soc.* **84**, 499.

Branton, D. and Moor, H. (1964). *J. Ultrastruct. Res.* **11**, 401.

Brown, D. D. and Gurdon, J. B. (1964). *Proc. natn. Acad. Sci., U.S.A.* **51**, 139.

Bopp-Hassenkamp, G. (1959). *Protoplasma* **50**, 243.

Brachet, J. (1967). *Nature, Lond.* **213**, 650.

Buvat, R. (1963). *Int. Rev. Cytol.* **14**, 41.

Callan, H. G. (1963). *Int. Rev. Cytol.* **15**, 1.

Callan, H. G. (1966). *J. Cell Sci.* **1**, 85.

Chadard, R. (1962). *Revue Cytol. Biol. vég.* **24**, 1.

Chipchase, M. I. H. and Birnstiel, M. L. (1963a). *Proc. natn. Acad. Sci., U.S.A.* **49**, 692.

Chipchase, M. I. H. and Birnstiel, M. L. (1963b). *Proc. natn. Acad. Sci., U.S.A.* **50**, 1101.

Chouinard, L. A. (1966). *Can. J. Bot.* **44**, 403.

Comb, D. G. and Katz, S. (1964). *J. molec. Biol.* **8**, 790.

Comb, D. G., Brown, R. and Katz, S. (1964). *J. molec. Biol.* **8**, 781.

Comb, D. G. and Zehavi-Willner, T. (1967). *J. molec. Biol.* **23**, 441.

Commerford, S. L. and Delihas, N. (1966). *Proc. natn. Acad. Sci., U.S.A.* **56**, 1759.

Cruft, H. (1966). *Biochem. J.* **101**, 36P.

Cruft, H., Mauritzen, C. M. and Stedman, E. (1957). *Phil. Trans. R. Soc. B* **241**, 93.

Das, N. K. (1963). *Science, N.Y.* **140**, 1231.

Das, N. K. (1965). *Expl Cell Res.* **40**, 360.

Das, N. K., Siegal, E. P. and Alfert, M. (1965). *Expl Cell Res.* **40**, 178.

Davidson, D. (1964). *Expl Cell Res.* **35**, 317.

De, D. M. (1961). *Nucleus* **4**, 1.

Deeley, H. E. M., Davies, H. G. and Chayen, J. (1957). *Expl Cell Res.* **12**, 582.

Diers, L. (1966). *J. Cell Biol.* **28**, 527.

Evans, G. M. and Rees, H. (1966). *Expl Cell Res.* **44**, 150.

Evans, H. J. (1964). *Expl Cell Res.* **35**, 381.

Fawcett, D. W. (1964). *In* "Modern Developments in Electron Microscopy". (B. M. Siegel, ed.), p. 257. Academic Press, London.

Fellenberg, G. (1965). *Planta* **64**, 287.

Fellenberg, G. and Bopp, M. (1966). *Z. Pfl. Physiol.* **55**, 337.

Filner, P. (1965). *Expl Cell Res.* **39**, 33.

Flamm, W. G. and Birnstiel, M. L. (1964a). *Expl Cell Res.* **33**, 616.

Flamm, W. G. and Birnstiel, M. L. (1964b). *Biochim. biophys. Acta* **87**, 101.

Flamm, W. G., Birnstiel, M. L. and Filner, P. (1963). *Biochim. biophys. Acta* **76**, 110.

Franke, W. W. (1966). *J. Cell Biol.* **31**, 619.

Gall, J. G. (1967). *J. Cell Biol.* **32**, 391.

Georgiev, G. P., Ananieva, L. N. and Kozlov, J. V. (1966). *J. molec. Biol.* **22**, 365.

Godward, M. B. E. and Jordan, E. G. (1965). *Jl. R. Micr. Soc.* **84**, 347.

Graham, C. F., Arms, K. and Gurdon, J. B. (1966). *Devl Biol.* **14**, 349.

Greenberg, H. and Penman, S. (1966). *J. molec. Biol.* **21**, 527.
Gurdon, J. B. (1966). *Endeavour* **25**, 95.
Gurdon, J. B. and Brown, D. D. (1965). *J. molec. Biol.* **12**, 27.
Guttman, R. (1957). *J. biophys. biochem. Cytol.* **3**, 129.
Haemmerling, J. (1963). *A. Rev. Pl. Physiol.* **14**, 65.
Harding, C. V. and Feldherr, C. (1959). *J. gen. Physiol.* **42**, 1155.
Harris, P. and Bajer, A. (1965). *Chromosoma* **16**, 624.
Harris, H. and LaCour, L. F. (1963). *Nature, Lond.* **200**, 227.
Hawker, L. E. (1965). *Biol. Rev.* **40**, 52.
Hotta, Y. and Stern, H. (1963). *J. Cell Biol.* **19**, 45.
Hotta, Y., Ito, M. and Stern, H. (1966). *Proc. natn. Acad. Sci., U.S.A.* **56**, 1184.
Howard, A. and Dewey, D. L. (1961). *Expl Cell Res.* **24**, 623.
Huang, R. C. and Bonner, J. (1962). *Proc. natn. Acad. Sci., U.S.A.* **48**, 1216.
Huang, R. C. and Bonner, J. (1965). *Proc. natn. Acad. Sci., U.S.A.* **54**, 960.
Hyde, B. B. (1964). *In* "The Nucleohistones". (J. Bonner and P. Ts'o, eds), p. 163. Holden-Day, Inc., London.
Hyde, B. B., Sankaranarayanan, K. and Birnstiel, M. L. (1965). *J. Ultrastruct. Res.* **12**, 652.
Ingle, J., Key, J. L. and Holm, R. E. (1965). *J. molec. Biol.* **11**, 730.
Inoue, S. and Bajer, A. (1961). *Chromosoma* **12**, 48.
Ishida, M. R. (1961). *Cytologia* **26**, 359.
Israel, H. and Sagawa, Y. (1964). *Caryologia* **17**, 301.
Israel, H. and Sagawa, Y. (1965). *Caryologia* **18**, 15.
Iwai, K. (1964). *In* "The Nucleohistones". (J. Bonner and P. Ts'o eds), p. 59. Holden-Day Inc., London.
Jensen, W. A. (1957). *Proc. natn. Acad. Sci., U.S.A.* **43**, 1038.
Jensen, W. A. (1964). *J. Cell Biol.* **23**, 669.
Jensen, W. A. (1965). *Am. J. Bot.* **52**, 781.
Jensen, W. A., Kavaljian, L. G. and Martinot, S. (1960). *Expl Cell Res.* **20**, 361.
Jensen, W. A., Pollock, E. G., Healey, P. and Ashton, M. (1964). *Expl Cell Res.* **33**, 523.
Johns, E. W. and Butler, J. A. V. (1962). *Biochem. J.* **84**, 436.
Johnston, F. B., Nasatir, M. and Stern, H. (1957). *Pl. Physiol., Lancaster* **32**, 124.
Johnston, F. B., Setterfield, G. and Stern, H. (1959). *J. biophys. biochem. Cytol.* **6**, 53.
Jones, K. W. (1965). *J. Ultrastruct. Res.* **13**, 257.
Kallio, P. (1963). *Suomal. Tiedeakar. Toim.* (A) IV **70**, 1.
Karasaki, S. (1965). *J. Cell Biol.* **26**, 937.
Kaufmann, B. P. and Das, N. K. (1955). *Chromosoma* **7**, 19.
Kaufmann, B. P., MacDonald, M. and Gay, H. (1948). *Nature, Lond.* **162**, 814.
Kemp, C. L. (1966). *Chromosoma* **19**, 137.
Kusanagi, A. (1966). *Chromosoma* **20**, 125.
La Cour, L. F. (1963). *Expl Cell Res.* **29**, 112.
La Cour, L. F. (1966). *In* "Chromosomes Today". (C. D. Darlington and K. R. Lewis, eds), Vol. 1, p. 150. Oliver and Boyd, Edinburgh.
La Cour, L. F. and Crawley, J. W. C. (1965). *Chromosoma* **16**, 124.
Lafontaine, J. G. and Chouinard, L. A. (1963). *J. Cell Biol.* **17**, 167.
Leaver, J. L. and Cruft, H. J. (1966). *Biochem. J.* **101**, 665.
Ledbetter, M. C. and Porter, K. R. (1963). *J. Cell Biol.* **19**, 239.
Li, P. H. and Anderson, W. R. (1967). *Nature, Lond.* **214**, 86.

38   R. F. LYNDON

Lin, C. Y., Key, J. L. and Bracker, C. E. (1966). *Pl. Physiol., Lancaster* **41**, 976.
List, A. (1963). *Am. J. Bot.* **50**, 320.
Loening, U. E. (1965). *Proc. R. Soc.* B **162**, 121.
Loewenstein, W. R., Kanno, Y. and Ito, S. (1966). *Ann. N. Y. Acad. Sci.* **137**, 708.
Lu, B. C. (1966). *Expl Cell Res.* **43**, 224.
Lyndon, R. F. (1963). *J. exp. Bot.* **14**, 419.
Lyndon, R. F. (1967). *Ann. Bot.* **31**, 133.
Manton, I. (1964). *Jl R. micr. Soc.* **83**, 471.
Marinos, N. G. (1960). *J. Ultrastruct. Res.* **3**, 328.
Martin, P. G. (1966). *Expl Cell Res.* **44**, 84.
Mattingly, A. (1963). *Expl Cell Res.* **29**, 314.
Mazia, D. (1961). *In* "The Cell". (J. Brachet and A. E. Mirsky, eds), Vol. 3, p. 77. Academic Press, London.
McLaren, A. D. and Bradfute, O. E. (1966). *Physiologia Pl.* **19**, 1094.
McLeish, J. (1959). *Chromosoma* **10**, 686.
McLeish, J. (1963). *Proc. R. Soc.* B **158**, 261.
McLeish, J. (1964). *Nature, Lond.* **204**, 36.
McLeish, J. and Sunderland, N. (1961). *Expl Cell Res.* **24**, 527.
Menzel, M. Y. and Price, J. M. (1966). *Am. J. Bot.* **53**, 1079.
Mirsky, A. E. and Ris, H. (1951). *J. gen. Physiol.* **34**, 475.
Mitchison, J. M. (1966). *Int. Rev. Cytol.* **19**, 97.
Moor, H. and Muhlethaler, K. (1963). *J. Cell Biol.* **17**, 609.
Moses, M. J. (1964). *In* "Cytology and Cell Physiology". (G. H. Bourne, ed.), 3rd edition, p. 423. Academic Press, London.
Olszewska, M. J. (1959). *Expl Cell Res.* **16**, 193.
Painter, T. S. and Biesele, J. J. (1966). *Proc. natn. Acad. Sci., U.S.A.* **56**, 1920.
Partanen, C. R. (1965). *Am. J. Bot.* **52**, 204.
Paul, J. and Gilmour, R. S. (1966). *J. molec. Biol.* **16**, 242.
Peacock, W. J. (1965). *Natn. Cancer Inst. Monog.* **18**, 101.
Penman, S. (1966). *J. molec. Biol.* **17**, 117.
Perry, R. P. (1965). *Natn. Cancer Inst. Monog.* **18**, 325.
Peveling, E. (1961). *Planta* **56**, 530.
Pickett-Heaps, J. D. and Northcote, D. H. (1966). *J. Cell Sci.* **1**, 109.
Porter, K. R. and Machado, R. D. (1960). *J. biophys. biochem. Cytol.* **7**, 167.
Prensky, W. and Smith, H. H. (1964). *Expl Cell Res.* **34**, 525.
Prescott, D. M. (1964). *In* "The Nucleohistones". (J. Bonner and P. Ts'o eds) p. 193. Holden-Day Inc., London.
Rasch, E. and Woodard, J. W. (1959). *J. biophys. biochem. Cytol.* **6**, 263.
Rees, H. and Evans, G. M. (1966). *Expl Cell Res.* **44**, 161.
Resch, A. and Peveling, E. (1964). *Z. Naturforsch.* **19B**, 506.
Rho, J. H. and Bonner, J. (1961). *Proc. natn. Acad. Sci., U.S.A.* **47**, 1611.
Rho, J. H. and Chipchase, M. I. H. (1962). *J. Cell Biol.* **14**, 183.
Ris, H. (1961). *Can. J. Genet. Cytol.* **3**, 95.
Ris, H. (1966). *Proc. R. Soc.* B **164**, 246.
Rossner, W. (1961). *Chromosoma* **12**, 717.
Rothfels, K., Sexsmith, E. Heimburger, M. and Krause, M. O. (1966). *Chromosoma* **20**, 54.
Rozijn, T. H. and Tonino, G. J. M. (1964). *Biochim. biophys. Acta* **91**, 105.
Selman, G. G. (1966). *J. Embryol. exp. Morph.* **16**, 469.
Setterfield, G. (1961). *Can. J. Bot.* **39**, 469.

Sharp, L. W. (1943). "Fundamentals of Cytology". McGraw-Hill, New York.
Shephard, D. C. (1965). *Expl Cell Res.* **37**, 93.
Sheridan, W. F. and Stern, H. (1967). *Expl Cell Res.* **45**, 323.
Sirlin, J. L., Jacob, J. and Birnstiel, M. L. (1965). *Biochim. biophys. Acta.* **108**, 716.
Sonneberg, B. P. and Zubay, G. (1965). *Proc. natn. Acad. Sci., U.S.A.* **54**, 415.
Sparvoli, E., Gay, H. and Kaufmann, B. P. (1965). *Chromosoma* **16**, 415.
Stange, L. (1965). *A. Rev. Pl. Physiol.* **16**, 119.
Steffensen, D. M. (1966). *Expl Cell Res.* **44**, 1.
Steffensen, D. M. and Bergeron, J. A. (1959). *J. biophys. biochem. Cytol.* **6**, 339.
Stern, H. and Mirsky, A. E. (1952). *J. gen. Physiol.* **36**, 181.
Sunderland, N. and McLeish, J. (1961). *Expl Cell. Res.* **24**, 541.
Swanson, C. P. (1958). "Cytology and Cytogenetics". MacMillan, London.
Tamiya, H. (1964). *Symp. Soc. exp. Biol.* **17**, 188.
Taylor, J. H. (1953). *Expl Cell Res.* **4**, 164.
Taylor, J. H. (1958). *Am. J. Bot.* **45**, 123.
Taylor, J. H., Woods, P. S. and Hughes, W. L. (1957). *Proc. natn. Acad. Sci., U.S.A.* **43**, 122.
Thomas, A. J. and Sherratt, H. S. A. (1956). *Biochem. J.* **62**, 1.
Trosko, J. E. and Wolff, S. (1965). *J. Cell Biol.* **26**, 125.
Tuan, D. Y. H. and Bonner, J. (1964). *Pl. Physiol., Lancaster* **39**, 768.
Uhl, C. (1965). *Genetics* **51**, 191.
Van't Hof, J. (1963). *Cytologia* **28**, 30.
Van't Hof, J. (1967). *Expl Cell Res.* **45**, 638.
Werz, G. (1965). *Brookhaven Symp. Biol.* **18**, 185.
Whaley, W. G., Mollenhauer, H. H. and Leech, J. H. (1960). *J. biophys. biochem. Cytol.* **8**, 233.
Wilkins, M. H. F. and Zubay, G. (1959). *J. biophys. biochem. Cytol.* **5**, 55.
Wimber, D. E. (1961). *Expl Cell Res.* **23**, 402.
Wimber, D. E. and Presnky, W. (1963). *Genetics* **48**, 1731.
Wolfe, S. L. (1965). *J. Ultrastruct. Res.* **12**, 104.
Wolff, S. (1965). *Natn. Cancer Inst. Monog.* **18**, 155.
Woodard, J., Rasch, E. and Swift, H. (1961). *J. biophys. biochem. Cytol.* **9**, 445.
Woods, P. S. (1960). *In* "The Cell Nucleus". (J. S. Mitchell ed.), p. 127. Butterworths, London.
Woods, P. S. and Zubay, G. (1965). *Proc. natn. Acad. Sci., U.S.A.* **54**, 1705.
Zalokar, M. (1960). *Expl Cell Res.* **19**, 559.
Zubay, G. and Doty, P. (1959). *J. molec. Biol.* **1**, 1.

CHAPTER 3

The Structure and Possible Function of the Vacuole

J. DAINTY

School of Biological Sciences, University of East Anglia, Norwich, England

I. STRUCTURE AND ORIGIN

Vacuoles are an obvious and characteristic feature of plant cells. In the older, pre-electron microscope literature the size of vacuoles, their distribution among various types of cells and various types of plants, the nature of the contents and inclusions and the pH etc. have been described and discussed, although most of the discussion of function has been and still is almost pure speculation. Some further observations have been made in recent years (Voeller, 1964; de Robertis *et al.*, 1965); these have added something, although not a very great deal, to our total knowledge.

All cells contain what might be called a vacuolar system represented by the endoplasmic reticulum, the Golgi complex and the nuclear envelope. In plant cells this vacuolar system has added to it the plant vacuole(s) to which we usually reserve the name vacuole. All these vacuoles, vesicles, cisternae and so on, seem to be essentially "aqueous inclusions" in the cytoplasm bounded by phospholipid membranes. On the whole, as judged by the evidence gained from electron microscope pictures, these phospholipid membranes, and the plasmalemma, are very similar so-called unit membranes. It is true that some of them may appear fractionally wider than others and some may be "rough" and others "smooth". It may be, too, that some are of the Danielli type of bimolecular layer of lipid, while in others the membrane may be made up of subunits, micelles of lipid coated with protein. However, at present, we would say that they are all basically similar phospholipid membranes. The special name of tonoplast is given to the membrane bounding the large central vacuole of mature plant cells.

There has, of course, been some speculation as to the origin of the characteristic vacuoles of plant cells. Some think of them as originating by being budded off, as vesicles, from the Golgi complex and subsequently growing and coalescing to produce the final large central vacuole (Marinos, 1963). Others think of a similar origin from the endoplasmic reticulum (Buvat, 1963) or that they arise from the synthesis of a highly hydratable macromolecule in the cytoplasm which "draws" water to it leading to the creation of a little aqueous bubble around this macromolecule and this bubble subsequently acquires a phospholipid membrane as a boundary (Guilliermond, 1941).

These speculations have not had much physico-chemical basis which is not surprising for there is little physico-chemical understanding of the nature of cytoplasm. However, one or two things can be said with respect to this system in which, apparently, a homogeneous aqueous phase or phases can separate out and/or coexist with a complex colloidal phase. If the phases are in thermodynamic equilibrium with respect to water, then the chemical potential of water must be the same in the vacuoles as in the cytoplasm. The chemical potential of water can be written as the sum of three components (plus the standard chemical potential of pure water at atmospheric pressure):

$$\mu_w = \mu_w^0 + RT\ln a_w + P\bar{V}_w + \Gamma$$

In this expression $RT\ln a_w$ (a_w is the activity of the water) expresses the contribution due to dissolved solutes; $P\bar{V}_w$ ($\bar{V}_w$ is the partial molar volume of water) is the effect of hydrostatic pressure (P) and Γ is the so-called matric potential which depends on the interaction of the water with macromolecules and colloidal constituents. The $RT\ln a_w$ and Γ terms are negative. This separation of μ_w into components is probably not thermodynamically justifiable but it forms a useful basis for discussion.

If we assume that the $P\bar{V}_w$ terms are the same in a vacuole and in the cytoplasm (although this may not be true), then only the two negative terms need to be considered. In a large vacuole it seems certain that Γ is negligible compared to its value in the cytoplasm. Thus equality of μ_w can only be achieved by having a higher solute concentration in the vacuole than in the cytoplasm. (If the vacuole is to grow then the vacuolar solute concentration must be higher still to make μ_w (vacuole) less than μ_w (cytoplasm).) Since the cytoplasmic colloids probably carry a net negative charge, the Donnan effect operating on ionized solutes tends to make the solute concentration in the cytoplasm *higher* than in the vacuole; this, of course, only makes it still more difficult to get a higher solute concentration in the vacuole. Thus it is tentatively concluded that we must expect, at the vacuolar surfaces, inwardly directed solute "pumps" the function of which is to produce and maintain the necessary higher vacuolar solute concentration. There is not much experimental evidence containing the relative solute concentrations in the vacuole and the cytoplasm. What little there is comes from ion analyses on

D

large coenocytic algae; these are quoted in Table I and it can be seen that the total ionic concentration in the vacuole is, in general, greater than that in the cytoplasm. It could still be that there are other solutes in the cytoplasm which would invalidate this evidence.

From the above thermodynamic considerations about μ_w, the chemical potential of water, a vacuole might start in a small region centred on a particularly hydrophilic (and water structure-ordering) macromolecule because here there could be a large, negative contribution to μ_w from Γ. But such a vacuole could not develop without a fairly rapid increase in the local solute concentration for the Γ contribution would rapidly decrease as the

TABLE I

Ionic concentrations (mM) in "flowing" cytoplasm (i.e. not including the stationary chloroplast layer) and the vacuole of certain giant algal cells.

	Nitella flexilis (Kishimoto and Tazawa, 1965)		Nitella translucens (MacRobbie, 1962)		Nitella translucens (Spanswick and Williams, 1964; Spanswick et al., 1967)	
	cytoplasm	vacuole	cytoplasm	vacuole	cytoplasm	vacuole
Potassium	125	80	120	79	93	67
Sodium	5	27	54	37	37	73
Chloride	36	135	?	150	65	160

vacuole enlarged. However, there would appear to be nothing against such an origin on thermodynamic grounds. One of the big problems in connection with such an origin is the appearance, presumably at an early stage because of the apparent early necessity for solute pumping systems, of a phospholipid membrane around the incipient vacuole. This implies the synthesis of phospholipid in the cytoplasm and its "adsorption" as a bimolecular layer, or its equivalent, at the surface of the developing vacuole. We seem to know little about the mechanism of such an adsorption of phospholipid. It may be a "passive" process, involving a decrease in free energy, but it seems more likely that metabolic energy is involved in ordering the phospholipid molecules and then subsequently maintaining the structure of the membrane.

Most people are probably more attracted to the idea that vacuoles do not arise *de novo* but are products of a pre-existing vacuolar system, whether Golgi, endoplasmic reticulum or more non-specific vacuoles and vesicles. Again much phospholipid synthesis is needed and the phospholipids have to be "slotted-in" to the pre-existing vacuolar membranes. There are also the same physico-chemical problems of the expansion of vacuoles which requires a lower μ_w in the vacuoles than in the cytoplasm. In addition, a new problem arises, that of the mechanism of "budding-off" from the pre-existing vacuolar system. This implies, I think, some heterogeneity in the membranes, perhaps of charge, which can allow approach, fusion and separation of the phospholipid systems. Local differences in charge, perhaps due to calcium, and local differences in ion pumping activities may be vital here.

II. ION TRANSPORT

I have so far raised some questions and unsatisfactorily discussed some of the physico-chemical problems associated with the origin and development of vacuoles. It seems that there is little information as yet to resolve the problems involved. A little is known, however, about the permeability properties of the tonoplast, the phospholipid membrane surrounding the large central vacuole of mature plant cells. This information is largely gained from studies on giant coenocytic algal cells and it is possible that it is not completely relevant to the situation in higher plant cells.

The large internodal cells of various members of the Characeae have been most frequently studied and fairly detailed pictures are beginning to emerge, particularly for two species, *Nitella translucens* and *Chara australis*. A kinetic analysis of the exchange of the ions sodium, potassium and chloride between the bathing medium and the cells of *N. translucens*, together with a knowledge of the concentration of these ions in the vacuole and cytoplasm of these cells, shows that the ion fluxes across the tonoplast are up to a hundred times greater than the fluxes across the plasmalemma (MacRobbie, 1962, 1964, 1966). It therefore appears that the tonoplast in these cells is much more permeable to ions than is the plasmalemma. Certain other evidence supports this conclusion. By inserting suitable microelectrodes, the electrical resistance of the plasmalemma and tonoplast can be separately measured; it turns out that the resistance of the tonoplast is at least ten times smaller than that of the plasmalemma in *C. australis* (Hope and Walker, 1961). Also most of the electrical potential difference between the vacuole and the external medium is across the plasmalemma (about 140 mV, cytoplasm negative, across the plasmalemma and not more than 20 mV, cytoplasm also negative, across the tonoplast) (Spanswick and Williams, 1964; Hope and Walker, 1961). The tonoplast does not seem so selective, with respect to cation permeability at least, as the plasmalemma. Thus, in the two most thoroughly investigated species, the tonoplast seems to be a fairly permeable, non-selective, membrane as compared with the plasmalemma. (Although the tonoplast of *N. translucens* and *C. australis* is one or two orders more permeable to ions than the plasmalemma, it is still only of the same order of permeability as a typical animal cell plasma membrane.)

The information obtained with other plant cells is quite dubious. Four marine or brackish water algae have been examined and no clear idea can be obtained from the results as to whether the tonoplast is more or less permeable to sodium, potassium and chloride ions than the plasmalemma (Gutknecht and Dainty, 1968). This is clearly an area where intensive work is needed.

One curious feature of the tonoplast fluxes in *N. translucens* has been observed by MacRobbie (1966). She finds a correlation between the influxes of potassium and chloride across the tonoplast and the influx of chloride across the plasmalemma. The correlation is such that, for every chloride ion crossing the plasmalemma, about 60 molecules of potassium (plus sodium ?) chloride cross the tonoplast; sometimes it is a small integral number times 60 molecules.

I have previously argued that the origin, growth and existence of vacuoles implies a solute pump, located at the tonoplast, and directed towards the vacuole. The most reliable evidence relevant to this comes from the work on *N. translucens*. The ionic concentrations in the "flowing cytoplasm" and in the vacuole are given in Table I. The electrical potential difference across the tonoplast is about 20 mV, with the cytoplasm negative. From these figures the electrochemical potential differences for sodium, potassium and chloride ions between the vacuole and the cytoplasm can be calculated. They show that both potassium and, particularly, sodium are at a higher electrochemical potential in the vacuole, whereas chloride is approximately in electrochemical equilibrium (Spanswick and Williams, 1964; Spanswick *et al.*, 1967). This result means, fairly unequivocally, that both potassium and, particularly, sodium are "pumped" against the electrochemical potential gradient from the cytoplasm to the vacuole. Similar measurements have been made on the marine alga *Valonia ventricosa* by Gutknecht (1966); here it is even more clear that sodium and potassium are pumped from the cytoplasm into the vacuole. Thus, from what little is known, there seem to be inwardly directed cation pumps at the tonoplast of giant algal cells.

Much less is known about the tonoplast in higher plant cells for the experimental difficulties are very much greater. Individual cells are quite small and the cytoplasm in mature cells is often less than one micron thick, hence it has so far proved practically impossible to measure directly ionic concentrations in the cytoplasm and almost impossible to measure the electrical potential difference between cytoplasm and vacuole. Additionally, flux measurements have to be made on tissues with the accompanying complications of extracellular space and heterogeneous populations of cells. Nevertheless, a few hints have been obtained of the possible situation at the tonoplast. The electrical potential difference between the cytoplasm and vacuole has been measured in root hair cells (Etherton and Higinbotham, 1960); it was found to be small, similar to the situation in the giant algal cells. Some ion flux measurements have been made on carrot root storage tissue and on excised barley roots (Pitman and Saddler, 1967) which indicate that the tonoplast permeability is fairly high, although the ratio of tonoplast permeability to plasmalemma permeability does not seem so high as in the giant algal cells which have been studied. However, because of the difficulties of a kinetic analysis of flux data from plant tissue, I do not feel that too much reliance can be placed on these permeability statements yet. Thus there is a suggestion, but only this so far, that higher plant cells are not too different from algal cells from the ionic relations point of view. One thing which is clearly different is that the major anion in the vacuole of higher plant cells is an organic acid anion, most commonly malate. Whether this has to be pumped across the tonoplast into the vacuole, as I suspect, or whether it moves passively in response to an electrical potential difference generated by cation pumps are questions which as yet cannot be resolved.

III. FUNCTION

One can at present only guess the function of vacuoles. It is clearly recognized that membranes and membrane-bounded organelles are a very important feature of all cells. It is also fairly certain that many of the chemical reactions of the cell takes place on or are closely associated with membranes; it is only necessary to think of photosynthesis, the Krebs cycle and oxidative phosphorylation, protein synthesis and active transport to see that this is so. Thus, phospholipid membrane-bounded compartments must have originated at a very early stage of evolution and have subsequently evolved to have various functions. One can speculate that a very early function of a phospholipid membrane, perhaps the external plasma membrane, was "secretory" or "excretory", being concerned with developing an ion-pumping system to maintain the integrity of primitive protoplasm, i.e. to stop it from being diluted out of existence by the inflow of water. It would appear from the earlier discussion that it is probably necessary for these phospholipo-protein membranes to retain their pumping properties if vacuoles are to form, grow and maintain their identity. Membranes are active transport sites for many solutes other than ions and I therefore envisage the primary function of vacuoles as secretory. It is well known that small vacuoles or vesicles (of, for example, the Golgi apparatus) perform this function with respect to processes such as the transport of cell wall material to and through the plasmalemma or to the site of origin of a new cell wall in a dividing plant cell. Such phospholipid-bounded vesicles would seem well adapted to fusion and subsequent emptying with the plasmalemma; this is a type of inverse pinocytosis. Small vacuoles certainly provide this kind of function in animal cells.

In plant cells, besides the small vacuoles or vesicles in the cytoplasm, the characteristic feature is the large central vacuole. Certainly one can envisage that its major function, or rather the major function of the tonoplast, is secretory, i.e. putting things, usually at a different concentration, into the vacuole. Thus, as is amply documented, the vacuole can act as a subcellular storage organ of useful metabolites or of toxic excretory products. The huge development of the vacuole may be partly associated with the lack of development of an efficient circulatory system in plants and of a kidney or other excretory system. However, it seems plausible to me that the development of the large central plant vacuole is associated with the development of cell walls and the need for turgid cells for skeletal purposes. It is true that the presence of a large vacuole is not essential to produce the high hydrostatic pressure inside plant cells. However, the presence of the vacuole ensures that the hydrostatic pressure is produced with great economy in the production of protoplasm which is now confined to a relatively thin film around the periphery of the cell. Given the primitive highly vacuolated plant cell, the vacuole can be used as a storage and dumping organ and to other advantages as well. The transport from cell to cell via the plasmadesmata becomes more rapid because of the cyclosis of the thin film of protoplasm. The development of special transporting cells (the phloem vessels, the tracheids and xylem vessels) follows fairly naturally from highly vacuolated standard plant cells. Indeed, together with the cell wall and the chloroplast, the large central vacuole is an *essential* feature of plants above the level of microscopic algae.

REFERENCES

Buvat, R. (1963). *Int. Rev. Cytol.* **14**, 41.
De Robertis, E. D. P., Narinski, W. W. and Salz, F. A. (1965). "Cell Biology", 4th Ed, W. B. Saunders Co., Philadelphia and London.
Etherton, B. and Higinbotham, N. (1960). *Science, N. Y.* **131**, 409.
Guilliermond, A. (1941). *Chronica Botanica*, Waltham, Massachusetts.
Gutknecht, J. (1966). *Biol. Bull. mar. biol. Lab., Woods Hale* **130**, 331.
Gutknecht, J. and Dainty, J. (1968). *Oceanography mar. Biol.* (in press). **6**, 163.
Hope, A. B. and Walker, N. A. (1961). *Aust. J. biol. Sci.* **14**, 26.
Kishimoto, U. and Tazawa, M. (1965). *Pl. Cell Physiol., Tokyo* **6**, 507.
MacRobbie, E. A. C. (1962). *J. gen. Physiol.* **45**, 861.
MacRobbie, E. A. C. (1964). *J. gen. Physiol.* **47**, 859.
MacRobbie, E. A. C. (1966). *Aust. J. biol. Sci.* **19**, 371.
Marinos, N. G. (1963). *J. Ultrastruct. Res.* **9**, 177.
Pitman, M. G. and Saddler, H. D. W. (1967). *Proc. natn. Acad. Sci., U.S.A.* **57**, 44.
Spanswick, R. M. and Williams, E. J. (1964). *J. exp. Bot.* **15**, 193.
Spanswick, R. M., Stolarek, J. and Williams, E. J. (1967). *J. exp. Bot.* **18**, 1.
Voeller, B. R. (1964). *In* "The Cell". (J. Brachet and A. E. Mirsky, eds), Vol. VI, Academic Press, New York and London.

CHAPTER 4

Structure, Function and Developmental Changes in Mitochondria of Higher Plant Cells

Department of Botany, University College, Swansea, Glamorgan, Wales

I. INTRODUCTION

The concept of mitochondria has undergone considerable evolution since the organelles were originally discovered and described (under the name of "bioblasts") by Altmann in 1890 in fixed preparations of animal cells. During the next 50 years, many cytological observations on mitochondria accumulated with only speculation about their function, although shrewd guesses were made; the particles came to be generally considered to be ". . . centres of constructive metabolism" and already in 1912 Kingsbury proposed a respiratory function (Hackett, 1955). During this period great confusion existed about just what cell inclusions should be termed mitochondria. Studies on the metabolic reactions now known to be associated with mitochondria at first proceeded quite separately. When the Krebs cycle sequence of reactions was elucidated in the 1930s, its cellular location was not known; the first reports of particulate succinoxidase in higher plants, in 1939 and 1940, were published without the significance of the particulate nature being recognized (Millerd, 1956). In the 1940s and 1950s, however, different lines of research

47

converged. While the refinement of differential centrifugation and analytical techniques enabled the isolation and biochemical characterization of sub-cellular fractions, electron microscopy made it possible to distinguish mito-chondria from other cytoplasmic inclusions and to equate subcellular frac-tions with structural entities in the cell. In a review published in 1951, Newcomer still accepts as a mitochondrion almost any cytoplasmic inclusion of appropriate size, while admitting that all "mitochondria" need not be identical. Those "mitochondria" obviously include what now would be termed proplastids. Within a few years, emphasis shifted to functional definitions. Hackett also provides a primary morphological definition of mitochondria as ". . . variously shaped particles, usually 0·5 to 1·0 μ in diameter and up to 10 μ or more in length, which are composed largely of lipids and proteins . . . and generally stain with Janus green B". At the same time, however, he cautiously produces a biochemical definition as " . . . par-ticles associated with cytochrome oxidase" and accepts a working definition on the basis of centrifugal forces used in organelle sedimentation (Hackett, 1955). Goddard and Stafford (1954) already put the functional characters first: "It seems best to define mitochondria in terms of their specific chemical activities, with chemical and morphological details as secondary factors . . . as cellular particles associated with enzymes of the cytochrome system, the Krebs cycle, fatty acid oxidation and with oxidative phosphorylation. These lipoprotein and pentose nucleic acid-containing particles may vary in size from . . . about 0·1 to 6·0 μ in diameter, and range in shape from spheres to small rods." All that holds at the present day but now it seems imperative to include one more criterion in the description, namely mention of the fine structure of the organelles. The present writer would offer the following definition:

Mitochondria are cytoplasmic organelles with dimensions ranging from less than 1 μ to several μ and of variable, labile shape. They have a smooth outer membrane and a highly infolded inner one and are composed pre-dominantly of lipoproteins, with small amounts of specific RNA and DNA, and are capable of carrying out certain biochemical reactions, notably the Krebs cycle, electron transport via the cytochromes and oxidative phosphory-lation. The mitochondrion has thus finally emerged as an organelle clearly definable by structural, chemical and metabolic criteria.

This paper is concerned with mitochondria in higher plants; most of the data comes in fact from angiosperms, with a limited number of observations from gymnosperms, ferns and bryophytes. The primary aim will be to de-scribe mitochondrial structure *in situ* and to evaluate their activities in the cell. Information about the metabolic activities of mitochondria comes, however, in the first place from *in vitro* experiments with isolated particles. Moreover, work on the activities of higher plant mitochondria has lagged behind that conducted on animal, particularly mammalian, mitochondria largely because of technical difficulties in handling the plant material. Many investigations by plant physiologists have been of a confirmatory nature to establish the presence in plant mitochondria of reactions known to occur in the animal organelles and, in many cases, this has been achieved only in the past few years. Therefore, after a discussion of mitochondrial structure, a section of this paper will be devoted to reviewing the activities of isolated plant mitchondria before passing on to consider their activities *in vivo*, developmental changes, growth and inheritance.

II. OBSERVATIONS WITH THE LIGHT MICROSCOPE

There is much confusion in this field, especially among the earlier literature, for different workers have used different definitions for mitochondria. Some authors have included all kinds of small organelles in the category; others have applied the term to organelles of one narrowly defined shape excluding other morphological forms which rank as mitochondria under the present definition (see Newcomer, 1951; Guilliermond, 1941). In addition to confused terminology, erroneous observations have most probably arisen because the particles are near the limit of resolution of the light microscope. It is not intended to attempt a sorting out of all the data here; discussion will be confined to observations which seem with reasonable certainty applicable to mitochondria according to the definition assumed here.

In unstained living cells mitochondria are best observed under phase contrast when they appear darker than the ground cytoplasm. The vital dye Janus green B is very widely used to distinguish mitochondria from other particles of similar size such as sphaerosomes (Steffen, 1955; Sorokin, 1955). For strict proof, it should be shown that the particles not only take up the dye but reduce it under anaerobic conditions and reoxidize it when oxygen is readmitted (Sorokin, 1955). Tetrazolium dyes, the Nadi reagent and various fluorescent dyes have been used with unfixed preparations but Janus green is considered to be the most specific. For detailed studies on the reaction of plant mitochondria with Janus green, the reader is referred to the work of Sorokin (1938, 1941, 1955, 1956).

Mitochondria are universally observable in higher plant cells appearing as spheres 1 μ or less in diameter, or as rods and filaments of similar width but several μ long, sometimes branched. The number per cell has been estimated at *ca* 90 in grass root tip epidermis (Avers, 1961); *Veronica* embryo haustorial cells also contain *ca* 90, while the endosperm cells contain 57 (Steffen, 1955). Much larger numbers can be present, however; from published electron micrographs the writer counted 80 mitochondrial profiles *per thin section* of a not quite complete cell of *Arum maculatum* spadix (Simon and Chapman,

1961) and 115 in a similar portion of a *Tradescantia* pollen mother cell (Sakai and Shigenaga, 1964); the numbers *per cell* must have been much higher. For liver, values of 500 to 2500 per cell are quoted (Schneider, 1959). Mitochondria may aggregate in certain cellular locations; e.g. in tulip perianth epidermis they congregate next to the inner wall (Sorokin, 1955) and in several cell types they cluster round the nucleus (Anderson, 1936).

The great value of *in vivo* observations by light microscopy lies in revealing the capacity of mitochondria for movement and their lability of shape. The organelles are carried along by cytoplasmic streaming but also perform independent motions—wriggling (Sorokin, 1955) and "pulsating" (Honda *et al.*, 1966). The shape can undergo spontaneous "pleomorphic" changes; the organelles divide and coalesce among themselves (Honda *et al.*, 1966). Changes in mitochondrial morphology can be induced by manipulation; pressure, for instance, can cause a reversible disappearance as seen under phase contrast (Wildman *et al.*, 1962) and swelling takes place in hypotonic media (Steffen, 1955). Seeming coalescence of mitochondria with nuclei or plastids has been reported; in view of electron microscopic observations, it is likely that in many cases the organelles only came into close contact (see below, Section III). The non-green jacket of chloroplasts can push out protuberances which break off, forming particles indistinguishable from mitochondria under phase contrast (Wildman *et al.*, 1962).

Light microscopy also offers opportunities for the cytochemical localization of enzyme activities and chemical compounds. The smallness of mitochondria hampers observation but some success has been achieved. The decolouration of Janus green in anaerobic conditions depends on enzymatic reduction of the dye by dehydrogenases (Lazarow and Cooperstein, 1953) and the Janus green reaction of mitochondria has lent strong support to the identification of the organelles as centres of dehydrogenase activity. The Nadi reagent has been used to locate cytochrome oxidase in the mitochondria and tetrazolium salts in combination with different substrates to locate enzymes such as succinic dehydrogenase (Avers, 1961).

III. Fine Structure

The electron microscope has confirmed the presence of mitochondria in all higher plant cells examined. Round or oval profiles predominate and elongate figures are frequent but great care must be taken in the deduction of three-dimensional shapes from single sections. Not only spheres but rods in cross-section will produce circular outlines, while elongate profiles may represent cylinders or flattened discs; curved discs can be cut as rings and discs with thicker edges can appear respectively as rings or as dumbbell shapes with a narrow connection according to the sectioning plane (Manton,

1961). The shapes can be quite complex. Isolated mitochondria are spherical. Mitochondria of all Eukaryota possess the same basic structure. An outer smooth membrane surrounds an inner membrane with many infoldings, the cristae or microvilli, projecting into the enclosed matrix. The thickness of the membranes is ca 50 Å; the width of the total mitochondrial envelope, i.e. outer and inner membrane plus the intervening space, is 150–200 Å— precise values depend on the fixation. With negative staining of unsectioned membranes, complex subunits can be seen on the inner membrane and cristae; in higher plant mitochondria, these have a "head" of 90–110 Å diameter and a "stem" measuring 35–40 by 40 Å (Parsons $et\ al.$, 1965). Freeze-etched onion ($Allium\ cepa$) root mitochondria display particles of 100 Å diameter on the cristae (Branton and Moor, 1964). These dimensions are very similar to those reported for mitochondrial subunits from $Neurospora\ crassa$—head 85 Å, stalk 40–50 Å (Stoeckenius, 1965) and beef heart—head 80–100 Å, stalk 30–40 by 50 Å (Fernández-Morán $et\ al.$, 1964). Thus all mitochondria seem to be constructed from the same fundamental building blocks. Some authors have considered the subunits to be myelin-figure like artefacts (Sjöstrand $et\ al.$, 1964) but by now, the particles have been seen also in thin sections (Ashhurst, 1965) and they persist in beef heart preparations after removal of 95% of the lipid, a treatment which should cause myelin figures to collapse (Fleischer $et\ al.$, 1967). The outer membrane does not bear these particles and has a different enzymatic makeup (see Section IV C). In plant mito-chondrial preparations, the outer membrane is more susceptible to fixation injury than the inner and may be lost in pellets. Parsons $et\ al.$ (1965) noted pits, 25–30 Å in diameter, in negatively stained outer membranes of isolated potato and mung bean ($Phaseolus\ aureus$) mitochondria but believe these may be indicative of damage.

The pattern of the membrane infoldings varies between species and tissues. In higher plant mitochondria, the infoldings are mainly tubular or saccular, rather than plate-like (as in many mammalian mitochondria); hence some authors prefer to term them microvilli rather than cristae. Sometimes circular profiles of cristae occur (Fig. 1); it is not clear what these represent in three dimensions. The system must possess great flexibility in view of the pleo-morphic changes visible $in\ situ$ by light microscopy.

The two most commonly employed fixatives, osmium tetroxide (with or without glutaraldehyde prefixation) and potassium permanganate, can give somewhat differing pictures of mitochondrial structure. With permanganate, the membranes are very smooth and regular and the intracristal spaces are narrow (Fig. 1). With osmium, the membranes often appear more wavy and diffuse (Figs 2 and 4); the outer may be faint and even broken. In osmium-fixed mitochondria the width of the intracristal space varies; it may be practically as narrow as with permanganate fixation (Fig. 3) or dilated to varying degrees (Figs 2, 6, 7). The mitochondria with dilated cristae usually also possess a more electron-dense matrix than the narrow-cristate ones. Osmium-fixed mitochondria can almost be divided into two types as narrow-cristate, light-matrix (Fig. 3) and swollen-cristate, dark-matrix (Figs 2 and 6), types. In any cell, all mitochondria are as a rule of the same type; occasionally both kinds coexist (Weintraub et al., 1966).

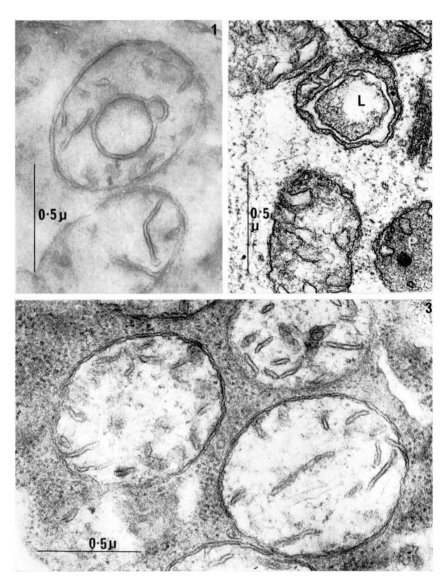

A scanning of as many original and published electron micrographs of osmium-fixed material as could be found with sufficiently distinct mitochondria yielded 26 tissues with clearly narrow-cristate, light-matrix mitochondria, 6 with the swollen-cristate, dark-matrix type and 8 with mitochondria of intermediate appearance. To some extent, the division must have depended on personal judgement but it gives an indication of a prevalence of the narrow-cristate type. Mitochondria of both types occurred in diverse tissues but no active young meristem had strongly swollen-cristate mitochondria although intermediate forms occurred in meristematic tissues. Isolated mitochondria, on the other hand, often have highly swollen cristae and very dark matrices and frequently both types are mixed in a pellet.

Interpretation of these observations must be undertaken with extreme caution because of the danger of fixation artefacts. There is an inclination to regard the swollen cristae as indicative of fixation damage or degeneration *in situ*. Permanganate fixation always produces a narrower separation of cristae and in freeze-etched onion root cells, the intracristal space seems to be narrow (Branton and Moor, 1964). Mitochondria of animal tissues are almost without exception narrow-cristate even when the matrix is very dense. Malhotra (1966) found that in quick-frozen, freeze-substituted mouse tissue there was no separation at all between the crista membranes and suggested that the routine osmium picture already represents some swelling during fixation. In plant tissues the mitochondria sometimes change during ageing from the narrow to the swollen-cristate type and this change can occur also during isolation (Weintraub *et al.*, 1966); some pellets show the swelling of cristae to an extreme degree. From such data, a tentative case can be made out for regarding the swollen-cristate state as indicative of damage. With mitochondria fixed *in situ*, however, one must allow for two possibilities: either the cristae were already dilated *in vivo* or the organelles were in a state of susceptibility to damage, manifested by swelling during fixation. The latter is probable in cases where permanganate fixation of the same material has shown narrow cristae (unless one postulates that permanganate causes a contraction!). The precariousness of this speculation is emphasized by the data of Hackenbrock (1966) who manipulated isolated rat liver mitochondria to assume

---

FIG. 1 Mitochondria in cells of sycamore (*Acer pseudoplatanus*) grown in suspension culture and fixed in potassium permanganate. (Photograph by C. J. Smith, Swansea).
FIG. 2 Mitochondria from cells as in Fig. 1, fixed in glutaraldehyde and osmium tetroxide and stained with uranyl acetate in potassium permanganate followed by lead citrate. The cristae are dilated, the matrix dark with light central spaces (L); P, proplastid. (Photograph by C. J. Smith, Swansea).
FIG. 3 Mitochondria from etiolated mung bean (*Phaseolus aureus*) hypocotyl, fixed in glutaraldehyde and osmium textroxide and stained with lead citrate. The cristae are narrow and the matrix light.

reversibly either state; the swollen-cristate, dark-matrix form appeared during conditions allowing active phosphorylation. A similar appearance of mitochondria can perhaps be caused by different circumstances.

Osmium fixation preserves more details in the mitochondrial matrix than permanganate; the latter usually produces a uniform, electron-transparent matrix comparable with the cytoplasmic background. With osmium fixation, mitochondria may show light areas containing filaments and clumps staining

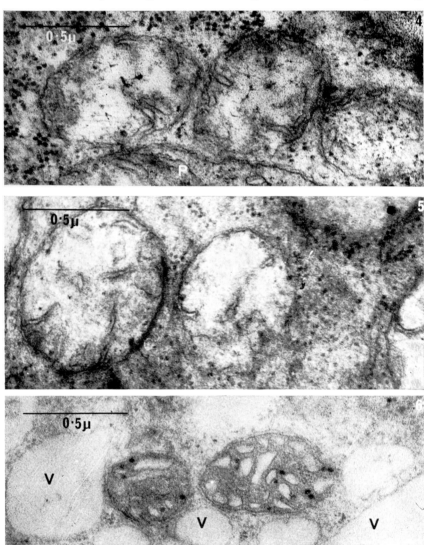

well with uranyl acetate (Fig. 4); such material was identified as DNA in animal mitochondria by Nass and Nass (1963) and in swiss chard (*Beta vulgaris*) leaf mitochondria the removal of the filaments by deoxyribonuclease has been demonstrated (Kislev *et al.*, 1965). Under carefully controlled conditions, Yotsuyanagi and Guerrier (1965) were able to discern DNA masses in mitochondria of young onion root cells with permanganate fixation; the material behaved identically with nuclear chromatin in all staining treatments and was removed by deoxyribonuclease. The light areas with DNA filaments are most conspicuous in mitochondria of young cells. Ribosome-like granules can be seen in mitochondria (Fig. 7) and the removal of these with ribonuclease in swiss chard leaf mitochondria has been achieved (Kislev *et al.*, 1965). Very electron-dense granules, *ca* 20–40 mμ in diameter, are sometimes present in the matrix and are associated with the cristae (Fig. 6) probably representing deposits of insoluble phosphate (Greenawalt *et al.*, 1964). Dark central bodies of unknown nature have been seen in mitochondria of bean (*Phaseolus vulgaris*) leaves (Weintraub *et al.*, 1966) and in young mung bean leaf (*Phaseolus aureus*) mitochondria (Fig. 7). Lance-Nougarède (1966) discovered crystalline protein inclusions in epidermal cell mitochondria of lentil (*Lens culinaris*) leaf.

The matrix, when electron-dense, sometimes has a granular appearance; Weintraub *et al.* (1966) interpret the granularity as representing electron-transparent particles 130–140 Å in diameter, embedded in a densely-staining ground substance.

Close associations between mitochondria and other organelles are frequently seen in electron micrographs; mitochondria may be enclosed in deep nuclear pockets (Mota, 1964; Öpik, 1965a; Wettstein and Zech, 1962) or within plastid cavities (Vesk *et al.*, 1965). Such relationships would account for reports based on light microscope observations on living cells of mitochondrial fusion with nuclei or chloroplasts and production of mitochondria from these organelles. There is no really convincing evidence of fusion of mitochondria and nuclei; Mota (1964) interprets his micrographs as indicating such fusion in *Chlorophytum capense* aerial roots but, in the present writer's opinion, the pictures certainly indicate close adpression but fail to prove

---

Fig. 4–6 Mitochondria from bean (*Phaseolus vulgaris*) cotyledon storage parenchyma, fixed in glutaraldehyde and osmium tetroxide.

Fig. 4 Meristematic ripening cotyledon, stained with uranyl acetate and lead citrate. DNA filaments are prominent and the cristae are diffuse. P, plastid.

Fig. 5 Mature cotyledon, 24 hr germinated, stained with lead citrate. Cristae are better defined and the matrix is light.

Fig. 6 Senescent cotyledon, 5 days germinated, stained as Fig. 5. Cristae are swollen and the matrix is dark and contains phosphate granules. V, vacuole.

fusion. Plastids, however, can bear protrusions with a mitochondrion-like structure (Fig. 8); see also Vesk *et al.* (1965). The electron microscope gives only a static picture but, if such projections were to break off, they would be indistinguishable from mitochondria in fine structure and these projections may well represent the pieces of plastid envelope seen by Wildman *et al.* (1962) to produce mitochondrion-like particles in living cells.

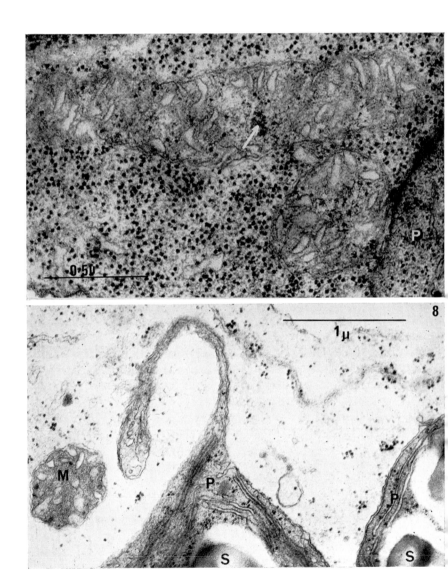

IV. PROPERTIES OF ISOLATED MITOCHONDRIA

A. ISOLATION METHODS

It is beyond the scope of this review to go into detailed considerations of isolation procedure. It has, however, become increasingly clear how profoundly the properties of the isolated particles depend on this and in recent years notable improvements in method have been made; hence a brief section will be given to the topic.

The isolation of highly active mitochondria from higher plant tissues has not proved easy largely because of damage caused by vacuolar contents. For many animal tissues, it suffices to adjust the osmotic potential of the medium, most commonly with sucrose, and perhaps to add a buffer and EDTA (ethylene diamine tetracetate). With a number of plant tissues, this procedure yields some success but with others such simple media produce practically no activity. While the precise optimal conditions vary from tissue to tissue, the cumulative experience of many workers has shown the beneficial effect of the following:

a. Media of high pH, up to 8·2, in the case of acid tissues (Lieberman, 1958).

b. The presence of EDTA in the medium; this probably acts by chelating vacuolar ions and is particularly necessary in the case of highly vacuolate material (Lieberman and Biale, 1955; Lund *et al.*, 1958).

c. The presence of reductants such as cysteine or ascorbic acid or citrate or succinate which ensure that the mitochondria are kept in a reduced state (Pierpoint, 1959).

d. The addition of high molecular weight compounds; e.g. PVP (polyvinylpyrrolidone) has been very successful with apple tissue where it acts by binding polyphenols (Hulme *et al.*, 1964); BSA (bovine serum albumin) protects by binding fatty acids and basic proteins (Hanson *et al.*, 1965).

Great care to avoid mechanical damage is also necessary.

Two media which have been used with considerable success are those developed by Pierpoint (1959, 1960) and Wiskich and Bonner (1963). Pierpoint's medium was developed for green leaves which have given more trouble than non-green material; it consists of sucrose, 0·4M; Tris (tris-

---

FIG. 7 Mitochondria in young etiolated mung bean (*Phaseolus aureus*) leaf; fixed in glutaraldehyde and osmium tetroxide and stained with lead citrate and uranyl acetate. Note the dark central body in the elongate mitochondrion (arrow) and intramitochondrial ribosome-like granules. P, plastid.

FIG. 8 Plastid P with mitochondrion-like attachment in germinating bean (*P. vulgaris*) cotyledon; M, probable mitochondrion, S, starch grain.

E

58 H. ÖPIK

hydroxymethylaminomethane) buffer, 0·2M; KH_2PO_4, 0·01M; EDTA, 0·005M and sodium citrate (or succinate), 0·02M, all at a pH of 7·8–7·9. This medium, with some modifications, has since been used for several green tissues, e.g. tomato (*Lycopersicon esculentum*) stem (Wu and Scheffer, 1960) and bean (*Phaseolus* and *Vicia*) leaf (Weintraub *et al.*, 1966). The medium of Wiskich and Bonner contains mannitol, 0·37M; sucrose, 0·25M; cysteine, 0·004M; EDTA, 0·005M at a pH of 7·2–7·5; originally developed for sweet potato root (*Ipomoea batatas*), this medium has proved the basis for satisfactory isolation of mitochondria from white potato (*Solanum tuberosum*) tuber (Verleur and Uritani, 1965) and numerous other tissues (Parsons *et al.*, 1965).

Honda *et al.*, (1966) have evolved a very complex medium simultaneously suitable for the preservation of mitochondria, nuclei and plastids. This contains sucrose, Tris buffer, EDTA, magnesium acetate, manganese acetate, BSA, dextran, Ficoll (a sucrose polymer of mol. wt 400,000) and a reductant (either glutathione, cysteine, ascorbic acid or mercaptoethanol) at a pH of 7·8. A total osmolarity of 0·08 was found best for leaves of spinach, tomato and tobacco on morphological criteria. To prevent mechanical damage, the cells are broken by a single slicing with an array of closely set sharp blades. With this treatment, extracted mitochondria retain not only rod shapes but their capacity for movement and pleomorphic changes. So far, data on the metabolic activity of mitochondria isolated in this medium are not available.

The values of centrifugal force used to sediment plant mitochondria have varied from 1700 *g* to over 20,000 *g*, most experimenters working with 10,000 to 20,000 *g*. There is now evidence that the higher forces really are too high, bringing down submitochondrial particles. Smillie (1956) found that practically all the succinoxidase of pea leaves was sedimented in two fractions obtained at 2700 *g* for 30 min and 6700 *g* for 15 min. A similar optimum *g*-value was found for pea stem mitochondria by Mosolova and Sissakian (1961); Kasinsky *et al.* (1966) use 6400 *g* for 20 min to obtain a pure preparation from mung bean hypocotyl. On the other hand, Hanson *et al.* (1959) produced very pure mitochondria (as judged by electron microscopic examination of the pellets) from maize (*Zea mays*) root with 10,000 (or 12,000) *g* for 10 min. The optimum force must depend on the tissue in hand and the viscosity of the medium but the comment of Mosolova and Sissakian (1961) that ". . . the majority of studies on plant mitochondria have been carried out not with pure mitochondria but with mitochondria-enriched fractions" appears justified in many cases. This probably accounts for a large proportion of the variation in reported values of chemical composition and enzymatic activities although these parameters are, of course, affected also by the degree of intactness of the particles. It is encouraging to see the electron microscopic examination of pellets becoming a routinely applied check on purity and intactness. Very

TABLE I

Chemical composition of higher plant mitochondria. The values marked with an asterisk* have been calculated from the authors' original data, assuming that all the nitrogen referred to was protein nitrogen, that the nitrogen content of protein was 6·25% and that the phosphorus content of nucleic acids was 10%. For the potato tuber mitochondria, Levitt (1954) by an indirect calculation obtained a total nucleic acid content of ca 20% of the protein.

Tissue	% of dry weight				μg/mg protein		Reference
	Protein	Lipid	RNA	DNA	RNA	DNA	
Bean (Vicia faba) root	37–39				130*		Brown et al., 1953
Beet (Beta vulgaris) petiole	29	ca 39			11–13*	1·9–3·7*	Martin and Morton, 1956b
Castor bean (Ricinus communis) endosperm					42*		Akazawa and Beevers, 1957a
Mung (Phaseolus aureus) hypocotyl						0·8	Suyama and Bonner, 1966
Pea (Pisum sativum) leaf, etiolated						4·8–9·6*	Smillie, 1956b
Pea (Pisum sativum) leaf, green					40–43*	3·2–4·8*	Smillie, 1956c
Pea (Pisum sativum) seedling, etiolated	35–40	30	0·5–1·0	0·7–0·9			Stafford, 1951
Pea (Pisum sativum) seedling, etiolated	37	40					Mosolova and Sissakian, 1961
Potato (Solanum tuberosum) tuber	39*	22	+	+			Levitt, 1954a
Tobacco (Nicotiana tabacum) leaf					102*	11*	McClendon, 1952
Wheat (Triticum vulgare) root	37–39				11–15*	5·8–7·0*	Martin and Morton, 1956c

TABLE II

Cytochromes present in plant mitochondria, with molar ratios where available. Molar ratios for beef heart and yeast mitochondria given for comparison. Species marked with an asterisk* belong to the Araceae.

Tissue	Cytochrome			Comments	Reference
	$a + a_3$	b	c		
Mung (*Phaseolus aureus*) hypocotyl	1	1	2	3 of b type, 2 of c type	Bryant et al., 1963
Mung (*Phaseolus aureus*) hypocotyl	+	+	+	b type predominant; 2 (or 3?) of b type	Kasinsky et al., 1966
Wheat (*Triticum*) root	1	5	3	2 of b type, 2 of c type	Lundegårdh, 1960
*Arum maculatum** spadix	+	+	+	b_7 present	Bendall and Hill, 1956
*Symplocarpus foetidus** flowers	+	+	+	b_7 present	Chance and Hackett, 1959
Beef heart	3	1	1·5		Green and Fleischer, 1963
Yeast	1	1	1·5		Lundegårdh, 1960

pure preparations can be achieved with density gradient centrifugation but this method has been hardly used as yet with plant mitochondria.

The large-scale preparation of mitochondria has for a long time been the prerogative of animal physiologists. No botanical laboratory can match the record of D. E. Green's group of having produced 200 kg of mitochondria by 1962 (Green, 1962). Only in recent years have plant physiologists begun to extract mitochondria from kilogram quantities of material (Kasinsky et al., 1966; Suyama and Bonner, 1966). The availability of really pure and intact mitochondria in reasonable quantities should enable more rapid progress in the study of their properties and the clearing up of contradictory observations from earlier work. Mung bean hypocotyl seems to be a likely candidate for the place assumed by rat liver and beef heart for work on animal mitochondria.

There is one additional complication inherent to higher plant material in that tissues of one single cell type are practically impossible to obtain. Thus all mitochondrial preparations from natural plant organs will contain a mixed population of mitochondria from several cell types. This could cause complications; mammalian mitochondria are known to possess tissue-specific properties. The only way of overcoming this problem would be to use tissue or cell cultures as source of mitochondria.

B. CHEMICAL COMPOSITION

Some analytical data on higher plant mitochondria are summarized in Table I. The lipid is mainly phospholipid (Levitt, 1954a; Martin and Morton, 1956b, c). The water content of castor bean (*Ricinus communis*) endosperm mitochondria in 0·5M sucrose was estimated at 69–75 % (Akazawa and Beevers, 1957a) but this varies with the osmolarity of the medium. The composition is basically similar to that of animal mitochondria. The amount of mitochondrial material that has been obtained per unit weight of tissue varies very widely; e.g. a survey of nine papers gave 0·03–4·8 mg mitochondrial nitrogen per g fresh weight but this value is so dependent on isolation methods that the figures give little clue about the actual proportion of mitochondria in the tissues. Martin and Morton (1956) obtained *ca* 8·5 times as much mitochondrial material per unit weight of tissue from young, rapidly growing wheat (*Triticum vulgare*) roots than from mature, fairly inactive silver beet (*Beta vulgaris*) petiole by identical isolation procedures and Lund et al. (1958) state that mitochondria contain the major proportion of cytoplasmic protein in maize root.

The nucleic acids found in mitochondria have been under suspicion of being contaminants, the DNA arising from nuclear fragments and the RNA from "microsomes". It is clear that earlier preparations were in fact contaminated with nucleic acid from other cellular sites and the higher values of

TABLE III

Examples of plant mitochondrial preparations with complete Krebs cycle activity. The "oxidation" criterion is based on enhancement of oxygen uptake; "sparker" requirement for pyruvate is given positive both in cases of absolute requirement and of stimulation. "Acid interconversions" refers to chromatographic identification of other cycle acids synthesized from (labelled) acids supplied. All the leaf tissues were green; all the seedlings and seedling parts, etiolated. Blank spaces imply absence of test, not a negative result.

Tissue	Oxidation of		Criteria for activity			Reference
	Pyruvate	Other acids	"Sparker" for pyruvate	Malonate inhibition	Acid Inter-conversions	
Apple (*Pyrus malus*) fruit	+	+ +	+		+	Hulme et al., 1964
Arum maculatum spadix	+	+ +	+ +			Hackett and Simon, 1954
Avocado (*Persea americana*) fruit	+	+ +		+ +	+ +	Avron and Biale, 1957
Bean (*Phaseolus vulgaris*) hypocotyl	+	+ +	+			Beaudreau and Remmert, 1955
Castor bean (*Ricinus communis*) endosperm	+	+ +		+		Beevers and Walker, 1956
Cauliflower (*Brassica oleracea*) bud	+	+	+			Laties, 1953
Lupinus albus cotyledon	+	+ +	+		+	Brummond and Burris, 1953
Mung (*Phaseolus aureus*) hypocotyl	+	+ +				Millerd et al., 1951
Pea (*Pisum sativum*) seedling	+	+ +	+ + +	+ +	+ +	Davies, 1953
Pea (*Pisum sativum*) leaf	+	+ +	+ + +	+ +	+ +	Smillie, 1956a
Soybean (*Glycine max*) hypocotyl	+	+ +				Switzer and Smith, 1957
Spinach (*Spinacia oleracea*) leaf	+	+ +				Zelitch and Barber, 1960
Tobacco (*Nicotiana tabacum*) leaf	+	+ +	+	+ +	+	Pierpoint, 1960
Tomato (*Lycopersicon esculentum*) stem	+	+ +	+ +	+ +		Wu and Scheffer, 1960
Sweet potato (*Ipomoea batatas*) root	+	+	+	+ +	+	Lieberman and Biale, 1956

Table I are suspect but there is now no doubt that small amounts of nucleic acid are integral parts of the organelles. The RNA content of beef heart mitochondria is 7·0 μg/mg protein (Green et al., 1966) and the DNA content of animal and micro-organism mitochondria is 0·3–2·2 μg/mg protein (Tewari et al., 1966). The mitochondrial DNA from higher plants has a specific gravity distinct from the nuclear and the total amount in a mung bean hypocotyl mitochondrion from a recent estimate is ca $5 \cdot 10^{-10}$ μg (Suyama and Bonner, 1966). RNA from cauliflower (Brassica oleracea) buds has been isolated in the form of ribosome-like particles and resolved into 18S and 28S components, the former with a base composition different from the cytoplasmic RNA (Pollard et al., 1966). Further evidence for the presence of RNA in plant mitochondria stems from observations that ribonuclease has a deleterious effect on their activity (Hanson et al., 1965). Electron microscopic evidence for mitochondrial nucleic acids has already been presented.

The cytochromes of higher plant mitochondria are of the same basic types as in yeast and animals but the proportion of b types is high (Table II). A special cytochrome, b_7, has been found only in the floral parts of some aroids (Bendall and Hill, 1956; Chance and Hackett, 1959).

Other components present in plant mitochondria are coenzymes, especially nicotinamide nucleotides, ascorbic acid (Buvat, 1963), ions and carbohydrates (Levitt, 1954).

C. METABOLIC ACTIVITIES

1. The Krebs Cycle

By 1948, animal mitochondria had been established as the carriers of the Krebs cycle for complete oxidation of pyruvate. For plant mitochondria, the issue was in doubt for some years; particulates were at first found to be inactive or capable of oxidizing only a limited number of acids or the enzyme activities appeared to be located in a nonparticulate phase (Brummond and Burris, 1954). Subsequent improvements in isolation and assay technique, however, have produced plant mitochondrial preparations which fulfil to a reasonable degree the criteria for complete Krebs cycle activity, viz. oxidation of the cycle acids, the requirement of a "sparker" acid for pyruvate oxidation, conversion of added acids to other members of the cycle and malonate inhibition of oxidation (Table III). In many more examples at least some of the steps have been identified and the variety of tissues investigated is sufficient to allow the generalization that higher plant mitochondria carry out the complete Krebs cycle.

Mitochondria from higher plants will also readily oxidize NADH and at a lower rate, NADPH (Table IV). This holds even for intact, tightly coupled preparations (Ikuma and Bonner, 1967) in contrast to animal mitochondria which will oxidize the reduced coenzymes only when damaged.

TABLE IV

Examples of identification of oxido-reduction enzymes in plant mitochondrial preparations. "D" indicates that the cytochrome oxidase activity was increased by digitonin; brackets indicate low activity. Blank spaces imply absence of test, not a negative result. Species marked with an asterisk* belong to the Araceae.

Tissue	Oxidases			Reductases				Reference
	NADH	NADPH	Cytochrome c	Succinate-cytochrome c	NADH-cytochrome c	NADPH-cytochrome c	Dia-phorase	
54 species, dicotyledons			+, (+)					Webster, 1952
12 species, higher plants			+, D					Simon, 1958b
Apple (Pyrus malus) fruit					+		+	Hulme et al., 1965
Arum maculatum* spadix			+, D					Simon, 1957
Bean (Phaseolus vulgaris) cotyledon			+, D					Öpik, 1965b
Maize (Zea mays) root	+	+						Cunningham, 1964
Mung (Phaseolus aureus) hypocotyl	+	+						Ikuma and Bonner, 1967
Pea (Pisum sativum) leaf, etiolated	+	+	+ +					Smillie, 1956b
Pea (Pisum sativum) leaf, green	+	+	+ +		+ +			Geronimo and Beevers, 1964
Pea (Pisum sativum) stem, etiolated	+	+	+, D		+		+	Ragland and Hackett, 1961
Peanut (Arachis hypogaea) cotyledon		(+)	+	+ +				Cherry, 1963
Potato (Solanum tuberosum) tuber			+ +	+	+			Verleur and Uritani, 1965
Silver beet (Beta vulgaris) petiole			+ +	+	+		+	Martin and Morton, 1956b
Spinach (Spinacia oleracea) leaf		+	+	+	+	+		Zelitch and Barber, 1960
Symplocarpus foetidus* flower	+	+	+ +	+	+			Hackett, 1956
Tobacco (Nicotiana tabacum) leaf	+	+	+	+	+			Pierpoint, 1960
Wheat (Triticum vulgare) root				+	+			Martin and Morton, 1956c
Zantedeschia aethiopica* flower			+					Hatch and Millerd, 1957

2. Electron Transport; Cytochrome Oxidase

Cytochrome oxidase activity has been demonstrated in mitochondria from many higher plant species (Table IV); the enzyme resembles yeast and animal cytochrome oxidase in substrate affinity (Webster, 1952). Succinic-cytochrome c reductase and NADH-cytochrome c reductase have been found active in plant mitochondria (Table IV); the NADPH reductase has been demonstrated in fewer cases and the activity is higher in the microsome fraction (Martin and Morton, 1956).

3. Oxidative Phosphorylation and Coupling

Earlier plant mitochondrial preparations had low P/O values (ratio of atoms phosphate esterified to atoms of oxygen taken up). Millerd et al. (1951) obtained P/O values of ca 1 with all acids for mung bean hypocotyl mitochondria; in other instances no phosphorylation at all could be demonstrated. Later, however, Freebairn and Remmert (1957) obtained P/O values of 2–3 for various acids with cabbage particles and Zelitch and Barber (1960) reported values of 2·3 for α-ketoglutarate and 2·7 for pyruvate with spinach (Spinacia oleracea) leaf mitochondria; other examples of similar values can be found in the literature.

Recent investigations have also produced fairly tightly coupled plant mitochondria with a previously unattained level of respiratory control defined as the ratio of oxidation rates in the presence and absence of ADP or the ratio of oxidation in State III to oxidation in State IV in the terminology of Chance and Williams (1955). Numerical examples of plant mitochondrial respiratory control ratios are: sweet potato 1·4–1·9 with succinate, 8·2–10·4 with malate (Wiskich and Bonner, 1963); mung bean hypocotyl up to 5·3 (Ikuma and Bonner, 1967); avocado fruit (Persea gratissima) 1·58–4·75, increasing with maturity (Lance et al., 1965). The mitochondria in the above examples were all isolated in complex media and with low-force mechanical disruption. Blending or grinding in a pestle and mortar suffice to diminish respiratory control in avocado fruit (Lance et al., 1965).

These respiratory control ratios are still lower than those of animal mitochondria which average around 20 and may reach up to 65 (Honda et al., 1966). It remains to be seen whether this reflects a true difference between the plant and animal particles or whether there will yet be improvements in the plant values.

4. Values of the Q_{O_2} (N)

The value of the Q_{O_2} (N), i.e. the rate of oxidation per unit weight of mitochondrial (protein) nitrogen, is considered to be a measure of the efficacy (or the "goodness") of the preparation. This value depends on the intrinsic

*

activity of the mitochondria, the degree of contamination with inactive material, the assay conditions (such as substrate concentration, coenzyme supply) and the extent of damage sustained during isolation. It is therefore not surprising that Freebairn and Remmert (1956) obtained a range of Q_{O_2} (N) values of 9–1020 (at 30°C) with a total of 11 tissues! As with Krebs cycle activity and oxidative phosphorylation, one can trace in the literature a steady "pushing upwards" of plant mitochondrial Q_{O_2} (N) values. In most cases, succinate is the substrate giving the fastest rates. Among the highest values reported to date are: pea root with succinate at 22–23°, 2280 (Strickland, 1960); maize scutellum with α-ketoglutarate at 29°, 2810 (Hanson et al., 1965); tomato fruit with pyruvate + malate at 30°, 2854 (Dickinson and Hanson, 1965); Arum maculatum spadix with succinate at 25°, 5250 (Simon and Chapman, 1961). These are within the range reported for animal material, especially when one considers that the temperatures used for plant mitochondrial assays are lower than the 37° generally employed for animal particles.

It is seen that well-preserved plant mitochondria carry out the Krebs cycle, electron transport and oxidative phosphorylation at high rates. While it is premature to state categorically that *all* low values of oxidation, P/O and respiratory control obtained with mitochondria from young, healthy tissues result from extraction damage, this is certainly the case in many instances.

5. The β-oxidation of Fatty Acids

The enzymes for this reaction series are firmly bound to mitochondria in mammalian tissues. Kmetec and Newcomb (1956) found that the mitochondria from cotyledons of germinating peanut (*Arachis hypogaea*) oxidize palmitate and Stumpf and Barber (1956) further reported that whole mitochondria were needed for the activity. Rebeitz and Castelfranco (1964), however, claimed that the palmitate-oxidizing system from the same tissue was located mainly in the supernatant from a 10,000-*g* centrifugation and in germinating castor bean seeds also most of the β-oxidation activity appears in the 10,000-*g* supernatant (Yamada and Stumpf, 1965). Thus the location of β-oxidation enzymes in higher plant cells is not known with certainty.

6. Other Metabolic Activities

In Table V are listed, in the upper section, various enzyme activities that have been reported in higher plant mitochondria and in the bottom section, some more complex reactions. With the exception of ATP-ase, each enzyme has been reported only from a few preparations and the possibilities of adsorption from other fractions must be kept in mind. Whether hexokinase, for instance, sediments as a mitochondrial enzyme or remains soluble depends entirely on the method of preparation (Saltman, 1953). The possession of hexokinase would give the mitochondria control over glycolysis and the PPP (pentose phosphate pathway) and if the other glycolytic enzymes are truly native to the particles, the mitochondria could themselves carry out some glycolysis but this point has not apparently been critically investigated with plant mitochondria. The presence of transminases and glutamic dehydrogenase in mitochondria is probably significant for the Krebs cycle is the path-

TABLE V

Enzyme activities found in plant mitochondrial preparations.

Activity	Reference
1. Single enzymes	
Adenosine triphosphatase	Numerous instances
Adenylate kinase	Davies, 1956
Alcohol dehydrogenase	Davies, 1956
Aldolase	Davies, 1956
Ascorbic acid oxidase	Young and Conn, 1956
Formic dehydrogenase	Davies, 1956
Glucose-6-phosphate dehydrogenase	Giorgio et al., 1959
Glutamic dehydrogenase	Davies, 1956
Glutathione reductase	Young and Conn, 1956
Hexokinase	Bonner and Millerd, 1953
	Saltman, 1953
Lactic dehydrogenase	Davies, 1956
Malic enzyme	Davies, 1956
Nicotinamide nucleotide transhydrogenase	Davies, 1956
Oxaloacetic carboxylase	Davies, 1956
Ribonuclease B	Hanson et al., 1965
Transaminases	Smith, 1962
2. Complex activities	
Conversion of pentose to heptose	Giorgio et al., 1959
Conversion of malonate to CO_2	Giovanelli and Stumpf, 1957
Conversion of malonate to Krebs cycle acids	Young and Shannon, 1959
Incorporation of amino acids into protein	Webster, 1954
	Das and Roy, 1961
Uptake of Ca, Mg and PO_4 ions	Hodges and Hanson, 1965.

way of ultimate oxidation of amino acids and the source of carbon skeletons for amino acid synthesis. Mitochondrial protein synthesis and ion uptake are dependent on an energy supply either from concurrent substrate oxidation or from added ATP; the species of proteins synthesized by plant mitochondria have not been identified. The particles listed in Table V as carrying out some of the PPP reactions were isolated from etiolated pea stem by Giorgio et al.

(1959) at 2900 g for 10 min. Ragland and Hackett (1961) failed to substantiate these findings, however, obtaining particles with typical mitochondrial activity in this fraction and the PPP enzymes are generally considered to be soluble.

7. *The Question of Lysosomes and Mitochondrial Heterogeneity*

In the 1950s, workers on animal mitochondria became aware of the heterogeneity of many of their mitochondrial preparations (De Duve *et al.*, 1955). Subfractionation of crude preparations led to the isolation of the lysosomes as a distinct class of particles containing hydrolytic enzymes and recognizable in the electron microscope as single-membrane bound, approximately circular profiles with electron-dense contents. The presence of lysosomes in plant tissues is more sparsely documented; since the subject is covered by Dr. P. B. Gahan in Chapter 13, it will not be further considered here. It is, however, worth while paying attention to the findings of Avers (1961) that, in grass root epidermal cells, the number of particles staining with Janus green equalled that staining with the Nadi reagent for cytochrome oxidase but the numbers staining with tetrazolium salts for several Krebs cycle dehydrogenases were consistently less. This could mean heterogeneity among the cytochrome oxidase-containing particles, i.e. mitochondria.

8. *The Precise Intramitochondrial Location of Enzymes*

The fractionation of mammalian mitochondria into subunits carrying specific enzyme activities has been achieved to a high degree of precision largely by the school of D. E. Green using beef heart particles. It is proposed that the inner membrane bears the electron transport chain, i.e. all the apparatus for electron transfer from NADH or succinate to oxygen, the remaining Krebs cycle dehydrogenases being on the outer membrane (Bachmann *et al.*, 1966). The inner membrane is thought to consist of elementary particles, mol. wt 2×10^6 and further resolvable into four lipoprotein complexes: I, NADH-coenzyme Q reductase; II, succinate-coenzyme Q reductase; III, coenzyme Q-cytochrome *c*-reductase and IV, cytochrome oxidase (Green and Fleischer, 1963). The relationship of these complexes to the visible subunits is not quite clear, there being some discrepancies between the size seen in electron microscopy and the analytically estimated particle weights. The outer membrane is resolved into a particulate "K fraction" forming an integral part of the membrane and a more easily solubilized "S fraction". The K fraction carries the higher molecular weight enzymes (the pyruvic, α-ketoglutaric and β-hydroxybutyric dehydrogenases), while the S fraction includes the lower molecular weight enzymes (isocitric and malic dehydrogenase, fumarase, aconitase, condensing enzyme and the fatty acid oxidizing enzymes (Bachmann *et al.*, 1966; Allmann *et al.*, 1966;

Green *et al.*, 1966)). If the above structure is correct for beef heart mitochondria, in all probability it applies to higher plant mitochondria as well.

The enzymes relegated to the S fraction of the outer membrane have previously been regarded as soluble in the matrix (Green *et al.*, 1966; Davies, 1956). Their easy loss from mitochondria has been put down to leakage but this can equally well be interpreted as solubilization from the membrane. Breakage and loss of outer membranes is often visible in mitochondrial pellets. Mitochondria from different sources vary in the strength with which the outer membrane enzymes are held (Bachmann *et al.*, 1966); this might explain the contradictory reports on the location of fatty acid oxidases in plant mitochondria. The often-noted excess of succinoxidase activity over the oxidation rates of other Krebs cycle acids could result not only from the resistance of this system but from the excess of cristae (bearing the succinoxidase) over outer membrane which bears the dehydrogenases for the other acids.

What, then, is left for the matrix? Electron micrographs show the mitochondrial nucleic acids residing here; the matrix therefore is a likely location for the mitochondrial protein synthesizing system. A specific site has not been suggested for the mitochondrial transaminases and glycolytic enzymes and the matrix presumably contains also low molecular weight compounds such as amino acids and ions in solution. There is evidence for a large amount of soluble protein in the matrix of liver mitochondria (Green, 1962) and it has been proposed that the matrix exists as a colloidal gel since it does contract *in vitro* when given the appropriate treatments (Burgos *et al.*, 1964; Klein and Neff, 1960).

V. MITOCHONDRIAL ACTIVITIES IN THE CELL

A. RESPIRATORY FUNCTIONS

1. *Quantitative Rôle of Mitochondria in Respiration; the Krebs Cycle*

There are two aspects to evaluating the quantitative rôle of mitochondria in respiration: firstly, to what extent does the substrate breakdown pass via the Krebs cycle and secondly, how much of the electron transport proceeds through the cytochromes. Theoretically, it would be feasible, for instance, for the major part of substrate breakdown to occur extramitochondrially via the PPP while the reduced coenzyme was fed into the mitochondria for terminal oxidation.

Functioning of the Krebs cycle has been amply documented in many plant tissues (Millerd, 1960); the assessment of its quantitative rôle *in vivo* is, however, more difficult. The oxidation rates of Krebs cycle acids by isolated mitochondria and the respiration rates of intact tissues have been compared

TABLE VI

Oxidation rates of plant mitochondria expressed as per cent of the oxygen uptake of the intact tissue. Values marked with an asterisk* have been derived by calculation from the authors' original data; D indicates that digitonin was used in the cytochrome oxidase assays. Stage β of *Arum* spadix is prior to its rise in respiration rate, stage δ is at the peak.

Tissue	Oxidation of				Reference
	Succinate	α-keto-glutarate	NADH	Cyto-chrome	
Arum spadix, stage β	73	55		82, D	Simon, 1958a
Arum spadix, stage δ	16	15		12, D	Simon, 1958a
Avocado (*Persea americana*) fruit, preclimacteric minimum		60*			Millerd et al., 1953
Avocado (*Persea americana*) fruit, preclimacteric rise		21*			Millerd et al., 1953
Avocado (*Persea americana*) fruit), climacteric maximum		8*			Millerd et al., 1953
Bean (*Phaseolus vulgaris*) cotyledon	40			236, D	Öpik, 1965b
Maize (*Zea mays*) root		20–33*			Lund et al., 1958
Pea (*Pisum sativum*) internode	32			40	Price and Thimann, 1954
Symplocarpus foetidus flower	10		40	20	Hackett, 1956

to see whether, at least potentially, the mitochondrial activity would suffice to mediate the respiration; some examples are given in Table VI. The writer is not aware of any case where mitochondrial oxidation of a Krebs cycle acid has equalled or exceeded the respiration rate of the corresponding plant tissue although the *Arum* spadix activity (Table VI) could be considered sufficient, allowing for isolation losses. Mostly the mitochondrial activities amount to less than half the respiration rate.

Price and Thimann (1954) argued that it would suffice for the mitochondrial oxidation rate with any one acid to equal one-sixth of the respiration rate for with six oxidative steps in the complete oxidation of hexose, any one Krebs cycle step would *in vivo* be proceeding at one-sixth of the total oxidation rate. On this surmise, many of the observed mitochondrial rates become adequate. For the argument to hold, however, the oxidation rates with several acids should be additive whereas in fact they are not; with two substrates applied simultaneously, the rate equals the higher of the rates with the single substrates (Wu and Tsou, 1955; Öpik, 1965b). The maximum Krebs cycle activity attainable with isolated mitochondria is thus lower than the respiration rate.

However, in view of the possibilities of extraction loss, failure to obtain sufficient Krebs cycle activity *in vitro* by no means precludes the mitochondria from having enough activity *in vivo*. Extraction methods producing really intact mitochondria are not necessarily suited for quantitative extraction and quantitative comparisons between respiration rate and the activity of mitochondria isolated in complex media do not appear to have been undertaken. On the other hand, the possession of enough activity in an isolated mitochondrial fraction does not prove that all this activity is realized *in vivo* at any particular instant. Feeding of radioactive substrates indicates that the Krebs cycle is blocked in freshly cut potato slices, yet the isolated mitochondria can oxidize Krebs cycle acids (Laties, 1964).

One must accordingly turn to *in vivo* experiments with intact tissue. The chief tool in this investigation has been the employment of malonate as a specific Krebs cycle inhibitor. A high degree of inhibition is obtained in some instances; the respiration of spinach leaf is inhibited 90% (Millerd, 1960); that of *Arum* spadix, up to 80% (Simon, 1958a) and of rose petals, up to 70% (Spiegelman et al., 1958). These figures represent the *minimum* fraction of respiration running through the cycle under normal circumstances for the application of an inhibitor of one pathway would be expected to drive respiration into any alternative pathway that may exist. Butt and Beevers (1961) have actually shown that the application of inhibitors of glycolysis stimulates the PPP in maize roots. Taking further into account the slowness of malonate penetration and its competitive nature so that its effect depends on the (unknown) concentration of succinate at the reaction sites, such values point to the Krebs cycle as the major if not exclusive pathway of substrate oxidation in these cases.

In other cases the malonate sensitivity of plant respiration has been found to be low. Sometimes perhaps the inhibitor has failed to reach the reaction sites. Moreover, malonate can be metabolized by plant tissues, passing via malonyl coenzyme A into the Krebs cycle (Shannon et al., 1959; Young and Shannon, 1959). Nevertheless it would be rash to explain away all failures to obtain malonate inhibition of respiration on such grounds for there is good independent evidence for the operation of the alternative respiratory pathway, the PPP, from studies with labelled substrate. A quantitative measure of the participation of the PPP can be deduced by measuring the C-6/C-1 ratio, i.e.

$$\frac{C^{14}O_2 \text{ produced from C-6 labelled glucose}}{C^{14}O_2 \text{ produced from C-1 labelled glucose}}$$

under otherwise identical conditions. In the PPP, carbon atom 1 is released first as CO_2 in the very first steps of the cycle whereas in the glycolytic pathway followed by the Krebs cycle, carbon atoms 1 and 6 are released simultaneously and last. If there were no complicating factors, the C-6/C-1 ratio would be 1·0 for glycolysis and 0 for the PPP. In practice, recycling of the pentoses to hexoses soon effects the release of carbon atom 6 by the PPP also; thus the ratio can only give the minimum participation of the PPP. Out of 12 tissues tested by Beevers and Gibbs (1954), only one (maize root tip) gave a ratio of ca 1, the remainder ranging from 0·75 in sunflower (Helianthus annuus) leaf and stem to 0·36 in carrot (Daucus carota) petiole. These figures suggest that well over half the respiration can proceed via the PPP, especially in older tissues. Cooperation between the PPP and the Krebs cycle is possible, however, with the trioses formed in the PPP joining the glycolytic sequence and entering the Krebs cycle as pyruvate.

In conclusion, the mitochondrial Krebs cycle is a major respiratory pathway and in some tissues mediates at least 90% of the respiration. In tissues with an active PPP, however, the exact proportion of respiration passing through the Krebs cycle cannot be estimated on data available at present.

2. Terminal Oxidation; Cytochrome Oxidase

Quantitative comparisons between the cytochrome oxidase activity of isolated mitochondria and the oxygen uptake of the intact tissue are open to the same criticisms as comparisons of Krebs cycle activity and respiration rate. An additional problem is encountered in that the large substrate molecule, cytochrome c, has difficulty in reaching the reaction sites. Penetration can be facilitated by agents loosening the lipoprotein membrane structure; brief digitonin treatment was found by Simon (1958b) to be the most effective procedure with mitochondria from a range of plant tissues, increasing the activity by 2·8 to 52-fold. The differences in the magnitude of enhancement reflect, presumably, the different extents to which the individual preparations had already been affected by extraction, the treatment having the greatest effect on relatively intact particles.

Values of the cytochrome oxidase activity of plant mitochondria range from a few per cent to over 100% of the oxygen uptake of the intact tissues, sometimes exceeding the rate of oxidation of Krebs cycle acids by the same preparation and sometimes falling short of it (Table VI). With digitonin treatment, the cytochrome oxidase activity of germinating bean (*Phaseolus vulgaris*) cotyledons exceeds the respiration rate considerably and for *Arum* spadix at the younger developmental stage it is almost sufficient. Even digitonin-treated mitochondria probably give underestimates of activity for the treatment is itself deleterious, activity falling rapidly with increased treatment time (Simon, 1958b).

In whole homogenates of wheat, barley (*Hordeum vulgare*) and pea seedlings, cytochrome oxidase activity has been found to be in excess of that required to account for the respiration rate (Fritz and Beevers, 1955).

A large volume of work has been conducted with terminal oxidase inhibitors *in vivo*. Higher plant tissues tend to show considerable resistance towards cyanide, azide and carbon monoxide to the extent that a concept of a "ground respiration" resistant to inhibitors of cytochrome oxidase has arisen. In wheat roots, for example, the cyanide-insensitive respiration equals 25–50% of the total (Lundegårdh, 1960). Often the sensitivity of plant organs decreases as the tissues age and the inhibitors may even become stimulatory at low concentrations in older tissues. This occurred in 10 species of angiosperm and gymnosperm leaves investigated by McDonald and De Kock (1958); in maize, for instance, the respiration of young leaves was 90% inhibited by 2×10^{-4}M cyanide, while that of old leaves was stimulated by 47%. During senescence, sensitivity redeveloped in some cases. The respiration of freshly cut potato discs is sensitive to cyanide and carbon monoxide but on washing, as the respiration rate rises, the sensitivity falls (Thimann *et al.*, 1954).

The insensitivity of plant tissues towards inhibitors of cytochrome oxidase, together with the low cytochrome oxidase activities of many mitochondrial preparations, led to propositions that a large part of plant oxygen uptake proceeds through soluble terminal oxidases, viz. ascorbic acid oxidase and polyphenol oxidase which are highly active in many plant extracts. More critical work has established cytochrome oxidase as the chief terminal oxidase in many tissues. Etiolated pea internode contains enough ascorbic acid oxidase to mediate 40 times the actual respiration rate yet inhibitor data, and the high oxygen affinity of the tissue (half saturation of respiration rate with less than 3% oxygen), indicate that not over 10% of the respiration normally proceeds through ascorbic acid oxidase (Eichenberger and Thimann, 1957). The intense respiration of aroid floral parts is notorious for high cyanide resistance; 10^{-3} M cyanide and 95% carbon monoxide stimulate respiration in the flowers of the aroids *Philodendron* and *Peltandra* yet the oxygen affinity of the floral respiration is again too high for any known enzyme except cytochrome oxidase, half-saturation being reached at 0·002 atm of oxygen (Yocum and Hackett, 1957). Mitochondria isolated from aroid flowers do possess cytochrome oxidase activity (Tables IV and VI). The b_7 cytochrome of the aroid flowers may act as a terminal oxidase in the presence of cyanide, being autoxidizable, and other b-type cytochromes of plants also possess some degree of autoxidizability and offer possible cyanide-insensitive shunts.

Direct evidence for the participation of cytochromes in plant respiration has been obtained from spectrophotometric examination of living material (Lundegårdh, 1960).

Conclusive evidence for the participation of soluble oxidases in plant respiration is, on the other hand, scant. Inhibition by low concentrations of dieca (sodium diethyldithiocarbamate) has been taken as indicative of ascorbic acid oxidase activity (James, 1953) but dieca inhibits cytochrome oxidase at higher concentrations and can be oxidized in living tissues to a potent inhibitor of succinic dehydrogenase (Keilin and Hartree, 1940). If soluble oxidases are active, their most probable rôle lies in the oxidation of the NADPH produced in the PPP. The rate of oxidation of externally added NADPH by isolated mitochondria is low; in grasshopper spermatids, the oxidation and reduction of intra- and extra-mitochondrial nicotinamide nucleotides proceed quite separately (Chance and Theorell, 1959). Marré (1961) considers that there is no evidence for the oxidation of extramitochondrial NADPH through the cytochrome chain and Ragland and Hackett (1965) come to a similar conclusion from tracer studies. Not all the NADPH from the PPP is oxidized by oxygen; it acts as a donor of hydrogen in reductive reactions.

Space does not permit a more detailed weighing of the evidence here but the current consensus of opinion regards cytochrome oxidase as the most important terminal oxidase in plant tissues. The insensitivity to inhibitors like cyanide can possibly be accounted for by the functioning of soluble oxidases and/or autoxidizable b-type cytochromes as alternative pathways in the presence of the inhibitor. The stimulations of respiration by low inhibitor concentrations have been attributed to the inhibitors complexing with deleterious heavy metal ions which have accumulated in the tissues.

3. *Developmental Changes in Mitochondrial Activity and Structure*

The respiration rate of meristems is high per unit fresh weight but this results from the high proportion of protoplasm, as opposed to vacuolar and cell wall material, in this region. Per cell, the rate increases during cell expansion and differentiation; a peak may be reached around the stage of completion of expansion with a slight decline thereafter (Brown and Broadbent, 1951). In successive maize root segments up to 3·5 cm from the apex, the rate per unit fresh weight also reaches a peak in the elongation region (Lund *et al.*, 1958). The changes in maize root respiration are paralleled by increases in the Q_{O_2} (*N*) and P/O values of the isolated mitochondria. In the developing *Arum* spadix, too, the activity of isolated mitochondria as Q_{O_2} (*N*) and as Q_{O_2} (fresh weight) goes up in parallel to the respiration rate (Simon, 1958a). In both tissues, there is an increase in the quantity of mitochondrial material in the pellets; Clowes and Juniper (1964) observed by electron microscopy an increase in the number of mitochondria per cell during the differentiation of maize root cap cells. The changes in the Q_{O_2} (*N*), however, imply a differentiation of the mitochondria to acquire greater oxidative efficiency and this also is borne out by electron microscopy; an increase in cristae was observed in the maize root and *Arum* mitochondria. Generally, the mitochondria of meristematic cells contain few cristae and differentiation is accompanied by increases in the density of cristae. Since the cristae carry the oxidative enzymes, it is understandable that a greater proportion of cristae per mitochondrion gives an increased Q_{O_2} (*N*); in the *Arum* spadix, there is an almost direct proportionality between the average number of cristae per mitochondrial cross-section and the Q_{O_2} (*N*) (Simon and Chapman, 1961). Meristematic tissues have been noted to have respiratory quotients exceeding unity, implying an excess of fermentation and providing further evidence for a low mitochondrial oxidation rate in these tissues. Combined evaluation of the observations on fine structure and the metabolic investigations of whole tissue and subcellular fractions leads to the conclusion that growth and differentiation from a meristem are associated with an increase in mitochondrial respiration.

The germination phase in the life cycle of a higher plant is characterized by rapid and steep increases in respiratory activity. The behaviour of mitochondria during germination has been studied mainly in seed storage tissues which are available in quantity in the ungerminated seeds. Mitochondria can be seen in the cells of dry, dormant seeds but efforts at isolation from dry tissue yield preparations with very little, if any, activity—most probably because of the difficulty of homogenizing such hard, brittle material. On hydration, activity becomes manifest; as the water content of sugar pine (*Pinus lambertiana*) endosperm rose from 3 to 57% in six hours of imbibition, the Q_{O_2} (N) of the isolated mitochondria went up from 37 to 246 (Stanley, 1957). After hydration is completed, however, further striking increases occur in mitochondrial activity, e.g. in peanut cotyledons (Q_{O_2} (N), Cherry, 1963; Q_{O_2} (N) and per gram, Breidenbach *et al.*, 1966), in soybean (*Glycine max*) cotyledons (Q_{O_2} (N), Howell, 1961) and in castor bean endosperm (Q_{O_2} (N) and per organ, Akazawa and Beevers, 1957b). In these instances, the amount of mitochondrial material extractable per organ or per unit weight also increased and, where fine structure was examined concurrently, the mitochondria were found to have acquired more cristae as the Q_{O_2} (N) rose. Thus increases in respiration rate occurring during germination can be mediated largely by increased mitochondrial activity. In germinating bean (*Phaseolus vulgaris*) cotyledons, however, the extractable mitochondrial activity rose only very slightly and fell again quickly long before respiration had reached its peak; it could not be decided whether this reflected mitochondrial efficiency *in vivo* or reaction to isolation (Öpik, 1965b). All these mitochondrial activations take place in non-growing organs where there is neither cell division nor expansion; the function of the high respiration rates must be to energize the mobilization and translocation of reserve nutrients.

During germination, the mitochondrial oxidation rates of different substrates do not change in parallel; in peanut cotyledons, the succinate oxidation rate reaches a sharp peak at 8 days while α-ketoglutarate oxidation rises much more gradually and is at a maximum at 10–11 days (Cherry, 1963). It is not known whether this derives from a true difference in the enzyme proportions or whether we are once more being frustrated by differential effects of extraction. When the amount of cristae per mitochondrion rises, the rate of succinate oxidation, being dependent on enzymes located on the cristae only, could well increase more than the oxidation rates of other acids which depend on dehydrogenases on the outer membrane. Alternatively, since storage tissues contain more than one type of cell, if mitochondria from different cells should vary quantitatively in their ability to oxidize divers substrates, a change in the proportions of different types of mitochondria could effect the observed result.

The storage tissues of seeds are short-lived and a study of their behaviour during germination leads without a break into a study of senescence. As the tissues lose their reserves and deteriorate, the respiration rate falls and so does the activity of isolated mitochondria. In several cases, a decline in the P/O ratio has been found to precede a fall in the Q_{O_2} (N) (Cherry, 1963; Hanson *et al.*, 1959; Young *et al.*, 1960). The last-mentioned authors suggested that a fall in mitochondrial ATP production could be a primary cause of senescence. The supernatant fraction from these ageing organs has a deleterious effect on their mitochondria and on mitochondria from other tissues. One harmful component in the supernatants has been identified as long-chain fatty acids, possibly as protein complexes (E. W. Simon, Manchester, personal communication); another may be ribonuclease. In a detailed study of maize scutellum over a 5-day germination period, Hanson et al. (1965) found that the activity of isolated mitochondria depended very much on the pH of the medium. The respiration rate of the intact tissue came to a peak at 3 days; the P/O ratio and the Q_{O_2} (N) of mitochondria isolated at pH 6·8 declined, respectively, from day 2 and days 3–4 onwards while ribonuclease activity associated with the mitochondria rose steadily. With extraction at pH 7·6, a high P/O value persisted to day 4 and the Q_{O_2} (N) continued rising up to day 5 whereas the ribonuclease activity of the particles was much lower. It would seem that the respiratory decline *in vivo* results from a drop in mitochondrial activity controlled by agents such as ribonuclease or fatty acids in the cytoplasm and mitochondria freed from these influences during extraction can show high activity. The structure of mitochondria in 5-day-old maize scutellum was still normal and of the narrow-cristate, light-matrix type. In final stages of cotyledon senescence, mitochondria do degenerate structurally (Cherry, 1963; Öpik, 1965b).

Fewer data are available on mitochondrial metabolism in other kinds of senescing plant systems. In pea leaves, respiration rate falls in senescence and the isolated mitochondria exhibit first a fall in the P/O ratio, then in Q_{O_2} (N); feeding with labelled acetate confirms that Krebs cycle activity decreases *in vivo* and there is a loss of microvilli in the mitochondria (Geronimo and Beevers, 1964). These results suggest a similarity with the senescence of seed organs. Soluble fractions from senescent foliage leaves inhibit mitochondrial activity (Hanson et al., 1965).

Structural changes in mitochondria have been observed in various tissues during ageing, even when data on the metabolic activity have not been obtained. In *Elodea* and *Chrysanthemum* leaves, the maximum development of mitochondrial cristae coincides with maximum photosynthetic activity and in senescence, the density of cristae diminishes (Buvat and Lance, 1958). Figures 4–6 present a developmental sequence of mitochondrial structure in bean cotyledon tissue. In the meristematic primordium (Fig. 4), mitochondrial cristae are diffuse and the light spaces with DNA filaments are present in practically all profiles. In the mature cotyledon at the beginning of germination (Fig. 5), the cristae have become better defined; 32% of the profiles still contain the light spaces. In senescent cells (Fig. 6), the cristae have become dilated, the matrix has darkened and the light spaces have disappeared completely. How universal such a sequence is, and what it means exactly in terms of activity, remains to be seen. Swelling of cristae (as seen with osmium fixation) does seem to occur in a number of ageing tissues.

Cells engaged in active transport acquire highly cristate mitochondria. This holds for secretory cells of various types (Lüttge, 1966); in nectaries, the density of cristae has been seen to increase during the period of secretion and to regress again (Schnepf, 1964). Tapetal cells (Heslop-Harrison, 1963), phloem companion cells and the filiform apparatus of synergid cells (Jensen, 1965a) are all characterized by numerous and highly cristate mitochondria.

The developmental stages during which some detailed work on mitochondrial activity has been carried out comprise germination, certain aspects of senescence, differentiation from the apical meristem and the climacteric (see e.g. Hulme *et al.*, 1964).

Levitt (1954a, b) conducted analyses on mitochondrial composition from potato tubers stored at low and high temperatures as part of a study on frost resistance. Lyons *et al.* (1964) tackled the problem of hardiness by measuring physical properties of mitochondria isolated from hardy and non-hardy species, obtaining some suggestion that the mitochondrial membranes of hardy species possessed greater elasticity. Apart from some such scattered instances, the field of mitochondrial changes in many aspects of development is still largely unexplored.

To round off this section, the following generalizations can be made.

a. In *meristematic cells*, mitochondria are immature with few cristae and respiration is partly fermentative.

b. Growth and *differentiation* are accompanied by rises in mitochondrial oxidative activity resulting from synthesis of mitochondrial enzymes, visible as increases in cristae; the Krebs cycle and cytochrome oxidase pathways predominate in the respiration of actively growing tissues.

c. In *mature* tissues, an appreciable proportion of respiration may proceed via the PPP and perhaps also through soluble oxidases. This implies some fall in mitochondrial activity. High metabolic activity in mature tissues is correlated with highly cristate mitochondria and presumably high mitochondrial activity.

d. In *senescence*, mitochondrial activity falls; this appears to be controlled by chemicals in the ground cytoplasm. A dilation of cristae often accompanies ageing and in extreme stages of senescence, mitochondrial structure becomes disorganized.

B. NON-RESPIRATORY FUNCTIONS

The line between respiratory and non-respiratory functions of mitochondria cannot be drawn rigidly for the Krebs cycle, besides its rôle as a route for oxidation, also supplies intermediates for many biosynthetic pathways. It is particularly important as a source of carbon skeletons for amino acids; since transaminases are located in mitochondria, the organelles are probably centres of amino acid synthesis in the cell. Acids formed in the Krebs cycle often accumulate in vacuolar sap.

A few observations have been made on the accumulation of ions by mitochondria *in situ*. The mitochondrial fraction isolated from potato slices after incubation of the tissue in solutions of radioactive calcium and phosphate had a high specific activity (Long and Levitt, 1952). More circumstantial evidence comes from the observations of Florell (1957) that in wheat roots there was a direct correlation between the calcium content of the medium, the amount of mitochondria in the tissue and the capacity of the roots for bromide and nitrate absorption. In view of the existing theory of salt respiration, the role of mitochondria in cellular salt uptake wants further attention.

Amino acid incorporation into mitochondrial protein *in situ* has been demonstrated in several cases. In soybean hypocotyl segments incubated with a ^{14}C-labelled amino acid mixture, the specific activity of the mitochondria remained almost constant between the apex and 40 mm back where the tissue was considered mature; the specific activity of the "microsomes" (isolated at 75,000 g) fell so that in the mature segments the mitochondria had the higher specific activity (Chrispeels *et al.*, 1966). On exposure of tobacco (*Nicotiana rustica*) leaves to $^{14}CO_2$, even after a 5-min period, the protein of highest specific radioactivity was found in the mitochondrial fraction (Parthier, 1963) suggesting a very fast passage of newly assimilated carbon to mitochondria as well as a high protein synthesis activity. How great a proportion of mitochondrial protein is synthesized within the organelles is, however, not yet clear. Theoretically the amount of DNA in a plant mitochondrion could code for *ca* 100 polypeptide chains of 15,000 mol. wt. Labelling experiments *in vivo* and *in vitro* have indicated, however, that Krebs ascites tumour cell mitochondria synthesize only certain of their insoluble proteins, others, including cytochrome c, being formed in the ground cytoplasm (Haldar *et al.*, 1966). Rat liver mitochondria seem to be capable only of structural, not enzyme, protein synthesis and protein synthesized on "microsomes" is transferred to the mitochondria (Kadenbach, 1967). Thus not all the radioactive protein found in mitochondria subsequent to *in vivo* incubation with labelled precursors has necessarily been synthesized there in the first place. In studies of mitochondrial protein synthesis, bacterial contamination is a dangerous source of error.

Green (1962) comments that the density of cristae in mitochondria is inversely proportional to their non-respiratory functions. The low density of cristae in meristematic cells and their low Q_{O_2} (N) probably reflect not mere inactivity on the part of the particles but a high activity in protein (and nucleic acid?) synthesis. It is in these cells that the mitochondria must keep growing and multiplying most actively to keep pace with cell division.

VI. ORIGIN, GROWTH AND INHERITANCE

Mitochondrial origin has been a point of contention almost ever since the organelles were first discovered. There are three possibilities: *de novo* formation from previously unorganized cytoplasm; formation from pre-existing mitochondria by fission and formation from other cellular organelles. Each of these propositions has received warm support. Bound up with the question of origin is the evaluation of the degree of genetic autonomy of mitochondria.

A. *DE NOVO* FORMATION

De novo formation is most difficult to prove or to disprove. It would mean gradual growth, starting with a sub-mitochondrial body, so that the beginnings would be invisible in the light microscope while the electron microscope gives only a static picture with no chance of following an organelle through its growth and, at best, one can hope to recognize stages of development among a mixed population of organelles of varying size and complexity. The mitochondria of meristematic cells are certainly of simpler structure than in mature tissue and can have very little internal structure indeed. Small membrane-bound organelles have been pointed out as possible "promitochondria" but it cannot be proved that these do grow into mitochondria and even if they do, this does not prove that the promitochondria arise *de novo* rather than by division of pre-existing ones. There is no really convincing evidence for a sequence of mitochondrial formation *de novo*. The *de novo* formation hypothesis does not assume genetic autonomy of mitochondria and leaves one with the problem of accounting for the starting point, the core around which the mitochondrion springs up.

B. DIVISION

This hypothesis stands on firmer ground for mitochondrial division can be plainly seen in living cells. Many of the observations derive from mature cells where the mitochondria also keep coalescing and the total mass of mitochondria does not increase. This kind of division may, therefore, not be strictly comparable to mitochondrial multiplication in a meristem; nevertheless it offers support to the theory. Electron micrographs display mitochondrial profiles with narrow regions which would be compatible with subsequent division (but see Section III). Division is usually assumed to occur by fission but might also proceed by a cristal ingrowth forming a complete plate and fragmentation along this (Manton, 1961). As indirect evidence in favour of division in higher plant cells may be quoted the fact that some unicellular algae possess one single mitochondrion which divides at each cell division (Manton, 1961). The division hypothesis ascribes a high degree of autonomy to mitochondria as self-reproducing particles. Even if many mitochondrial proteins are synthesized extramitochondrially, the organelles are still self-reproducing if no mitochondria can arise without pre-existing mitochondria.

C. FORMATION FROM OTHER ORGANELLES

Practically every organelle in the plant cell has been proposed as giving rise to mitochondria. A case can be made for chloroplasts, which in the light microscope can be seen to shed mitochondrion-like particles (Wildman et al., 1962) and in the electron microscope show mitochondrion-like attachments (Fig. 8). It is still uncertain how these observations should be interpreted. The chemical nature of the detached organelles cannot be determined. The light microscopic observations are again confined to mature cells, in which mitochondria are not multiplying, but young ripening bean cotyledon cells, which may still be dividing, show plastids with mitochondrion-like projections in electron micrographs (Öpik, 1968). In non-chlorophyllous plant cells, there are still proplastids as possible sources of mitochondria although in germinating bean cotyledons, protuberances (seen in electron micrographs) develop only in green plastids and not from the etiolated proplastids of dark-grown seedlings (H. Öpik, unpublished results). In animal cells, plastid origin is ruled out. It would be strange indeed if after all the similarities observed between plant and animal mitochondria, the two did not possess the same mode of origin also. If formation of mitochondria from plastids can occur, it is not likely to be the sole mode of origin.

The endoplasmic reticulum and the Golgi apparatus have been put forward as generators of mitochondria with little concrete support. The observation of two organelles in electron micrographs in close contact does not mean that one is giving rise to the other. Wildman et al. (1962) noted in living cells of tobacco leaf hairs an apparent coalescence of mitochondria with a "cytoplasmic network", thought to be the endoplasmic reticulum, when pressure was applied, the organelles reappearing on release of pressure. This could be due to a change in hydration with consequent change in refractive index and does not furnish much support for the origination of mitochondria from the endoplasmic reticulum.

From a series of electron micrographs covering the development of the egg cell of the fern Pteridium aquilinum, Bell and Mühlethaler (1962) conclude that during oogenesis all the mitochondria (and plastids) degenerate to be replaced by outbuddings from the nuclear membrane. Autoradiography combined with electron microscopy further suggests that DNA is synthesized in the mitochondria as they are being formed (Bell and Mühlethaler, 1964). Pictures capable of interpretation as representing nuclear budding of organelles have also been obtained from angiosperm tapetal cells (Heslop-Harrison, 1963). A theory that during gametogenesis cellular organelles are scrapped then reformed from the nucleus and reproduce by division for the rest of the life cycle is certainly attractive. It would permit simultaneously a considerable autonomy of the organelles and an ultimate control by the nucleus which would supply their genetic material in the first instance. At the moment, however, the hypothesis rests on the sole observations cited above. A search for nuclear formation of organelles during oogenesis in the fern *Dryopteris filix-mas* and the liverwort *Sphaerocarpus donnelli* proved unsuccessful (Diers, 1964); Jensen (1965b) could find no sign of the process in cotton (*Gossypium hirsutum*) egg-cell formation and Larson (1965) states that in pollen of *Parkinsonia maturata* mitochondria multiply by division, although the evidence is not specified. This subject decidedly calls for further examination.

To sum up so far: of the hypotheses for mitochondrial origin, division of pre-existing mitochondria is the best documented with some evidence for the formation from nuclear membranes at certain stages of the life cycle and perhaps also from plastids.

A solution of the ultimate origin does not exhaust the queries about mitochondrial development. If mitochondria reproduce by division, one is left to ask what force makes them divide and what controls their rate of multiplication to keep pace with cell growth and division. It is not known whether mitochondrial turnover occurs in mature plant cells; the incorporation of radioactivity into mitochondrial protein of non-growing tissue (Chrispeels *et al.*, 1966; Parthier, 1963) suggests turnover. If nuclear budding of mitochondria is accepted, one is left wondering what stimulates the initial degeneration, as well as the budding itself.

The mitochondria also present a problem in morphogenesis. On one level of organization, this is manifested by the arrangement of the cristae as sacs, microvilli or flat plates; the amoeba *Pelomyxa carolinensis* produces an extraordinarily regular pattern of wavy tubules (Pappas and Brandt, 1959). On a finer level, the construction of the supramolecular complexes which comprise the mitochondrial subunits and the fitting together of subunits into successively larger blocks and finally to membranes is also a complicated process. To some extent the molecular union can result automatically from the physicochemical properties of the constituents as is shown by the reformation of complexes by dissociated molecules *in vitro*. However, the entire membrane is so intricate that the involvement of structural templates may be necessary (Green and Hechter, 1965).

Mitochondria are present in both the egg cell and the pollen of higher plants. The cytoplasm of germinating pollen is very rich in highly cristate mitochondria (Larsen, 1965) which is probably a reflection of the fast growth of the pollen tube, whereas the egg cell before fertilization is less active and its mitochondria are not so highly developed (Jensen, 1965b). It is probable that mitochondria are carried into the egg by the male nucleus but it is not absolutely certain. By means of light microscopy of fixed material, Anderson (1936) was able to ascertain that male nuclei are surrounded by mitochondria at all stages up to nuclear fusion in the egg. No mitochondrial mutants that could serve as markers to study transmission are known in higher plants; in obligately aerobic organisms, any drastic mitochondrial mutations may well be lethal while small differences would pass unnoticed with present analytical tools.

VII. FINAL COMMENTS

When prepared with appropriate techniques, higher plant mitochondria compare favourably in activity with mitochondria from mammalian sources. They mediate a large proportion of plant respiration but some substrate breakdown certainly passes extramitochondrially via the PPP and soluble oxidases may mediate some of the terminal oxidation. Mitochondrial oxidative activity is at a peak in young tissues and the proportion of respiration passing through them seems to decrease as tissues age. There is room for much further investigation on developmental changes in mitochondrial activity. The non-respiratory activities of mitochondria have been studied less than the respiratory reactions and merit more attention.

The basic similarities in the structure and function of mitochondria from the most diverse sources have been established; it is now time to look for the variations. We are vaguely aware of differences between mitochondria from various tissues or from the same tissue at different developmental stages but uncertain as to wherein the true basis of the difference lies. One preparation oxidizes malate at a higher rate than citrate, another reacts in the opposite way; are these true differences in the enzymatic makeup of the mitochondria or are they acquired during isolation? If such differences are real, they must be under genetic control (no matter where this control is located) and maybe, with respect to such quantitative differences, mitochondrial mutants will some day be recognized.

It is not yet known whether all the mitochondria of a cell are functionally and genetically equivalent; the data of Avers (1961; see Section IV c 7) suggest functional heterogeneity. If mitochondria carry their own genome, it is quite conceivable that a cell contains a genetically mixed mitochondrial population, any non-deleterious mutation having a chance of being perpetuated. If mitochondrial genetic material is derived from the nucleus in the course of gametogenesis (nuclear budding), then all the organelles in a cell, and indeed in an organism, are more likely to be genetically uniform (unless a different type is inherited from each parent) for any mitochondrial mutations occurring during the vegetative life of the plant would be eliminated at gametogenesis.

Metabolically the mitochondria must cooperate very intimately with the rest of the cell; the cytoplasm supplies the mitochondria with substrate and phosphate acceptors while the mitochondria supply the cell with ATP and metabolic intermediates. Mitochondrial movement must favour exchange of metabolites. We have some idea as to how the cell regulates the respiratory activity of its mitochondria although the effect of light on mitochondrial activity in chlorophyllous cells is still obscure. The greatest deficiencies in our knowledge of mitochondria as parts of the cellular whole lie in the mode of mitochondrial reproduction, the way this is geared to the development of the cell and the extent of genetic autonomy of the mitochondria. In this connection, location of the sites of mitochondrial protein synthesis is of great importance. These topics require the study of whole cells, tissues and organisms. Tools for studying mitochondria *in vitro* have been perfected to a reasonable degree; it is now necessary to perfect the methods for studying them *in vivo*.

ACKNOWLEDGEMENTS

I am grateful to Mr. G. Asquith for help in preparing the figures and to Mr. C. J. Smith for permission to reproduce the electron micrographs of Figs 1 and 2.

REFERENCES

Akazawa, T. and Beevers, H. (1957a). *Biochem. J.* **67**, 110.
Akazawa, T. and Beevers, H. (1957b). *Biochem. J.* **67**, 115.
Allmann, D. W., Bachmann, E. and Green, D. E. (1966). *Archs Biochem. Biophys.* **115**, 165.
Anderson, L. E. (1936). *Am. J. Bot.* **23**, 490.
Ashhurst, D. E. (1965). *J. Cell Biol.* **24**, 497.
Avers, C. J. (1961). *Am. J. Bot.* **48**, 137.
Avron, M. and Biale, J. B. (1957). *Pl. Physiol., Lancaster* **32**, 100.
Bachmann, E., Allmann, D. W. and Green, D. E. (1966). *Archs Biochem. Biophys.* **115**, 153.
Beaudreau, G. S. and Remmert, L. F. (1955). *Archs Biochem. Biophys.* **55**, 468.
Beevers, H. and Gibbs, M. (1954). *Pl. Physiol., Lancaster* **29**, 322.
Beevers, H. and Walker, D. A. (1956). *Biochem. J.* **62**, 114.
Bell, P. R. and Mühlethaler, K. (1962). *J. Ultrastruct. Res.* **7**, 452.
Bell, P. R. and Mühlethaler, K. (1964). *J. molec. Biol.* **8**, 853.
Bendall, D. S. and Hill, R. (1956). *New Phytol.* **55**, 206.
Bonner, J. and Millerd, A. (1953). *Archs Biochem. Biophys.* **42**, 135.
Branton, J. and Moor, H. (1964). *J. Ultrastruct. Res.* **11**, 401.
Breidenbach, R. W., Castelfranco, P. and Peterson, C. (1966). *Pl. Physiol., Lancaster* **41**, 803.
Brown, G. L., Fitton Jackson, S. and Chayen, J. (1953). *Nature, Lond.* **171**, 1113.
Brown, R. and Broadbent, D. (1951). *J. exp. Bot.* **1**, 249.
Brummond, D. O., and Burris, R. H. (1953). *Proc. natn. Acad. Sci., U.S.A.* **39**, 754.
Brummond, D. O. and Burris, R. H. (1954). *J. biophys. biochem. Cytol.* **209**, 755.
Bryant, N. H., Bonner, W. and Sikes, S. V. (1963). *Pl. Physiol., Lancaster* **38**, XLIII.

Burgos, M. H., Aoki, A. and Sacerdote, F. L. (1964). *J. Cell Biol.* **23**, 207.
Butt, V. S. and Beevers, H. (1961). *Biochem. J.* **80**, 21.
Buvat, R. (1963). *Int. Rev. Cytol.* **14**, 41.
Buvat, R. and Lance, A. (1958). *C. r. hebd. Séanc. Acad. Sci., Paris* **247**, 1130.
Chance, B. and Hackett, D. P. (1959). *Pl. Physiol., Lancaster* **34**, 33.
Chance, B. and Theorell, B. (1959). *J. biol. Chem.* **234**, 3044.
Chance, B. and Williams, G. R. (1955). *J. biol. Chem.* **217**, 409.
Cherry, J. H. (1963). *Pl. Physiol., Lancaster* **38**, 440.
Chrispeels, M. J., Vatter, A. E., Madden, D. M. and Hanson, J. B. (1966). *J. exp. Bot.* **17**, 492.
Clowes, F. A. L. and Juniper, B. E. (1964). *J. exp. Bot.* **15**, 622.
Cunningham, W. P. (1964). *Pl. Physiol., Lancaster* **39**, 699.
Das, H. K. and Roy, S. C. (1961). *Biochim. biophys. Acta* **53**, 445.
Davies, D. D. (1953). *J. exp. Bot.* **4**, 173.
Davies, D. D. (1956). *J. exp. Bot.* **7**, 203.
Dickinson, D. B. and Hanson, J. B. (1965). *Pl. Physiol., Lancaster* **40**, 161.
Diers, L. (1964). *Ber. dt. bot. Ges.* **77**, 369.
De Duve, C., Pressman, B. C., Gianetto, R., Wattiaux, R. and Applemans, F. (1955). *Biochem. J.* **60**, 604.
Eichenberger, E. and Thimann, K. V. (1957). *Archs Biochem. Biophys.* **67**, 466.
Fernández-Morán, H., Oda, T., Blair, P. V. and Green, D. E. (1964). *J. Cell Biol.* **22**, 63.
Fleischer, S., Fleischer, B. and Stoeckenius, W. (1967). *J. Cell Biol.* **32**, 193.
Florell, C. (1957). *Physiologia Pl.* **10**, 781.
Freebairn, H. T. and Remmert, L. F. (1956). *Pl. Physiol., Lancaster* **31**, 259.
Freebairn, H. J. and Remmert, L. F. (1957). *Pl. Physiol., Lancaster* **32**, 374.
Fritz, G. and Beevers, H. (1955). *Pl. Physiol., Lancaster* **30**, 309.
Geronimo, J. and Beevers, H. (1964). *Pl. Physiol., Lancaster* **39**, 786.
Giorgio, F., Tua, C. and Tognoli, L. (1959). *Biochim. biophys. Acta* **36**, 19.
Giovanelli, J. and Stumpf, P. K. (1957). *Pl. Physiol., Lancaster* **32**, 498.
Goddard, D. R. and Stafford, H. A. (1954). *A. Rev. Pl. Physiol.* **45**, 115.
Green, D. E. (1962). *Comp. Biochem. Physiol.* **4**, 81
Green, D. E., Bachmann, E. and Allmann, D. W. (1966). *Archs Biochem. Biophys.* **115**, 172
Green, D. E. and Fleischer, S. (1963). *Biochim. biophys. Acta* **70**, 554.
Green, D. E. and Hechter, O. (1965). *Proc. natn. Acad. Sci., U.S.A.* **53**, 318.
Greenawalt, J. W., Rossi, C. S. and Lehninger, A. L. (1964). *J. Cell Biol.* **23**, 21.
Guilliermond, A. (1941). "The Cytoplasm of the Plant Cell", Chronica Botanica Co., Waltham, Mass., U.S.A.
Hackenbrock, C. R. (1966). *J. Cell Biol.* **30**, 269.
Hackett, D. P. (1955). *Int. Rev. Cytol.* **4**, 143.
Hackett, D. P. (1956). *J. exp. Bot.* **8**, 157.
Hackett, D. P. and Simon, E. W. (1954). *Nature, Lond.* **173**, 162.
Haldar, D., Freeman, K. and Work, T. S. (1966). *Nature, Lond.* **211**, 9.
Hanson, J. B., Vatter, A. E., Fisher, M. E. and Bils, R. F. (1959). *Agronomy J.* **51**, 295.
Hanson, J. B., Wilson, C. M., Chrispeels, M. J., Krueger, W. A. and Swanson, H. R. (1965). *J. exp. Bot.* **16**, 282.
Hatch, M. D. and Millerd, A. (1957). *Aust. J. biol. Sci.* **10**, 310.

86 H. ÖPIK

Heslop-Harrison, J. (1963). *Symp. Soc. exp. Biol.* **17**, 315.
Hodges, T. K. and Hanson, J. B. (1965). *Pl. Physiol., Lancaster* **40**, 101.
Honda, S. I., Hongladarom, T. and Laties, G. G. (1966). *J. exp. Bot.* **17**, 460.
Howell, R. W. (1961). *Physiologia Pl.* **14**, 89.
Hulme, A. C., Jones, J. D. and Wooltorton, L. S. C. (1964). *Phytochem.* **3**, 173.
Hulme, A. C., Jones, J. D. and Wooltorton, L. S. C. (1965). *New Phytol.* **64**, 152.
Ikuma, H. and Bonner, W. D. (1967). *Pl. Physiol., Lancaster* **42**, 67.
James, W. O. (1953). *A. Rev. Pl. Physiol.* **4**, 59.
Jensen, W. A. (1965a). *Am. J. Bot.* **52**, 238.
Jensen, W. A. (1965b). *Am. J. Bot.* **52**, 781.
Kadenbach, B. (1967). *Biochim. biophys. Acta* **134**, 430.
Kasinsky, H. E., Schichi, H. and Hackett, D. P. (1966). *Pl. Physiol., Lancaster* **41**, 739.
Keilin, D. and Hartree, E. F. (1940). *Proc. R. Soc.* B **129**, 277.
Kislev, N., Swift, H. and Bogorad, L. (1965). *J. Cell Biol.* **25**, 327.
Klein, R. L. and Neff, R. J. (1960). *Exp. cell. Res.* **19**, 133.
Kmetec, E. and Newcomb, E. H. (1956). *Am. J. Bot.* **43**, 333.
Lance, C., Hobson, G. E., Young, R. E. and Biale, J. B. (1965). *Pl. Physiol., Lancaster* **40**, 1116.
Lance-Nougarède, A. (1966). *C.r. hebd. Séanc. Acad. Sci., Paris* Ser. D **263**, 246.
Larson, D. A. (1965). *Am. J. Bot.* **52**, 139.
Laties, G. G. (1953). *Physiologia Pl.* **6**, 199.
Laties, G. G. (1964). *Pl. Physiol., Lancaster* **39**, 654.
Lazarow, A. and Cooperstein, S. J. (1953). *J. Histochem. Cytochem.* **1**, 234.
Levitt, J. (1954a). *Physiologia Pl.* **7**, 109.
Levitt, J. (1954b), *Physiologia Pl.* **7**, 117.
Lieberman, M. (1958). *Science, N.Y.* **127**, 189.
Lieberman, M. and Biale, J. B. (1955). *Pl. Physiol., Lancaster* **30**, 549.
Lieberman, M. and Biale, J. B. (1956). *Pl. Physiol., Lancaster* **31**, 425.
Long, W. G. and Levitt, J. (1952). *Physiologia Pl.* **5**, 610.
Lund, H. A., Vatter, A. E. and Hanson, J. B. (1958). *J. biophys. biochem. Cytol.* **4**, 87.
Lundegårdh, H. (1960). *In* "The Encyclopedia of Plant Physiology" (W. Ruhland, ed.), Vol. 12, part 1, p. 311. Springer, Berlin.
Lüttge, U. (1966). *Naturwissenschaften* **53**, 96.
Lyons, L. M., Wheaton, T. A. and Pratt, H. K. (1964). *Pl. Physiol., Lancaster* **39**, 262.
MacClendon, J. H. (1952). *Am. J. Bot.* **39**, 275.
MacDonald, I. R. and DeKock, P. C. (1958). *Physiologia Pl.* **11**, 464.
Malhotra, S. K. (1966). *J. Ultrastruct. Res.* **15**, 14.
Manton, I. (1961). *J. exp. Bot.* **12**, 421.
Marré, E. (1961). *A. Rev. Pl. Physiol.* **12**, 195.
Martin, E. M. and Morton, R. K. (1956a). *Biochem. J.* **62**, 696.
Martin, E. M. and Morton, R. K. (1956b). *Biochem. J.* **64**, 221.
Martin, E. M. and Morton, R. K. (1956c). *Biochem. J.* **64**, 687.
Millerd, A. (1956). *In* "The Encyclopedia of Plant Physiology". (W. Ruhland, ed.), Vol. 2, p. 573. Springer, Berlin.
Millerd, A. (1960). *In* "The Encyclopedia of Plant Physiology". (W. Ruhland, ed.), Vol. 12, part 1, p. 620. Springer, Berlin.

Millerd, A., Bonner, J., Axelrod, B. and Bandurski, R. (1951). *Proc. natn. Acad. Sci.*, *U.S.A.* 37, 855.
Millerd, A., Bonner, J. and Biale, J. B. (1953). *Pl. Physiol.*, *Lancaster* 28, 521.
Mosolova, I. M. and Sissakian, N. M. (1961). *Biokhimiya* 26, 488.
Mota, M. (1964). *Cytologia* 28, 409.
Nass, M. M. K. and Nass, S. (1963). *J. Cell Biol.* 19, 593 and 613.
Newcomer, E. H. (1951). *Bot. Rev.* 17, 53.
Öpik, H. (1965a). *Expl Cell Res.* 38, 517.
Öpik, H. (1965b). *J. exp. Bot.* 16, 667.
Öpik, H. (1968). *J. exp. Bot.* 19, 64.
Pappas, G. D. and Brandt, P. W. (1959). *J. biophys. biochem. Cytol.* 6, 85.
Parsons, D. F., Bonner, W. D. and Verboon, J. G. (1965). *Can. J. Bot.* 43, 674.
Parthier, B. (1963). *Biochim. biophys. Acta* 72, 503.
Pierpoint, W. S. (1959). *Biochem. J.* 71, 518.
Pierpoint, W. S. (1960). *Biochem. J.* 75, 504.
Pollard, C. J., Stemler, A. and Blaydes, D. F. (1966). *Pl. Physiol.*, *Lancaster* 41, 1323.
Price, C. A. and Thimann, K. V. (1954). *Pl. Physiol.*, *Lancaster* 29, 495.
Ragland, T. E. and Hackett, D. P. (1961). *Biochim. biophys. Acta* 54, 577.
Ragland, T. E. and Hackett, D. P. (1965). *Pl. Physiol.*, *Lancaster* 40, 1191.
Rebeitz, C. and Castelfranco, P. (1964). *Pl. Physiol.*, *Lancaster* 39, 932.
Sakai, A. and Shigenaga, M. (1964). *Cytologia* 29, 214.
Saltman, P. (1953). *J. biol. Chem.* 200, 145.
Schneider, W. C. (1959). *Adv. Enzymol.* 21, 1.
Schnepf, E. (1964). *Protoplasma* 58, 137.
Shannon, L. M., Young, R. H. and Dudley, C. (1959). *Nature, Lond.* 183, 683.
Simon, E. W. (1957). *J. exp. Bot.* 8, 20.
Simon, E. W. (1958a). *J. exp. Bot.* 10, 125.
Simon, E. W. (1958b). *Biochem. J.* 69, 67.
Simon, E. W. and Chapman, J. A. (1961). *J. exp. Bot.* 12, 414.
Sjöstrand, F. S., Anderson Cedergren, E. and Karlsson, O. (1964). *Nature, Lond.* 202, 1075.
Smillie, R. M. (1956a). *Aust. J. biol. Sci.* 9, 81.
Smillie, R. M. (1956b). *Aust. J. biol. Sci.* 9, 331.
Smillie, R. M. (1956c). *Aust. J. biol. Sci.* 9, 347.
Smith, J. E. (1962). *Biochim. biophys. Acta.* 57, 183.
Sorokin, H. (1938). *Am. J. Bot.* 25, 28.
Sorokin, H. (1941). *Am. J. Bot.* 28, 476.
Sorokin, H. (1955). *Am. J. Bot.* 42, 225.
Sorokin, H. (1956). *Am. J. Bot.* 43, 787.
Spiegelman, H. W., Chow, C. T. and Biale, J. B. (1958). *Pl. Physiol.*, *Lancaster* 33, 403.
Stafford, H. A. (1951). *Physiologia Pl.* 4, 696.
Stanley, R. G. (1957). *Pl. Physiol.*, *Lancaster* 32, 409.
Steffen, K. (1955). *In* "The Encyclopedia of Plant Physiology". (W. Ruhland, ed.), Vol. 1, p. 574. Springer, Berlin.
Strickland, R. G. (1960). *Biochem. J.* 77, 636.
Stoeckenius, W. (1965). *J. Cell Biol.* 17, 443.
Stumpf, P. K. and Barber, G. A. (1956). *Pl. Physiol.*, *Lancaster* 31, 304.
Suyama, Y. and Bonner, W. D. (1966). *Pl. Physiol.*, *Lancaster* 41, 383.
Switzer, C. M. and Smith, F. G. (1957). *Can. J. Bot.* 35, 515.

Tewari, K. K., Vötsch, W. and Mahler, H. R. (1966). *J. molec. Biol.* **20**, 453.
Thimann, K. V., Yocum, C. S. and Hackett, D. P. (1954). *Archs Biochem. Biophys.* **53**, 239.
Verleur, J. D. and Uritani, I. (1965). *Pl. Physiol., Lancaster* **40**, 1003.
Vesk, M., Mercer, F. V. and Possingham, J. V. (1965). *Aust. J. Bot.* **13**, 161.
von Wettstein, D. and Zech, H. (1962). *Z. Naturf.* **17** b, 376.
Webster, G. C. (1952). *Am. J. Bot.* **39**, 739.
Webster, G. C. (1954). *Pl. Physiol., Lancaster* **29**, 202.
Weintraub, M., Ragetli, H. W. J. and John, V. T. (1966). *Can. J. Bot.* **44**, 1017.
Wildman, S. G., Hongladarom, T. and Honda, S. I. (1962). *Science, N.Y.* **138**, 434.
Wiskich, J. T. and Bonner, W. D. Jr. (1963). *Pl. Physiol., Lancaster* **38**, 604.
Wu, C. and Tsou, C. (1955). *Scientia Sin.* **4**, 137.
Wu, L. and Scheffer, R. P. (1960). *Pl. Physiol., Lancaster* **35**, 708.
Yamada, M. and Stumpf, P. K. (1965). *Pl. Physiol., Lancaster* **40**, 653.
Yocum, C. S. and Hackett, D. P. (1957). *Pl. Physiol., Lancaster* **32**, 186.
Yotsuyanagi, Y. and Guerrier, C. (1965). *C. r. hebd. Séanc. Acad. Sci., Paris* **260**, 2344.
Young, J. L., Huang, R. C., Vanecko, S., Marks, J. D. and Varner, J. E. (1960). *Pl. Physiol., Lancaster* **35**, 288.
Young, L. C. T. and Conn, E. E. (1956). *Pl. Physiol., Lancaster* **31**, 205.
Young, R. H. and Shannon, L. M. (1959). *Pl. Physiol., Lancaster* **34**, 149.
Zelitch, I. and Barber, G. A. (1960). *Pl. Physiol., Lancaster* **35**, 205.

CHAPTER 5

Mitochondrial Biogenesis in Yeast

D. WILKIE

Department of Botany, University College, London, England

I. INTRODUCTION

Isolated mitochondria of yeast are able to incorporate amino acids into their structural protein but apparently not into specific proteins (Wintersberger, 1965). Such protein synthesis presumably proceeds by way of a DNA–RNA system since these nucleic acids are present in the mitochondrion. The idea of an intrinsic genetic system in the mitochondrion is substantiated by the finding that there is cytoplasmic inheritance of respiratory deficiency (the petite mutation) in *Saccharomyces cerevisiae*. The main points about this mutant are as follows: (1) it is apparently irreversible; (2) in crosses to normal, the deficiency is not inherited among sexual progeny; (3) biochemically there is loss of mitochondrial enzymes including cytochromes *a*, *b* and c_1 and an apparent loss of mitochondrial DNA; (4) there is morphological aberration in that the inner membrane is incomplete and (5) the mutation can be specifically induced by UV light and by acridines (for details and literature see Roodyn and Wilkie, 1967). From these facts it is generally believed that there is an extra-chromosomal genetic unit, assumed to be the mitochondrial DNA, necessary for mitochondrial development and which can be spontaneously lost or specifically eliminated by mutagens.

From electron microscope pictures it would appear that intact mitochondria can be transmitted to daughter cells in growing yeast cultures which are

F

actively respiring. Intercalary growth and fission of the organelle is also apparent so the perpetuation of the complete mitochondrial system can be visualized by these means. However, there are no detectable mitochondria in the cells of anaerobically-grown *S. cerevisiae* (Linnane *et al.*, 1962), one of many yeasts that are facultative anaerobes. Nonetheless, these cells inherit the necessary information for making mitochondria as can be seen on transferring them to aerobic conditions. It would seem then that it is not necessary to have intact mitochondria in order that the instructions for making the organelle are transmitted at cell division.

II. STUDIES WITH RESPIRATORY MUTANTS

A. UV INDUCTION OF RESPIRATORY DEFICIENCY

UV induction curves of the petite mutation (Wilkie, 1963) are linear in anaerobic cells leading to the conclusion that a single copy of the mitochondrial genetic unit survives mitochondrial disintegration under anaerobiosis. This copy has been termed the mitochondrial DNA master template. At each anaerobic cell division the master template replicates and the replica is inherited by the daughter cell. It is further theorized that on transfer to aerobic conditions many replicas will be made independently of cell division with a single replica per new mitochondrion. That the mitochondrial copies can function genetically is shown by the lag in the UV induction of petites in aerobic cells indicating multiple targets (Fig. 1). It is presumed the multiple targets comprise the master unit together with mitochondrial copies. It is clear, however, that the mitochondrial replicas which must be comparatively numerous in fully adapted cells cannot be accorded the heritability or stability of the master otherwise the UV dose required to destroy all copies would be very great indeed. Also it can be seen that the spontaneous mutation rate of the master in anaerobic cells is about 6×10^{-3} so if all copies are equivalent in aerobic cells the spontaneous rate here should be $(6 \times 10^{-3})^n$ where n is the number of genetic units. In fact the two rates differ only by a factor of about 3.

B. THE *GI* MUTANT

The case of mitochondrial transmission of the genetic unit is brought into sharper focus in the *gi* mutant. Unlike normal cells, repression of the mitochondrial system in this mutant either by anoxia or glucose repression, both of which give incompletely formed mitochondria (Yotsuyanagi, 1962), results in the apparent loss of the cytoplasmic genetic information among daughter cells which are petite. These facts were established by studies of cell lineages involving micromanipulation of daughter cells (Wilkie and Negrotti, 1968). In this mutant it thus appears to be necessary to have conditions for mitochondrial production and proliferation in order that the information be transmitted. Although genetic analysis of the *gi* character has been hampered by low viability of ascospores from crosses involving this mutant, the indications are fairly clear that the character is under the control of a nuclear gene. In terms of the master template, it is feasible that this gene regulates the replication of the unit. Following mutation of the gene and loss of function, the master can no longer replicate and be transmitted in which case genetic continuity of the unit would then depend on the proliferation of the copies in the mitochondria and their transmission in the intact organelle. Alternatively, the master unit may fail to replicate only under conditions of repression. This appears more likely since *gi* cells have a normal respiratory system regarding both content of cytochromes and genetic stability when growing on media containing non-fermentable substrate or sugars other than glucose. The finding of revertants to normal among *gi* populations of cells also tends to favour the alternative hypothesis; restoration of gene function could be seen to restore normal replication of the master unit.

Although it is not clear what the connection is between repression of the respiratory system and loss of genetic information in *gi* cells, this mutant is of major importance in current studies on the genesis and control of the mitochondrial genetic information.

C. INDUCTION OF RESPIRATORY DEFICIENCY WITH ACRIDINES

Acridines in very low concentrations have been found to cause 100% induction of the petite mutation in growing cultures where fermentable substrate is available. No other mutagenic effect is apparent at these levels of the dye (about 1 ppm) so it is many times more effective in destroying the mitochondrial genetic unit compared with its general mutagenic activity. This activity is believed to result from intercalation of the dye molecule into DNA (Lerman, 1964) causing errors in the replication process and depressing the formation of messenger RNA in the transcription process.

The concentration of acriflavin inducing the respiratory deficiency in yeast strains can be accurately determined by observing colony formation and development on a solid medium containing a non-fermentable substrate such as glycerol. Failure of cells to develop into visible colonies indicates 100% petite induction among daughter cells. In most strains of *S. cerevisiae* this is brought about at a concentration of around 0·5 ppm. The differential mutagenic effect of the dye on the respiratory system is emphasized by the fact that the induced petite cells will grow normally in medium containing between 200 and 500 ppm (depending on the strain) so long as fermentable substrate is available. This extreme sensitivity of both the mitochondrial and the postulated master units is indicative of a cytoplasmic location in each case. An analogy can be drawn between this sytem and that of episomes such as the F factor in bacteria. In this case, when the F factor is in the free cytoplasmic state (F+), it is highly susceptible to the action of acridine orange which eliminates this genetic unit from cell populations; when the factor is integrated in the bacterial chromosome, however, it is relatively resistant to the dye (Hirota, 1960). In the case of yeast, the cytoplasmic factor is the mitochondrial DNA, the relatively stable units being the nuclear genes.

Spontaneous mutants of *S. cerevisiae* showing resistance to acriflavin ranging from 0·5 to 10 ppm have been isolated from glycerol-dye plates (Thomas and Wilkie, 1967). The demonstration that there is no concomitant increase in resistance on sugar-dye media suggests that this is resistance of the mitochondrial system to mutagenic action and not a mutational change leading to alteration in permeability of the cell to the dye or to a mechanism for inactivation of the mutagen. In one particular case, a 50-fold increase in resistance to induction of respiratory deficiency has been accompanied by an actual 2-fold increase in sensitivity to acriflavin on a sugar-containing medium. Genetic analysis of a few of these mutants provides evidence that changes in nuclear genes form the basis of the resistance and so far cytoplasmic inheritance of resistance, which would reflect a direct heritable change in the mitochondrial DNA itself, has not been observed. Perhaps these mutant genes make an altered mitochondrial-DNA polymerase (see below) which is better able to recognize points of intercalation of the dye along the double helix and deal with these aberrations during replication.

The degree of intercalation may also be a factor and this can be determined by observing changes in thermal transition (melting point) of the DNA brought about by the process (Lerman, 1964). This is currently under investigation in these studies.

In all the foregoing discussion attention has been focused on the transmission and mutagenicity of the mitochondrial DNA, the tacit assumption being made that this DNA is the cytoplasmic genetic factor of the respiratory system of the yeast cell. A number of controversial points have been made not least of which is the theory of a master template. If it exists, its origin is still obscure. However, these speculations serve to put the problem in perspective and provide starting points for discussion and experiment.

At the present time attention is focused more on the isolation and characterization of the mitochondrial DNA in terms of its amount, base composition and function in regulating protein synthesis in the organelle. These aspects will now be considered.

III. NUCLEIC ACIDS IN YEAST MITOCHONDRIA

A. DNA

The mitochondria of all organisms so far examined have been found to contain DNA distinguishable from nuclear and other satellite DNA by differences in buoyant density and/or thermal transition point (see Nass *et al.*, 1965). Tewari *et al.* (1965) isolated a discrete native DNA from yeast mitochondria of low buoyant density of 1·685 g/cm³. Moustacchi and Williamson (1966) identified a similar satellite band in their preparations of whole cell DNA of yeast. Both groups of investigators report the absence of the mitochondrial DNA in cytoplasmic petite strains (see also Mounolou *et al.*, 1966) while Moustacchi and Williamson make the further observation that in the early stages of growth of cultures, during which the cells show glucose repression of the respiratory system, there is little synthesis of mitochondrial DNA relative to nuclear DNA. When cells approach the final stages of growth and are fully respiring, this relationship is reversed with the rate of synthesis of the former showing a relative increase over that of the nuclear DNA. These authors suggest that the specific inhibition of the synthesis of mitochondrial DNA may be the cause rather than the consequence of repression of respiratory enzyme synthesis in the presence of glucose. It is likely that repression by anoxia also leads to a relative loss of mitochondrial DNA. Evidence of this has been seen in this laboratory where satellite DNA of the mitochondrial type is greatly reduced in amount in anaerobically-grown cells of *S. cerevisiae* in thermal transition studies (K. Giles and D. Wilkie, unpublished results). These findings are consistent with a theory of breakdown of mitochondrial DNA under conditions of repression and resynthesis from a master DNA template under inducing conditions.

Based on the estimate of Avers *et al.* (1965) of a complement of 50 mitochondria in a stationary phase cell, the average amount of DNA per mitochondrion has been calculated as 1.6×10^{-10} µg. This amount could code for about 100 proteins of average size. This compares with an estimated 30 proteins encoded in the circular DNA of mouse liver mitochondria (Sinclair and Stevens, 1966).

The finding that isolated yeast mitochondria contain a DNA polymerase with properties similar to the DNA polymerases of bacteria and mammalian cells (Wintersberger, 1966) is evidence that mitochondrial DNA has genetic continuity. This means, in other words, that mitochondrial DNA can and probably does undergo replication under suitable conditions.

B. RNA

As for DNA, the mitochondria of a wide variety of organisms have been found to contain RNA in amounts ranging from about 10–20 µg/mg mitochondrial protein. Contamination with microsomes is a problem in these investigations but a useful feature of mitochondrial RNA is its insensitivity to ribonuclease when it is located in intact, undamaged mitochondria. This allows the cleaning of preparations by treatment with this enzyme so a good deal of contaminant RNA can be removed in this way.

Analysis of yeast mitochondrial RNA has been carried out by Winters-berger (1966) who was able to separate the RNA into three species by ultra-centrifugation. These sedimented with coefficients of about 23S, 16S and 4S. The 4S peak corresponds to SRNA while the 23S and 16S fractions correspond to the subunits of bacterial ribosomes which have a coefficient of the ribo-some of higher cells. Although this implies a close affinity between the bac-terial ribosome and the high molecular weight RNA of the mitochondrion, investigators in this field are not in agreement on this point as not all find a clear separation into these sedimenting fractions (see Rifkin et al., 1967). Kroon (1966) tentatively concludes in his analysis of rat liver mitochondria that one of the RNA components has a sedimentation rate corresponding to 23S but that a possible 16S peak was largely masked by the breakdown pro-ducts of cellular RNA. Nonetheless he expresses the view that these com-ponents represent the intact RNA of mitochondrial ribosomes of rat liver. Taken together, the available evidence indicates the presence of ribosomes in mitochondria but whether they are of the bacterial type awaits confirma-tion. Indirect evidence that they could be akin to the bacterial ribosome is provided by the studies on antibacterial antibiotics and their effects on mito-chondrial synthesis described below.

IV. PROTEIN SYNTHESIS IN ISOLATED MITOCHONDRIA

Isolated mitochondria of *S. cerevisiae* incorporate amino acids into their protein as demonstrated by Wintersberger (1965). Using ^{14}C-leucine and ^{14}C-phenylalanine, he showed that the incorporation depends on a functional electron transport system and that it is inhibited by puromycin, actinomycin, chloramphenicol and acriflavin but not by ribonuclease. The labelled amino acids were present to a large extent in an insoluble protein fraction containing RNA and only small amounts of radioactivity were detected in the soluble mitochondrial proteins (free enzymes). This is in agreement with the findings of Kadenbach (1967) for rat liver mitochondria in which it was also shown that the soluble proteins of the mitochondria are first synthesized in the cytoplasm by the microsomes (that is, they are coded for by nuclear genes in the usual way) and then pass into the developing organelle (see also Haldar et al., 1966; 1967).

The presence of transfer RNA and amino acid activating enzymes, a DNA-dependent RNA polymerase and probable ribosomes in yeast mito-chondria (Wintersberger, 1965; 1966) leaves little doubt that the organelle has its own machinery for synthesizing proteins. At the same time it is clear from the limited amount of DNA present that the mitochondrion itself does not carry sufficient information to specify these components of its protein-synthesizing system and code for mitochondrial proteins as well.

V. Effects of Antibiotics on Mitochondrial Synthesis

There are one or two brief reports in the literature of the inhibition of amino acid incorporation into mitochondrial proteins *in vitro* by the antibacterial antibiotic chloramphenicol. Linnane and his collaborators subsequently demonstrated the inhibition of mitochondrial enzyme synthesis by this antibiotic in the intact yeast cell (Huang *et al.*, 1966). These investigations were extended to include a range of antibacterial drugs such as tetracycline and erythromycin, with similar results (Clark-Walker and Linnane, 1966). The

TABLE I

Resistance levels of the respiratory system of yeast strains to various antibiotics and of spontaneous resistant mutants of these strains.

Strain	Resistance (mg/ml)*						
	CAP	TC	ER	CA	OL	SP	LI
22–4B	<0·1	0·1	<0·1	<0·5	<2	5	10
22–4B–CAPR	1	1	<0·1	<0·5	<2	5	10
41	0·1	0·1	0·1	0·5	10	2	10
41–CAPR	2	1	0·1	0·5	10	2	10
41–ERR	0·1	0·1	8	0·5	10	2	10
D243–P1	1	0·5	0·1	<0·5	5	<2	2
D243–P1–ERR	1	0·5	8	0·5	20	2	10
D243–F2	<0·1	0·25	0·1	<0·5	<0·5	<2	<2
D243–F2–ERR	1	1	8	<0·5	0·5	2	10
10–19B	1	4	0·5	<0·5	5	<2	10
10–19B–ERR	1	4	8	0·5	10	2	10
10 (diploid)	2	0·5	0·1	<0·5	2	<2	10
10–ERR	2	1	8	0·5	5	2	10
M (diploid)	1	0·5	0·1	0·5	5	10	10
M–CAPR	4	2	0·1	0·5	5	10	10
44Cl	0·5	0·5	0·5	<0·5	5	2	5
4Cl–TCR	1	2	0·5	<0·5	5	2	5

Abbreviations:
CAP, chloramphenicol; TC, tetracycline; ER, erythromycin; CA, carbomycin; OL, oleandomycin; SP, spiramycin. CAPR, ERR, TCR denote spontaneous resistant mutants to chloramphenicol, erythromycin and tetracycline, respectively.
* Range of concentrations used (mg/ml):
CAP, 0·1–4; TC, 0·1–4; ER, 0·1–8; CA, 0·5; OL, 0·5–20; SP, 2–10; LI, 2–10.
(From Wilkie *et al.*, 1967).

conclusion was drawn that the antibiotics were directly inhibiting the synthesis of mitochondrial enzymes. In more recent studies (Wilkie *et al.*, 1967) it has been established that the level of tolerance to these drugs is strain-dependent (Table I). In a detailed genetic analysis of various spontaneous resistant mutants to erythromycin (resistance is ability of cells to grow and divide by utilizing non-fermentable substrate in the presence of the drug and selective plating allows the detection and isolation of such cells), both nuclear genes and cytoplasmic factors have been identified in controlling resistance in respective cases (Thomas and Wilkie, 1968). It has been deduced that the cytoplasmic factors for resistance are carried in the mitochondrial DNA since it was found that these factors are lost when the petite mutation is induced in this category of resistant cell. Petite mutation in gene-determined resistance, on the other hand, has no effect on the transmission of resistance.

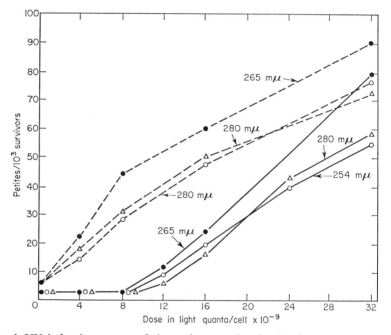

FIG. 1 UV induction curves of the petite mutation in *Saccharomyces cerevisiae*. Solid rule indicates aerobic cells; broken rule indicates anaerobic cells. (From Wilkie, 1963).

From the point of view of mechanism of resistance to erythromycin, it was found in those cases studied that gene mutants, but not mitochondrial DNA mutants, lost the character of resistance after being subjected to a period of anaerobic growth and then put down on the drug. If, however, aerobic growth was permitted once more before exposure to the drug, resistance was restored. Since anaerobic growth results in breakdown of mitochondrial membranes, these results indicate that resistance in gene mutants depends on the prior existence of membranes which have altered components so that they constitute a permeability barrier to the drug. By inference the nuclear genes involved are believed to be specifying these components. Furthermore, since the outer membrane synthesis is unaffected by the antibiotic (Clark-Walker and Linnane, 1967), these are more likely to be components of the inner membrane. The mechanism of resistance in the mitochondrial DNA mutants may be by alteration in the component of the protein-synthesizing machinery of the mitochondrion which is the site of action of the antibiotic. In the bacterial system this site is the 70S ribosome (see Vazquez, 1966) so it may be assumed that the mitochondrial "ribosome" is likewise the target for drug action. Further evidence for this may come from the study of the binding capacity of antibiotic to RNA fractions of sensitive and resistant mitochondria. If alteration in mitochondrial ribosomes is in fact the mechanism of resistance in mitochondrial DNA mutants (see Cooper *et al.*, 1967, for account of alteration of yeast 80S ribosomes in resistance to the antifungal drug cycloheximide) then, again by inference, mitochondrial DNA is specifying these units.

In summary, the picture that is emerging of mitochondrial biogenesis in yeast is that the organelle has limited auto-reproductive capacity and although possessing intrinsic genetic information, this may function only in specifying components of the organelle's protein-synthesizing system by means of which information of nuclear origin is processed in providing the proteins for assembly of the inner membrane.

REFERENCES

Avers, C., Pfeffer, C. and Rancourt, M. (1965). *J. Bact.* **90**, 481.
Clark-Walker, G. D. and Linnane, A. W. (1966). *Biochem. biophys. Res. Commun.* **25**, 8.
Clark-Walker, G. D. and Linnane, A. W. (1967). *J. Cell Biol.* **34**, 1.
Cooper, D., Banthorpe, D. V. and Wilkie, D. (1967). *J. molec. Biol.* **26**, 347.
Haldar, D., Freeman, K. and Work, T. S. (1966). *Nature, Lond.* **211**, 9.
Haldar, D., Freeman, K. and Work, T. S. (1967). *Biochem. J.* **102**, 684.
Hirota, Y. (1960). *Proc. natn. Acad. Sci., U.S.A.* **46**, 57.
Huang, M., Biggs, D. R., Clark-Walker, G. D. and Linnane, A. W. (1966). *Biochem. biophys. Acta* **114**, 434.
Kadenbach, B. (1967). *Biochem. biophys. Acta* **134**, 430.
Kroon, M. A. (1966). *In* "Regulation of Metabolic Processes in Mitochondria". (E. L. Slater, J. M. Tager, E. Quagliariello and S. Papa, eds), p. 396. Elsevier, Amsterdam.
Lerman, L. S. (1964). *J. cell. comp. Physiol.* **64**, Suppl. 1, 1.
Linnane, A. W., Vitols, E. and Knowland, P. G. (1962). *J. Cell Biol.* **13**, 345.
Mounolou, J., Jakob, H. and Slonimski, P. P. (1966). *Biochem. biophys. Res. Commun.* **24**, 218.
Moustacchi, E. and Williamson, D. H. (1966). *Biochem. biophys. Res. Commun.* **23**, 56.
Nass, M. M. K., Nass, S. and Afzelius, B. (1965). *Expl Cell Res.* **37**, 516.
*

Rifkin, M. R., Wood, D. D. and Luck, D. J. L. (1967). *Proc. natn. Acad. Sci.*, *U.S.A.* **58**, 1025.

Roodyn, D. B. and Wilkie, D. (1967). "The Biogenesis of Mitochondria". Methuen, London.

Sinclair, G. H. and Stevens, B. J. (1966). *Proc. natn. Acad. Sci.*, *U.S.A.* **56**, 508.

Tewari, K. K., Jayaraman, J. and Mahler, H. R. (1965). *Biochem. biophys. Res. Commun.* **21**, 141.

Thomas, D. Y. and Wilkie, D. (1967). In preparation.

Thomas, D. Y. and Wilkie, D. (1968). *Genet. Res.* **11**, 33.

Vazquez, D. (1966). *Biochem. biophys. Acta* **114**, 277.

Wilkie, D. (1963). *J. molec. Biol.* **7**, 527.

Wilkie, D. and Negrotti, T. (1968). *Biochem. biophys. Acta.* **153**, 341.

Wilkie, D., Saunders, G. and Linnane, A. W. (1967). *Genet. Res.* **10**, 199.

Wintersberger, E. (1965). *Biochem. Z.* **341**, 409.

Wintersberger, E. (1966). *In* "Regulation of Metabolic Processes in Mitochondria". (E. L. Slater, J. M. Tager, E. Quagliariello and S. Papa, eds), p. 439. Elsevier, Amsterdam.

Yotsuyanagi, Y. (1962). *J. Ultrastruct. Res.* **7**, 127.

CHAPTER 6

Carbon Pathways in Mitochondria with Special Reference to Fruit Metabolism

A. C. HULME and M. J. C. RHODES

*Agricultural Research Council, Food Research Institute,
Norwich, England*

I. INTRODUCTION

In this review the net has been spread wide to include many of the cellular processes which may be considered to *originate* in the carbon skeletons produced in plant mitochondria. Some may consider that the connection is often tenuous but the interaction of one series of reactions on another is becoming more and more evident. In fact, the present topic could, with some justification, cover almost the whole of plant biochemistry at the substrate level.

The mitochondrion is often regarded as the "power house" of the cell in that it is a major source of the energy required for cellular synthetic processes. In addition, the mitochondrion, by means of the system of enzymes of the Krebs (or tricarboxylic acid) cycle which it contains, also plays a rôle in providing carbon skeletons for these synthetic processes. Dr. Palmer will discuss the energy transfer functions of mitochondria later in this symposium (see p. 119); here, carbon pathways only will be considered. Since our interests

99

are concerned with the mitochondria of fruit tissues, we shall use some of the results we have obtained with these mitochondria to illustrate some aspects of the behaviour of plant mitochondria.

Of the pathways of carbon metabolism which appear to originate in the mitochondria, the only one which so far remains exclusively a prerogative of the mitochondrion is the fully integrated Krebs cycle. Many of the other systems present (e.g. β-oxidation of fatty acids and possibly the glyoxylate

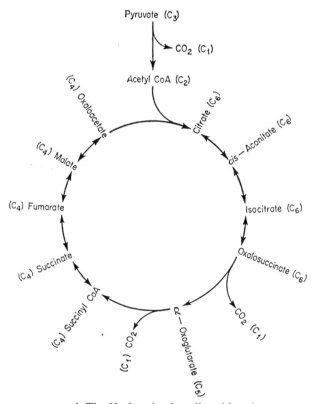

FIG. 1 The Krebs tricarboxylic acid cycle.

cycle) and some individual enzymes of the Krebs cycle, which were once thought to occur only in the mitochondrion, now appear also to be operative outside the mitochondrion. Critical surveys of the methods of isolating mitochondria and other cell fractions, especially from plant tissues, have shown that there are many pitfalls in assigning an enzyme system to a particular site. In the present state of knowledge it is not profitable to attempt a general assessment of the relative importance of the mitochondrion in the overall cell processes.

Plant mitochondria appear to have the same basic functions as animal mitochondria although differences in their physical and chemical (e.g. content of cytochromes) makeup do occur; more subtle differences in "fringe" activities appear in the literature from time to time.

The most important carbon pathway in the mitochondrion is the Krebs cycle (Krebs, 1943), which serves as the route for oxidation of pyruvate, or acetyl-CoA, originating from the metabolism of sugars or fatty acids. This pathway (see Fig. 1) consists of a cyclic series of reactions in which one molecule of acetyl-CoA in the presence of catalytic amounts of oxaloacetic acid (OAA) is completely oxidized to CO_2 during one complete turn of the cycle with the regeneration of the OAA. The cycle was originally discovered and studied in detail for animal tissues but there is now ample evidence that the entire cycle operates in most plant cells.

II. THE KREBS TRICARBOXYLIC ACID CYCLE

It is impossible to discuss the carbon pathways in mitochondria without describing the basic pattern of acid transformations which occur during the operation of the cycle. Most of you may be familiar with these details which have been published *ad nauseam* in textbooks and reviews. Nevertheless, in presenting the wider implications of mitochondrial activity, it is essential to have these basic sequences in mind (see Fig. 1).

The main functions of the Krebs cycle are:

(1) Production of reduced cofactors which are re-oxidized with concomitant conservation of energy as ATP during the passage of electrons through the cytochromes to oxygen (see Chapter 7).

(2) As a primary source of C_4, C_5 and C_6 carbon skeletons which can be drawn off for the synthesis of a variety of substances. In addition, under the appropriate physiological conditions, the cycle can serve as a means of breaking down C_4, C_5 and C_6 acids fed into it from outside the mitochondrion. The entry of these compounds into the mitochondrion from outside involves permeability factors which will be discussed later.

It is now well established that plant as well as animal mitochondria are able to carry out all the reactions of the Krebs cycle. Nevertheless, it does not follow that all mitochondrial preparations will vigorously oxidize all the intermediate acids. For example, the mitochondria may have been damaged or modified during the isolation procedures; conditions may be such that the mitochondrial membrane is impermeable to a particular acid or the mitochondrial preparation may be "contaminated" by enzyme inhibitors.

Apple mitochondria have been prepared in such a way that damage due to the high acidity of the sap and inhibition due to the presence of phenolic

TABLE I

Mitochondrial activity of preparations from peel, pulp and whole fruit tissue with various substrate acids of the Krebs cycle. Average of the first 2 hr.

Activity/hr/10 g tissue (μl gas, O_2-uptake)

Tissue	Citrate	Cis-aconitate	Isocitrate	Oxalo-succinate*	α-oxo-glutarate	Succinate	Fumarate	Malate	Pyruvate	Pyruvate Malate
Peel: Cox's O.P.	134	230	205	100	254	736	182	340	16	156†
Peel: King Edward						430		218	12	84†
Pulp: Cox's O.P.	49	74	60	70	72	245	52	92	10	47†

* Corrected for non-enzymic breakdown.
† "Sparking" amount of malate (2 μmole) with pyruvate (40 μmole). Allowance made for small malate oxidation.

substances have been overcome by the use of buffers and polyvinylpyrrolidone. The mitochondria will oxidize all the cycle acids to a greater or lesser degree (Table I). It will be seen that there is considerable variation in the oxidation rates of the various acids. To some extent this reflects the proximity of the particular acid to an oxidation step in the cycle and, probably, permeability differences of the mitochondrial membrane to a particular acid. The mitochondria oxidize pyruvate very slowly and its complete oxidation clearly requires the presence of catalytic amounts of a C_4 acid to provide OAA as an acceptor for the acetyl-CoA formed from pyruvate. Analysis, by paper chromatography, tracers and estimation of specific acids of mitochondrial digests oxidizing an individual acid, has demonstrated the accumulation of other key members of the cycle series of acids. In addition the presence of the individual dehydrogenases in apple mitochondria has also been demonstrated (Hulme et al., 1964a).

Certain of the intermediate acids accumulate (presumably in the vacuoie) in plants, whereas this does not normally occur in animal cells and microorganisms. Even in the leaves of tobacco there may be as much as 84 μmole of malic acid/g, whereas rat liver contains only $0 \cdot 2$–$0 \cdot 5$ μmole/g (Lioret and Moyse, 1963). A much greater accumulation occurs in a wide range of plants but is particularly noticeable in certain fleshy tissues, including those of fruits such as the orange, apple and plum. Of these acids, malate and citrate most commonly appear in large quantities. Aconitate, isocitrate, succinate and fumarate accumulate less frequently and oxaloacetate (OAA) and α-oxoglutarate only rarely. The accumulation of these acids cannot be explained purely in terms of consumption of acetyl residues in the Krebs cycle (from pyruvate) since the two carbons gained when this residue combines with OAA on entry into the cycle are balanced by the loss of two carbons as CO_2 in the regeneration of the OAA. Thus the accumulation of any acid intermediate or of any other compound at the expense of such an intermediate would immediately arrest the operation of the cycle. A C_4 acid is required to combine with the acetyl residue. Three enzymes are known which could provide C_4 acids from intermediates commonly found in tissues:

(1) Phosphoenolpyruvate (PEP) carboxylase:

$$PEP + CO_2 + H_2O \xrightarrow{Mg^{++}} OAA + P_i$$

(2) Malic enzyme:

$$Pyruvate + CO_2 + NADPH_2 \xrightleftharpoons{Mn^{++}} malate + NADP$$

3) PEP carboxykinase:

$$PEP + CO_2 + ADP \xrightleftharpoons{Mn^{++}} OAA + ATP$$

Only PEP carboxykinase is a possible mitochondrial enzyme; it would be necessary for the mitochondrial membrane to be permeable to PEP in order for this enzyme to produce OAA. Malic enzyme is known to be present in apples (Hulme *et al.*, 1963) but there is no evidence for its operation in the direction required to form malate. Walker (1962) suggests that reaction (1) is most likely to function *in vivo* as a source of C_4 acids since the equilibrium of the other two enzymes favours decarboxylation of these acids. There are other possibilities. For example, under conditions of protein degradation (during the germination of some seeds), α-oxoglutaric acid and OAA could be formed during transamination of the corresponding amino acids and could feed into the cycle if they were able to penetrate the mitochondrial membrane.

III. THE GLYOXYLATE CYCLE

Another possible way of maintaining the level of C_4 acids in the mitochondrion from acetyl residues alone is by means of the glyoxylic acid cycle, discovered in bacteria by Kornberg and Krebs (1957), which produces succinate. This can enter the Krebs cycle and allow the withdrawal of any

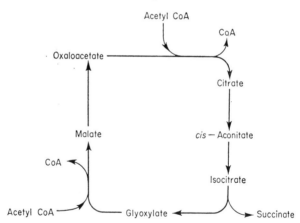

FIG. 2 The glyoxylate cycle.

cycle intermediate. In this cycle, which is shown in Fig. 2, two additional enzymes, isocitrate lyase and malate synthetase, act in association with the Krebs cycle so that the two decarboxylation stages are by-passed. During one turn of the glyoxylate cycle two acetyl-CoA moieties are fixed to form a C_4 acid (succinic) with concomitant regeneration of the catalytic OAA via malate.

The glyoxylate cycle was originally discovered in microorganisms metabolizing acetate and it has since been found in the mitochondria of germinating seeds rich in fat. So far it appears to be confined to such tissues and we have been unable to obtain any evidence for its presence in apple mitochondria. This cycle appears to be an important means of metabolizing the acetyl residues from fat reserves by their conversion to carbohydrate. Although the complete glyoxylate cycle appears to be present only in these fat metabolizing tissues, each of the two enzymes involved (isocitrate lyase and malate synthetase) have been found (not necessarily together) in a number of tissues (Yamomoto and Beevers, 1960; Morton and Wells, 1964). It is not clear whether in these cases the enzyme is associated with the mitochondrion. In pears (Meynhardt et al., 1965) as well as apples, the complete glyoxylic acid cycle does not appear to operate.

IV. OTHER SYSTEMS PRODUCING ORGANIC ACIDS

In addition to Krebs cycle acids, other organic acids, probably originating in the mitochondrion, may accumulate. The most common of these are oxalate, malonate and tartrate, all of which could arise from intermediates of the Krebs and glyoxylate cycles. The route of biosynthesis of oxalate was studied by Morton and his associates in *Oxalis* shoots. They provided convincing evidence that, in this tissue, the precursor of oxalate is glyoxylate produced by the action of isocitrate lyase (Morton and Wells, 1964). Two routes of biosynthesis of malonate have been found to operate in plant mitochondria. One of these is the carboxylation of acetyl-CoA to malonyl-CoA which is then acted on by a thioesterase to liberate malonate (Hatch and Stumpf, 1961). There is also evidence of malonate formation by the α-decarboxylation of oxaloacetate (Shannon et al., 1963). Possibly these two routes to malonate are related since Davies (1959) has suggested that the following reaction might well take place:

$$OAA + CoA + NAD \longrightarrow Malonyl\text{-}CoA + CO_2 + NADH_2$$

Very little is known concerning the metabolism of tartaric acid in spite of the fact that it is one of the earliest detected plant acids; it was used by Pasteur in his pioneer researches on optical activity. It is abundant in many fruits including the grape and it does not appear to arise directly from the Krebs cycle acids. Stafford and Loewus (1958) concluded that it was a product of carbohydrate metabolism outside the reactions involving the Krebs cycle. It has been suggested by Dr. W. M. Kliewer* that, in grapes, tartaric acid might be converted to pyruvate and OAA. Another organic acid, citramalate (2-methyl malate), has been found in apples (Hulme, 1954). Little is known of its origin and fate in plants but, since it has been found in rat liver mitochondria as citramalyl-CoA (Wang et al., 1961) and appears to be formed

* University of California, Davis, California—personal communication.

from glutamate in microorganisms, it could be of mitochondrial origin. It is still not clear whether the acids forming these relatively large accumulations in fruits arise directly in the fruits themselves or whether they are translocated there from the leaves. In apples there is some evidence that at certain stages of development there is an increase in malate in detached fruits. It seems likely, therefore, that at least some of the acid might arise directly in the fruit. The amount of organic acid which accumulates in the tissues argues against its possible storage in the cytoplasm. For example, the pH of the sap of apples is 4·0 to 4·5 and that of lemons as low as 2·5. In mature plant cells the cytoplasm occupies only a very small percentage of the total cell volume and the simplest conclusion is that the acid is stored in the cell vacuole. Since certain of the accumulating acids are formed in the mitochondrion, move to the vacuole and subsequently return into the mitochondrion, there are, presumably, at least three pools of acid in the cell. Radioisotope experiments carried out in Beevers' laboratory (McLennan *et al.*, 1963) have, indeed, demonstrated the presence of storage and turnover pools in a variety of plant tissues. Permeability of the tonoplast and the mitochondrial membrane will influence transport from pool to pool.

V. METABOLISM OF FATTY ACIDS IN MITOCHONDRIA

A. SYNTHESIS OF FATTY ACIDS

Until recently mitochondria were thought to be the main site of synthesis and breakdown of fatty acids in plant cells. Recent work suggests, however, that both these functions take place at least to an equal extent in other parts of the cell. Nevertheless, the mitochondrion is still the source of the primary building unit acetyl-CoA and, probably also, of malonyl-CoA. The recent work of Stumpf and his associates (Overath and Stumpf, 1964) indicated that fatty acid synthesis in plants involved a heat and acid stable protein of low molecular weight which subsequently became known as acyl carrier protein (ACP). This protein has a 4′-phosphopantetheine prosthetic group linked to a serine residue of the protein (Majerus *et al.*, 1964). It appears that the ACP reacts with acetyl and malonyl groups to form acetyl-ACP and malonyl-ACP and that it is these compounds which combine to form acetoacetyl-ACP. This is converted to butyryl-ACP which combines with a further malonyl residue. Repetitions of the whole process lead to the formation of long chain fatty acids. All the intermediates remain attached to ACP until the fully formed acid is released from the synthesizing system. Full details concerning the rôle of ACP in fat synthesis are given by Vagelos in a recent review (Vagelos *et al.*, 1966). Following the formation of a saturated fatty acid, there are special mechanisms for the production of corresponding unsaturated acids. Nagai and Bloch (1966) have recently obtained a system from chloroplasts which desaturates the ACP derivatives of fatty acids and involves $NADPH_2$, O_2 and ferredoxin. This system for desaturation of fatty acids differs from that found in animals and bacteria where the acyl-CoA derivatives are involved. While much, perhaps most, of the total fatty acids of plant cells is produced by soluble systems, chloroplasts and microsomes, evidence that fruit mitochondria can synthesize these acids has been provided by Mudd and Stumpf (1961). They showed that avocado mitochondria could perform *de novo* synthesis of C_{16} and C_{18} saturated and unsaturated acids when fed with labelled acetate or its CoA derivative. Recent work described above suggests that here too a protein similar to ACP could be involved.

B. DEGRADATION OF FATTY ACIDS

The breakdown of fatty acids in mitochondria with the release of the energy inherent in the highly saturated hydrocarbon chain occurs mainly by way of the so-called fatty acid spiral originally described by Lynen (1953)

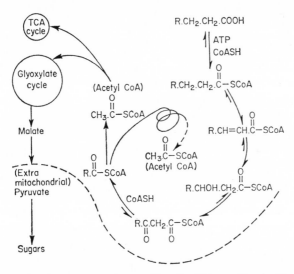

FIG. 3 Breakdown of fatty acids; the "fatty acid spiral".

and Green (1954) for animal tissues, where it is exclusively a mitochondrial process. There is now abundant evidence that the pathway also occurs in plants both in mitochondrial particles and soluble proteins of cell homogenates (Yamada and Stumpf, 1964; Rebeiz *et al.*, 1965). The spiral shown in Fig. 3 consists of a sequence of reactions in which an acyl-CoA is degraded in a C_2 sequence to acetyl-CoA. Each step in one stage of the spiral is also shown in Fig. 3. By a series of reductions and hydrations, the acyl-CoA yields acetyl-CoA and the two-carbon lower homologue of the original acid. The final product is acetyl-CoA which may then enter the Krebs or glyoxylate cycles. When odd-numbered acids are involved, the final product is propionyl-CoA. In plants it appears that the final propionic acid is converted to acetyl-CoA and CO_2 by a modified form of β-oxidation (Giovanelli and Stumpf, 1958; Hatch and Stumpf, 1962) in which β-hydroxypropionic acid is reduced to the corresponding aldehyde, which is further reduced and combined with CoA to form malonyl-CoA, which is then decarboxylated.

Another pathway of fatty acid oxidation which probably occurs in the mitochondrion is the so-called α-oxidation sequence which can also be regarded as a spiral system. This involves a two enzyme sequence of a specific fatty acid peroxidase and an NAD-dependent long-chain aldehyde dehydrogenase (Martin and Stumpf, 1959; Hitchcock et al., 1964). In each turn of the spiral the fatty acid is oxidatively decarboxylated to the next lower aldehyde. This aldehyde is then oxidized to the corresponding acid which re-enters the spiral. The overall cellular localization and relative importance of the α- and modified β-oxidation systems is at present uncertain.

VI. METABOLISM OF AMINO ACIDS AND PROTEINS

Each major synthetic route to amino acids branches off from an intermediate of either the glycolytate or tricarboxylic acid cycles. The keto acids of the Krebs cycle (excluding the unstable oxalosuccinic) may be readily transaminated with conversion of pyruvic to alanine, OAA to aspartic acid adn α-oxoglutaric to glutamic acid. While these processes may occur outside as well as inside the mitochondrion, the initial fixation of ammonia into amino acids takes place in the mitochondrion by the synthetic action of glutamic dehydrogenase. Transaminases are largely located in the mitochondrion; by their action a whole range of amino acids is produced from the three keto acids of the Krebs cycle. Some of these reactions, many of which occur in mitochondria, are shown in Fig. 4. The basic amino acid, arginine, has been shown to be formed from ornithine and carbamyl phosphate (synthesized from ammonia, ATP and CO_2) via citrulline and argininosuccinic acid in, for example, mung bean seedlings; the mitochondria appear to be involved in this process (Bone, 1959).

Moving in the opposite direction, a combination of transamination and deamination will lead to the formation of pyruvate, OAA and α-oxoglutarate. Even in tissues rich in glutamic dehydrogenase, the oxidation of glutamate proceeds by the transamination pathway, i.e. through α-oxoglutarate, in mitochondria (Müller and Leuthardt, 1950). It appears that the dehydrogenase has a purely synthetic function.

Although the chief site of protein synthesis is known to be in the microsomes, it would appear that mitochondria have at least a limited capacity for protein synthesis. Much of the difficulty in the investigation of mitochondrial protein synthesis is due to the ease with which the organelles become contaminated with bacteria during their isolation (Von der Decken *et al.*, 1966). Little protein synthesis work has been carried out with plants but preliminary data (Chaterjee, 1966) suggest that plant mitochondria behave similarly to those of animals, i.e. are concerned mainly with the synthesis of their own structural proteins. The specific respiratory enzyme proteins appear to be synthesized elsewhere. How these proteins become organized within the

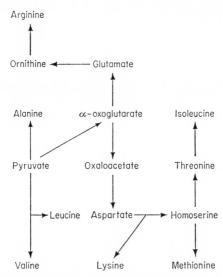

FIG. 4 Synthetic routes to amino acids.

developing mitochondrion is not clear (Roodyn, 1966). The breakdown of proteins, whether in the mitochondrion or in other regions of the cell, will eventually produce keto acids which may then enter the Krebs cycle.

VII. OTHER BIOSYNTHETIC PATHWAYS

Several intermediates in mitochondrial metabolism serve to initiate the routes of synthesis of a diversity of important compounds and secondary products which are located elsewhere in plant cells. For instance, acetyl-CoA combines with another mitochondrial intermediate, acetoacetyl-CoA, to form β-hydroxy-β-methyl-glutaryl-CoA which becomes oxidized to mevalonic acid, the precursor for the biosynthesis of terpenoid compounds including carotenoids and steroids. Mevalonic acid is also a precursor of the important growth regulator, gibberellic acid (Cross *et al.*, 1964). Acetyl-CoA is also involved in the biosynthesis of the "A" ring of flavanoid compounds which, among other functions, are responsible for many of the colours of flowers and the skins of some fruits.

Succinyl-CoA, formed in the Krebs cycle, is involved with glycine in the synthesis of haem compounds involving the cytochromes and the chlorophylls.

It has already been stated that carbamyl phosphate may be synthesized from ammonia, ATP and CO_2 in mitochondria. By combination with aspartic

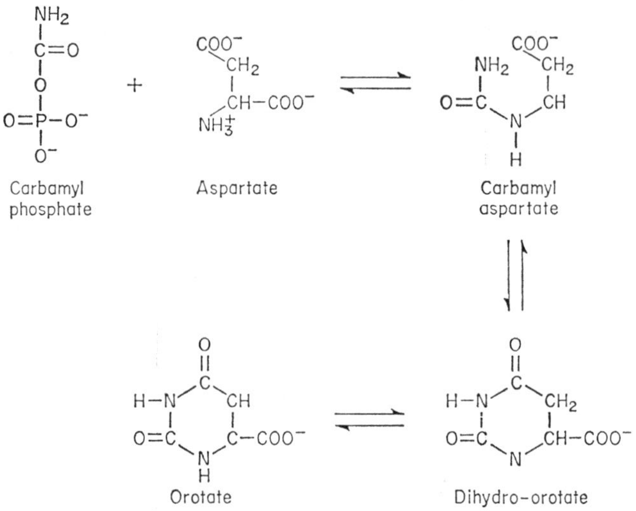

FIG. 5 Route of synthesis of orotic acid.

acid (also derived from processes taking place in the mitochondrion), orotic acid is formed in the manner shown in Fig. 5 (Reichard and Hansoff, 1956). Orotic acid is the key compound in the synthesis of the pyrimidines which are important structural units in nucleic acids.

VIII. General Control Mechanisms

We have discussed possible carbon pathways within the mitochondrion and routes of synthesis and breakdown leading from and returning to the mitochondrion. The relative importance of a process or series of processes will, however, depend on mechanisms regulating the speed and extent of such a process. These regulatory mechanisms may take a direct form or they may appear as permeability barriers to the free flow in and out of the mitochondrion and its compartments of substrates, cofactors, ions, etc. In dealing with the problem of these permeability barriers, the first important advance came from the realization that the penetration even of simple ions is not a function of their hydrated diameter (Chappell and Crofts, 1966). Chappell and Crofts showed further that only a few anions freely entered the mitochondrion, e.g. phosphate, acetate and propionate. Other anions of metabolically important acids, such as malate, succinate, malonate and mesotartrate, will penetrate only in the presence of P_i, while citrate cis-aconitate and D- and L-tartrate require both P_i and malate for penetration. Some important anions such as fumarate and maleate seem to be unable to penetrate the membrane. In these experiments metabolic inhibitors were (necessarily) present to prevent oxidation of the anion being studied. It seems possible that the permeability of the mitochondrial membrane to substrates may be different when the substrate is being actively metabolized.

With animal mitochondria it has been shown that acyl-CoA derivatives of long chain fatty acids cannot penetrate the mitochondrial membrane and that for penetration the acyl group must be transferred to carnitine, the betaine of β-hydroxybutyric acid (Bremer, 1962). In plants, however, the system must be different since carnitine appears to be absent from plant tissues. Similar permeability difficulties relate to the pyridine nucleotides and adenosine phosphates but this is outside the scope of this review.

The metabolite modulation of enzyme reactions, such as those of the Krebs cycle, has assumed great importance during the past 15 years since the work of Koch et al. (1952) which showed that purine inhibits purine synthesis in E. coli. This problem cannot be mentioned without a passing reference to the effect of the metabolic requirements of the cell in relation to the level of the ATP : ADP ratio. For example, the very commencement of the operation of the Krebs cycle depends on the activity of the enzyme citrate synthetase (condensing enzyme). Now, ATP decreases the affinity of this enzyme for its substrate, acetyl-CoA (Atkinson, 1966) so that when general metabolic activity is low and ATP, not being used up in synthetic reactions, is high then the cycle will be slowed down. Another enzyme of the cycle, fumarase, is similarly modified by ATP (Cohen and Penner, 1965). On the other hand AMP and ADP are *positive* modifiers (i.e. increase substrate-enzyme affinities) for isocitric dehydrogenase. By a combination of modifiers, acetyl-CoA may be switched from the Krebs cycle to the production of storage fats (Hathway and Atkinson, 1963).

The general question of product-inhibition of pathways has been widely studied recently in relation to amino acid synthesis in microorganisms (Atkinson, 1966). If there is a series of reactions at which a branch point occurs then we have a situation as shown in Fig. 6, where product A may go either to P, Q and R or the X, Y and Z. When end product R accumulates it may shut off its production by "allosterically" modifying the enzyme p' which is the first enzyme in the branch producing R. (This modification generally takes the form of altering the affinity of the enzyme for its substrate.) Then the flow of A will be switched to the X, Y, Z branch. There are several branching points around the Krebs cycle leading off to the synthesis of a number of compounds from simple amino and fatty acids to haems, sterols and phenolics. Is it possible that the products of reactions along these branch systems may inhibit the action of the first enzyme of the branch? There are few details available of such overall regulation of the Krebs cycle but specific examples have been known for some time, e.g. the inhibition of succinic dehydrogenase by OAA, the concentration of which may be regulated in a number of ways. This inhibition was originally thought to be a clear case of competitive substrate inhibition (Pardee and Potter, 1948). Here we have an

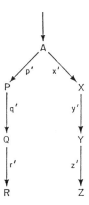

FIG. 6 Progression from a "branch point" in enzyme systems. A, P, Q, etc. are products of substrates; p′, q′, r′, etc. are enzymes.

example of a metabolite some way along a "normal" series of reactions affecting the activity of an enzyme several stages further back in the sequence; OAA inhibition is, in fact, a complicated process (Slater, 1966) and it may not be a simple competitive inhibition of succinic dehydrogenase; it may in fact be an example of "enzyme modification".

Payes and Laties (1963) have described a system in which OAA combines with glyoxylate to form γ-hydroxy-α-oxoglutarate which is seemingly a potent inhibitor of certain reactions of the Krebs cycle. This may be important in tissues in which isocitrate lyase is present.

IX. THE RÔLE OF OXALOACETIC ACID IN CONTROLLING THE KREBS CYCLE IN APPLE MITOCHONDRIA

Our own attention has been drawn to the effect of OAA on mitochondrial oxidations during a study of a certain type of physiological disorder of apple fruits which was preceded by an accumulation of this acid (Hulme *et al.*, 1964b). During the past decade abundant evidence has been obtained to emphasize the importance of OAA in the control of the metabolism of carbohydrate, fat and protein in mitochondria from animal tissues. Slater (1962) gives five ways in which this action may be exerted: (1), as a catalyst for the oxidation to CO_2 of acetate (bound to CoA) derived from the catabolism of fat and carbohydrate; (2), as a catalyst for the oxidation of glutamate to aspartate (this is concerned in the catabolism of protein); (3), as an inhibitor of the oxidation of malate to OAA; (4), as an inhibitor of the oxidation of succinate to fumarate and (5), as a catalyst in the synthesis of fat from carbohydrate.

With apple mitochondria addition to OAA inhibits the oxidation of both malate and succinate. As will be clear from Fig. 7, the inhibition decreases

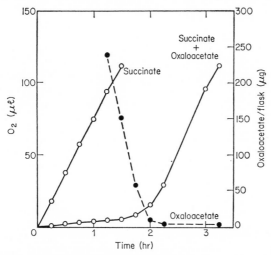

FIG. 7 The effect of added OAA on the oxidation of succinate by apple mitochondria and the concomitant changes in the amount of OAA in the digest.
O = O_2 uptake; ● = content of OAA.

with time and this is paralleled by the disappearance of OAA. For a given amount of OAA the oxidation of malate recovers more rapidly than that of succinate and at the same time the rate of disappearance of OAA is more rapid with malate (see Fig. 8). The small O_2-uptake in the early stages of the disappearance of OAA (when the OAA concentration is high) will be due to some oxidation of the OAA in the Krebs cycle. At this stage most of the OAA may be undergoing transformation in a coupled system, to be discussed later, which does not involve an overall uptake of O_2. As the oxidation of succinate *alone* progresses, OAA begins to accumulate and the rate of oxidation gradually decreases. During the oxidation of malate *alone*, OAA accumulates more rapidly so that when succinate is oxidized by apple mitochondria in the presence of malate a more rapid decrease (inhibition) in the rate of oxidation occurs (Hulme *et al.*, 1967). Inhibition by OAA is not due to the pyruvate formed from it (Hulme *et al.*, 1967). The rapidity with which *externally added* OAA inhibits oxidation of both succinate and malate suggests that the mitochondrial membrane cannot be entirely impermeable to OAA. Nevertheless, the more rapid disappearance of OAA with malate as compared with succinate could well be due to the assistance to the entry of OAA into

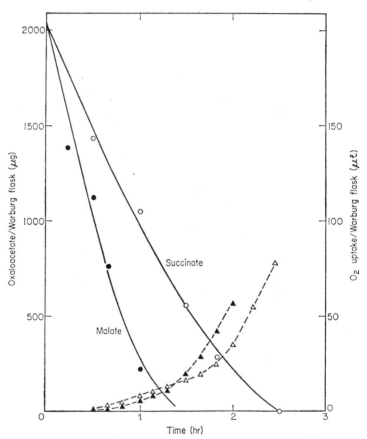

FIG. 8 O_2 uptake and content of OAA during the oxidation of succinate and malate by apple mitochondria.
●, O = O_2 uptake; ▲, △ = changes in content of OAA.

the mitochondrion which malate confers (Chappell and Crofts, 1966; see above p. 110). Alternatively, it could be that the "block" on succinate is extremely tight, whereas with malate the cycle is not immediately blocked. The NAD, always added to the digests, would allow some oxidation of malate in the cycle as far as succinate.

In a study of factors affecting the removal of OAA and, therefore, the relief from inhibition of succinate and malate oxidation by apple mitochondria, we have found that Mg^{++} and ATP greatly accelerate the disappearance of OAA (Hulme et al., 1967). These results are in general agreement with those of other workers using animal preparations (Pardee and Potter, 1948; Tyler, 1955). Small amounts of Al^{+++} are known to bring about the rapid decarboxylation of OAA (Krebs and Eggleston, 1945; Speck, 1949). This ion, at a concentration of 0·001M, both speeds the relief of OAA inhibition of malate oxidation and stimulates the rate of oxidation alone (Hulme et al., 1967).

The importance of OAA as an inhibitor of malate and succinate oxidation by apple mitochondria and its accumulation as the fruit itself becomes susceptible to low temperature injury in cold storage (see above) led us to a study of the possible routes by which OAA may be metabolized by apple mitochondria.

X. ROUTES FOR THE UTILIZATION OF OXALOACETIC ACID BY APPLE MITOCHONDRIA

When considering the metabolism of OAA the fact must be borne in mind that the acid undergoes spontaneous, non-enzymic breakdown to pyruvate and that this breakdown is accelerated by the presence of Mg^{++} (Hulme et al., 1967). Therefore, in the system of OAA and mitochondria (containing the various co-factors including CoA) pyruvate will always be available. This inevitable presence of pyruvate means that some utilization of "OAA alone" can occur by means of the Krebs cycle at least as far as the blocked succinate stage. The small but positive oxygen uptake (the NAD present will minimize the need for this) with apple mitochondria and the rapid appearance of small amounts of α-oxoglutarate confirm this.

OAA can also be transaminated to aspartate; we have found that relief from OAA inhibition can be effected by the addition of glutamate or cysteine sulphinic acid.

A system, first suggested for avocado mitochondria by Avron and Biale (1957), in which the action of the pyruvate dehydrogenase complex is coupled to the action of malic dehydrogenase can also metabolize OAA without the uptake of oxygen.

(1) $OAA \longrightarrow pyruvate + CO_2$

(2) $pyruvate + NAD + CoA \longrightarrow acetyl\text{-}CoA + NADH_2 + CO_2$

(3) $OAA + Acetyl\text{-}CoA \longrightarrow citrate + CoA$

(4) $OAA + NADH_2 \longrightarrow malate + NAD$

Overall reaction: $3OAA \longrightarrow citrate + malate + 2CO_2$

Reaction (2) provides the $NADH_2$ to drive reaction (4), the reverse of the normal Krebs cycle malate dehydrogenase reaction. Evidence for all these pathways of OAA degradation in apple mitochondria has been provided by Hulme et al. (1967a).

There is a striking change in the susceptibility of succinate oxidation to inhibition by OAA with apple peel mitochondria prepared from fruit at different stages of the climacteric rise in respiration, an important prelude to ripening. Preclimacteric mitochondria are inhibited for more than twice as long for a given amount of OAA as those prepared at the climacteric peak (Hulme et al., 1967b). This cannot be due to a simple process such as the presence of, or susceptibility to, the co-factor TPP as suggested by Lance et al. (1965) for avocado mitochondria. This change in susceptibility may be an important regulator of the progress of the climacteric and the onset of ripening. The mechanism involved is being studied.

Finally, in summary it can be said that OAA acts as both a catalyst and an inhibitor of the Krebs cycle. The standard free energy change of the action of malic dehydrogenase favours the formation of malate from OAA. The reaction only proceeds freely to OAA in the forward direction of the Krebs cycle when the NAD : $NADH_2$ ratio is relatively high and when the OAA level relative to malate is low. Within the cycle the latter condition is controlled by the availability of acetyl-CoA for condensation to form citrate. By means of the coupled system discussed above, under conditions in which oxygen uptake is limited and the level of $NADH_2$ is relatively high, OAA can be reduced to malate by the reverse operation of malic dehydrogenase. This formation of malate from OAA has recently been confirmed in animal tissues (Tager, 1966). There are other factors external to the Krebs cycle but still within the mitochondrion which can affect the level of OAA. For example, the transamination of OAA to aspartate and the diversion of acetyl-CoA into fat synthesis.

The realization that self-regulatory systems are widespread in plants is of recent origin and, no doubt, within the next decade research into the means by which mitochondrial activity is regulated by processes outside the mitochondrion (perhaps quite far removed from the relatively simple processes of the Krebs cycle) will lead to a much better understanding of how plant cells react to their environment and to the requirements of the plant as a whole.

REFERENCES

Atkinson, D. E. (1966). *A. Rev. Biochem.* **35**, 85.
Avron, M. and Biale, J. B. (1957). *J. biol. Chem.* **225**, 669.
Bonner, J. and Varner, J. E. (1965). "Plant Biochemistry," Academic Press, New York and London.

Bone, D. H. (1959). *Pl. Physiol., Lancaster* **34**, 171.
Bremer, J. J. (1962). *J. biol. Chem.* **237**, 2628.
Chappell, J. B. and Crofts, A. R. (1966). "Regulation of Metabolic Processes in Mitochondria". (J. M. Tager, S. Papa, E. Quagliariello and E. C. Slater, eds), p. 293. Elsevier, Amsterdam.
Chaterjee, S. K., Mukherjee, T., Das, H. K., Nath, K. and Roy, S. C. (1966). *Indian J. Biochem.* **3**, 239.
Cohen, L. H. and Penner, P. E. (1965). *Fedn Proc. Fedn Am. Socs exp. Biol.* **24**, 357.
Cross, B. E., Galt, R. H. B. and Hanson, J. B. (1964). *J. chem. Soc.* 295.
Davies, D. D. (1959). *Biol. Rev.* **34**, 407.
Giovanelli, J. and Stumpf, P. K. (1958). *J. biol. Chem.* **231**, 411.
Green, D. E. (1954). *Biol. Rev.* **29**, 330.
Hatch, M. D. and Stumpf, P. K. (1961). *J. biol. Chem.* **236**, 2879.
Hatch, M. D. and Stumpf, P. K. (1962). *Archs Biochem. Biophys.* **96**, 193.
Hathway, J. A. and Atkinson, D. E. (1963). *J. biol. Chem.* **238**, 2875.
Hitchcock, C. H. S., James, A. T. and Wood, B. J. B. (1964). *Proc. VIth Intern. Cong. Biochem., New York* **VII**, 377.
Hulme, A. C. (1954). *Biochim. biophys. Acta* **14**, 36.
Hulme, A. C., Jones, J. D. and Wooltorton, L. S. C. (1963). *Proc. R. Soc. B.* **158**, 514.
Hulme, A. C., Jones, J. D. and Wooltorton, L. S. C. (1964a). *Phytochem.* **3**, 173.
Hulme, A. C., Rhodes, M. J. C. and Wooltorton, L. S. C. (1967a). *J. exp. Bot.* **18**, 277.
Hulme, A. C., Rhodes, M. J. C. and Wooltorton, L. S. C. (1967b). *Phytochem.* **6**, 1343.
Hulme, A. C., Smith, W. H. and Wooltorton, L. S. C., (1964b). *J. Sci. Fd. Agric.* **5**, 303.
Koch, A. L., Putnam, F. W. and Evans, E. A. (1952). *J. biol. Chem.* **197**, 105.
Kornberg, H. L. and Krebs, H. A. (1957). *Nature, Lond.* **179**, 988.
Krebs, H. A. (1943). *Adv. Enzymol.* **3**, 191.
Krebs, H. A. and Eggleston, L. V. (1945). *Biochem. J.* **39**, 408.
Lance, C., Hobson, G. E., Young, R. E. and Biale, J. B. (1965). *Pl. Physiol., Lancaster* **40**, 1116.
Lehninger, A. L. (1964). "The Mitochondrion", W. A. Benjamin Inc., New York.
Lioret, C. and Moyse, A. (1963). *In* "Comparative Biochemistry". (M. Florkin and H. S. Mason, eds), Vol. 5, p. 203. Academic Press, New York.
Lynen, F. (1953). *Fedn Proc. Fedn Am. Socs exp. Biol.* **12**, 683.
McLennan, D. H., Beevers, H. and Horley, J. L. (1963). *Biochem. J.* **89**, 316.
Majerus, P. W., Alberts, A. W. and Vagelos, P. R. (1964). *Proc. natn. Acad. Sci., U.S.A.* **51**, 1231.
Martin, R. O. and Stumpf, P. K. (1959). *J. biol. Chem.* **234**, 2548.
Meynhardt, J. T., Maxie, E. C. and Romani, R. J. (1965). *S. Afr. J. agric. Sci.* **8**, 291.
Morton, R. J. and Wells, J. R. E. (1964). *Nature, Lond.* **201**, 477.
Mudd, J. B. and Stumpf, P. K. (1961). *J. biol. Chem.* **236**, 2602.
Müller, A. F. and Leuthardt, F. (1950). *Adv. Chim. Acta* **33**, 268.
Nagai, J. and Bloch, K. (1966). *J. biol. Chem.* **241**, 1925.
Overath, P. and Stumpf, P. K. (1964). *J. biol. Chem.* **239**, 4103.
Pardee, A. B. and Potter, V. R. (1948). *J. biol. Chem.* **176**, 1085.
Payes, B. and Laties, G. G. (1963). *Biochem. biophys. Res. Commun.* **10**, 460.
Rebeiz, C. A., Castelfranco, P. and Engelbrecht, A. H. (1965). *Pl. Physiol., Lancaster* **40**, 281.

Reichard, P. and Hanshoff, G. (1956). *Acta chem. scand.* **10**, 548.
Roodyn, D. B. (1966). *In* "Regulation of Metabolic Processes in Mitochondria", (J. M. Tager, S. Papa, E. Quagliariello and E. C. Slater, eds), p. 383. Elsevier Amsterdam.
Shannon, L. M., de Villis, J. and Leu, J. Y. (1963). *Pl. Physiol., Lancaster* **38**, 691.
Slater, E. C. (1962). *Chem. Weekbl.* **52**, 1.
Slater, E. C. (1966). *In* "Regulation of Metabolic Processes in Mitochondria". (J. M. Tager, S. Papa, E. Quagliariello and E. C. Slater, eds), p. 539. Elsevier, Amsterdam.
Speck, J. F. (1949). *J. biol. Chem.* **178**, 315.
Stafford, H. A. and Loewus, F. A. (1958). *Pl. Physiol., Lancaster* **33**, 194.
Tager, J. M. (1966). *In* "The Regulation of Metabolic Processes in Mitochondria". (J. M. Tager, S. Papa, E. Quagliariello and E. C. Slater, eds), p. 202. Elsevier, Amsterdam.
Tyler, B. D. (1955). *J. biol. Chem.* **216**, 395.
Vagelos, P. R., Majerus, P. W., Alberts, A. R. and Ailhaud, E. P. (1966). *Fedn Proc. Fedn Am. Socs exp. Biol.* **25**, 1485.
Von der Decken, A., Löw, H. and Sandell, S. (1966). *In* "Regulation of Metabolic Processes in Mitochondria". (J. M. Tager, S. Papa, E. Quagliariello and E. C. Slater, eds), p. 415. Elsevier, Amsterdam.
Walker, D. A. (1962). *Biol. Rev.* **37**, 215.
Wang, S. F., Adler, J. and Lardy, H. A. (1961). *J. biol. Chem.* **236**, 26.
Yamada, M. and Stumpf, P. K. (1964). *Pl. Physiol., Lancaster* **39**, (Suppl.) XXIV.
Yamomoto, Y. and Beevers, H. (1960). *Pl. Physiol., Lancaster* **35**. 102.

CHAPTER 7

The Energy Transfer Function of Mitochondria

J. M. PALMER

Department of Botany, King's College, University of London
London, England

I. INTRODUCTION

There are two major enzymatic pathways which are primarily involved in the transfer of energy. In photosynthesis, energy in the form of light is used by plants to cause electrons to move from water ($E'_0 = +0·81V$) to the electron carrier ferredoxin ($E'_0 = -0·42V$). Energy in this form is apparently of little use and it is converted to NADPH or ATP and finally to reduced carbon compounds mostly in the form of carbohydrates, fats and proteins. These compounds constitute the main store of energy in biological systems. The second process involved in the transfer of energy is cellular respiration; here the reduced carbon compounds are rearranged and pairs of hydrogen atoms are removed to produce reduced coenzymes. These electron donors are then oxidized and the energy liberated is conserved in the form of ATP. Figure 1 shows the main types of energy transfer processes which occur during cellular respiration. They can be divided into two groups, the first being glycolysis which is thought to take place in the soluble phase of the cytoplasm although there are reports (Barker et al., 1966) that it may be associated with a membrane system. Only a small amount of energy is

119

transferred during this process and is characterized by the substrate level phosphorylation which is catalysed by the enzyme phosphoglyceryl kinase. The major amount of energy transfer occurs in the second group and is located in the mitochondria and can be sub-divided into (a), substrate level phosphorylation and (b), oxidative phosphorylation. Substrate level phosphorylation is connected with the conversion of α-ketoglutarate to succinate via the high energy intermediate succinyl-coenzyme A. Work on plant mitochondria has shown that ATP rather than GTP is the final product of substrate

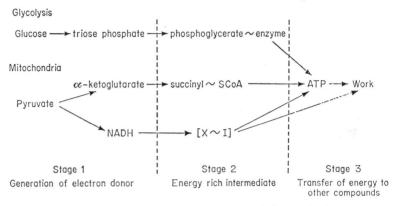

FIG. 1 The transfer of energy during cellular respiration.

level phosphorylation and that phosphohistidine may be an intermediate in the transfer process (Palmer and Wedding, 1966; Norman *et al.*, 1965).

The process of oxidative phosphorylation is quantitatively more important. Here reduced coenzymes are oxidized by molecular oxygen and the energy liberated coupled to the synthesis of ATP; this constitutes the main energy transfer function of the mitochondria.

II. OXIDATIVE PHOSPHORYLATION

It is convenient, for the purpose of discussion, to divide the process of oxidative phosphorylation into three sections: (a), the rearrangement of the carbon compounds so that the electrons can be withdrawn to produce the electron donor necessary for oxidative phosphorylation; (b), the transfer of electrons from the various donors to molecular oxygen and (c), the conservation of energy associated with this oxidation.

A. REARRANGEMENT OF CARBON COMPOUNDS ASSOCIATED WITH THE GENERATION OF ELECTRON DONORS

The mitochondria contain the enzymic apparatus necessary to produce electron donors from pyruvate derived from carbohydrates, fatty acids and amino acids. The central system for the production of electron donors is the tricarboxylic cycle which is outlined, more as a hydrogen metabolizing cycle than a carbon metabolizing cycle, in Fig. 2. The tricarboxylic acid cycle, as illustrated, uses acetyl-coenzyme A to produce carbon dioxide and reduced coenzymes; it is also able to use as a substrate any compound that can be first converted to any one of the intermediates of the cycle. Pyruvate entering the cycle is decarboxylated and then reduced to acetyl-coenzyme A by the enzyme complex pyruvate kinase, α-lipoic acid being the hydrogen acceptor

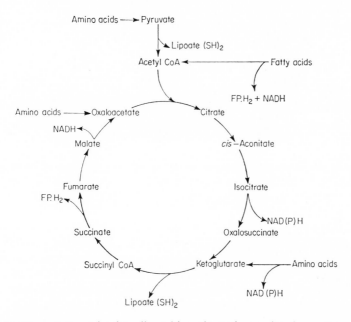

FIG. 2 Outline of the tricarboxylic acid cycle and associated reactions which produce the electron donors necessary for oxidative phosphorylation.

in this reduction. Fatty acids are another important source of substrates for cellular respiration, particularly in plant material which contains large amounts of oil and fat. The glycerol residue is converted to glycerol phosphate and is then directly oxidized by the electron transport system of the mitochondria to produce dihydroxyacetone phosphate which passes out of the mitochondria to be metabolized by the glycolytic system (Stumpf, 1955). The free fatty acid can then be converted into acetyl-coenzyme A by the process of β-oxidation and in this form can enter the tricarboxylic acid cycle. The enzymes responsible for β-oxidations of fatty acids are known to be associated with the mitochondria (Stumpf and Barber, 1956) and produce both $FADH_2$ and NADH as electron donors during the reaction.

G

Recently it has been shown (Rossi *et al.*, 1966a) that in sonicated animal mitochondria a second mechanism exists to activate fatty acids which is insensitive to the uncoupling activity of dinitrophenol and is closely coupled to the oxidation of α-ketoglutarate and involves the use of GTP, generated as

(1) Acyl–CoA synthetase (6.2.1.2)
    $R.CH_2.CH_2.COOH + CoA + ATP \rightleftharpoons R.CH_2.CH_2.CO.CoA + AMP + P\text{-}Pi$

(2) Acyl–CoA dehydrogenase (1.3.2.2.)
    $R.CH_2CH_2CO.CoA + FAD \rightleftharpoons R.CH.CH.CO.CoA + FADH_2$

(3) Enoyl–CoA hydranase (4.2.1.17)
    $R.CH.CH.CO.CoA + H_2O \rightleftharpoons R.CHOH.CH_2.CO.CoA$

(4) 3–hydroxyacyl–CoA dehydrogenase (1.1.1.35)
    $R.CHOH.CH_2.CO.CoA + NAD^+ \rightleftharpoons R.CO.CH_2.CO.CoA + NADH + H^+$

(5) Acetyl–CoA acytransferase (2.3.1.16)
    $R.CO.CH_2.CO.CoA + CoA \rightleftharpoons R.CO.CoA + CH_3CO.CoA$

FIG. 3   The enzymes and reactions involved in the production of acetyl coenzyme A from fatty acids during the process of β-oxidation.

the result of substrate level phosphorylation, as the energy source. The significance of this reaction is unknown but it does raise two interesting points. In the first case, it is a more efficient system than the mechanism involving ATP since only one phosphate molecule is removed from the GTP:

$$GTP + R\text{–}CH_2CO_2H + CoHSH \longrightarrow R\text{–}CH_2\text{–}CO\text{–}CoA + GDP + Pi,$$

rather than the pyrophosphate being removed from the ATP (see Fig. 3). Secondly, this activating system shows high activity towards fatty acids which are known to uncouple oxidative phosphorylation (Van den Bergh, 1966) and it is possible that this system may be able to act as a self defence mechanism, allowing the mitochondria to activate fatty acids when oxidative phosphorylation is completely uncoupled from electron transport.

In tissues where protein breakdown predominates, i.e. some germinating seeds and senescent tissue, it is possible to use amino acids as substrates for cellular respiration. Amino acids usually enter the tricarboxylic cycle as the corresponding keto acids formed by transamination with α-ketoglutarate acting as the acceptor for the amino groups. The glutamate thus formed can be converted to α-ketoglutarate by the enzyme glutamic dehydrogenase with the production of ammonia and NADPH. Both the transaminase and glutamic dehydrogenase are found in isolated mitochondria (Davies *et al.*, 1964).

Clearly the mitochondria have the ability to rearrange pyruvic acid, fatty acids and amino acids and produce a variety of electron donors (summarized in Table I) suitable for oxidation during oxidative phosphorylation.

B. OXIDATION OF ELECTRON DONORS

The next stage of the energy transfer process is the removal of electrons from the electron donors and their transfer to molecular oxygen with the controlled liberation of energy. The process is mediated by the electron transport chain which consists of proteins with firmly bound prosthetic groups such as iron porphyrins and flavin nucleotides which are attached to the inner membrane of the mitochondria. The composition of the electron transport chain is basically similar in both animals and plants although mitochondria from plants have lower concentrations of cytochromes. The greatest difference between the plant and animal system probably lies in the cytochrome b region of the chain. Plant mitochondria are thought to contain several different types of cytochrome b; Hackett (1959) has suggested that one of the cyto-

TABLE 1

Electron donors produced during the rearrangement
of carbon compounds.

Substrate	Initial electron donor produced
Pyruvate	reduced lipoic acid
	NADH
	reduced flavoprotein
Fats	α-glycerophosphate
	reduced flavoprotein
	reduced lipoic acid
	NADH
Amino acids	NADPH
	reduced lipoic acid
	NADH
	reduced flavoprotein

chrome b types is auto-oxidizable and may be important in mediating cyanide resistant respiration which is known to occur in some plant tissue (Laties, 1957); this theory has been contested, however (Bonner, 1966). Further discussion concerning the electron transport system in plant mitochondria is really beyond the scope of this paper but it has been reviewed recently (Davies et al., 1964; Bonner, 1966; Lieberman and Baker, 1965). Figure 4 shows a diagram of the electron transport chain as it is thought to be organized in an animal mitochondrion (Lehninger, 1964) and serves to show the points of entry of electrons from the various donors. The mechanism by which the electrons are moved from one member of the chain to the next is not understood although several theories have been advanced. One of the most interesting is that arising from the work of E. F. Korman (Green and Goldberger, 1966) who recognized from molecular models that certain compounds change shape when undergoing oxidation or reduction. It has been suggested that the ring system of NAD may rotate through an angle of 90° when undergoing reduction. From this data it has been possible to build up a model for electron transport in which the electrons are moved along the chain by a wave of conformational changes (Green and Goldberger, 1966).

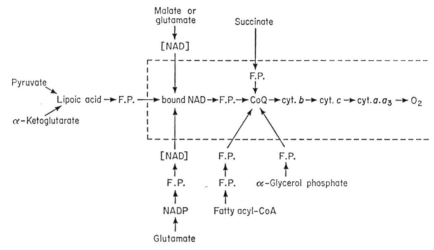

FIG. 4 The electron transfer system associated with mitochondria showing the points which electrons enter the chain from the various donors involved (Lehninger, 1964).

The importance of the electron transport chain from the point of view of energy transfer is that the components of the chain are redox couples, having negative potentials at the NAD end and increasingly positive redox potentials towards the oxygen end of the chain. As electrons are transferred from one component to the next there will be a liberation of energy given by the formula

$$F^{\circ} = -nF\Delta E'_0$$

where n = number of electrons transferred, F = a Faraday, $\Delta E'_0$ = difference in redox potential of the carriers involved. The values for $\Delta E'_0$ and ΔF° expected when two electrons move from one component to the next in the respiratory chain are given in Table II. If between 7 and 10 kcals are necessary to synthesize ATP from ADP under normal conditions then ATP formation can only occur when pairs of electrons move from NADH→FAD. Cytochrome b→cytochrome c and cytochrome $a \rightarrow \frac{1}{2}O_2$. Work involving the uses of various substrates and inhibitors (Davies et al., 1964) and the cross-over point theory (Chance, 1965a; Bonner, 1966) also show that phosphorylation occurs when electrons traverse the regions of the chain suggested from the thermodynamic considerations.

TABLE II

Thermodynamic relationships in the respiratory chain.

Carrier	E'_0 (mV)	$\Delta E'_0$ (mV)	$\Delta F°$ for 2e⁻ transfer (cal)
NAD	−320		
		+257	−11,853
Flavoprotein	− 63		
		+ 23	− 1061
Cytochrome b	− 40		
		+290	−13,375
Cytochrome c	+250		
		+ 40	− 1845
Cytochrome a	+290		
		+525	−24,213
Oxygen	+815		

C. CONSERVATION OF ENERGY LIBERATED DURING ELECTRON TRANSPORT

It is usually considered that under normal conditions the energy liberated during the process of oxidation is coupled to the synthesis of ATP. As yet little is known about the mechanism of this process although a considerable amount of research has been carried out in an attempt to clarify the problem. It has been established that with NADH as the electron donor three molecules of ATP are synthesized from ADP and inorganic phosphate for every pair of electrons transferred to oxygen; when succinate is used as the electron donor the P : O ratio is 2 (Rowan, 1966). Recently Lynn and Brown (1965) have suggested that in animal mitochondria, at least, the P : O ratio may be considerably higher than these values and at the present time this problem has not been satisfactorily resolved.

The mechanism by which the energy released by oxidation is utilized to synthesize ATP is of even greater complexity. There are two schools of thought concerning this problem. The first theory to be proposed was that the coupling was accomplished through a series of unknown energy-rich intermediates (Chance and Williams, 1956) and is generally known as the chemical coupling theory. More recently Mitchell (1961) has proposed the chemiosmotic theory in which the transfer of energy is caused by the generation of an electrochemical activity gradient of protons across a membrane (Mitchell, 1961, 1966a).

1. *The Chemical Coupling Theory*

This theory has been proposed mainly on the basis of results obtained using uncoupling agents such as dinitrophenol and arsenate or inhibitors of energy transfer such as oligomycin and atractyloside; it has been extensively reviewed on many occasions (Chance and Williams, 1956; Slater, 1966a; Griffiths, 1965). The scheme which is generally proposed is shown in Fig. 5; it involves two hypothetical non-phosphorylated intermediates $A \sim I$ and $X \sim I$ and a hypothetical phosphorylated intermediate $X \sim P$. In this scheme AH_2 is a reduced and B an oxidized member of the electron transport chain, respectively; before the hydrogen atoms or electrons can be moved from A to B,

$$AH_2 + B + I \rightleftharpoons A \sim I + BH_2$$
$$A \sim I + X \rightleftharpoons X \sim I + A$$
$$A \sim I + Pi \rightleftharpoons X \sim P + I$$
$$X \sim P + ADP \rightleftharpoons ATP + X$$

FIG. 5 Hypothetical energy-rich intermediates involved in the process of oxidative phosphorylation as visualized in the chemical coupling theory.

the hypothetical compound I must interact with A. If the compound I is not available to interact with compound A, electron transport is prevented; this is the basis for respiratory control by oxidative phosphorylation. There are several variations of this scheme and recently Green and Goldberger (1966) have proposed an alternative scheme shown in Fig. 6. In this system it is proposed that a carboxy group is involved in the formation of the energy-rich intermediate and that AMP rather than ADP is the primary energy acceptor (Ozawa, 1966); the ATP appears as the result of myokinase activity which is present at a high level in plant mitochondria (Palmer and Kalina, 1967). This

$$NADH + [Iox]COOH \rightleftharpoons [Ired]CO \sim NAD + H_2O$$
$$[Ired]CO \sim NAD + AMP \rightleftharpoons [Ired]CO \sim AMP + NAD$$
$$[Ired]CO \sim AMP + Pi \rightleftharpoons [Ired]COOH + ADP$$
$$2ADP \rightleftharpoons AMP + ATP$$

FIG. 6 Intermediates in the process of oxidative phosphorylation as described by Green and Goldberger (1966).

scheme also abolishes the requirement for the hypothetical phosphorylated energy-rich intermediate which is not in agreement with the phosphate [18] O exchange data which suggests inorganic phosphate is activated first and that the ADP supplies the oxygen involved in the terminal energy-rich bond of ATP (Low et al., 1963).

The chemical coupling theory does not explain in any way the actual mechanism of the initial energy conservation reaction (Fig. 5 first equation). Green and Goldberger (1966) suggested that a conformational change in the electron carriers A and B when passing through the oxidation reduction cycle may bring the reactive groups of A and I into close proximity so that an interaction can take place. There is evidence available from work on both animal and plant mitochondria to suggest that conformational changes of the mitochondrial membrane may precede phosphorylation (Boyer, 1965; Kenefick and Hanson, 1966).

2. The Chemiosmotic Theory

The details of this theory have been extensively discussed by Mitchell (1961, 1966a) and it is only necessary to mention the basic concepts in this paper. The theory is based on the suggestion that ATP is synthesized by reversing the activity of the enzyme ATPase and requires that the active site of this enzyme be situated in a membrane as shown in Fig. 7. It is also neces-

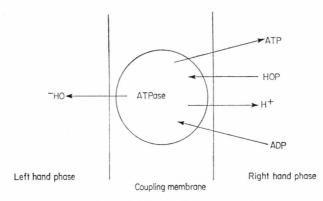

FIG. 7 ATP synthesis showing the production of H^+ and OH^- by the anisotropic ATPase proposed by Mitchell (1961, 1966a).

sary that this membrane should have permeability characteristics which allow the protons and the hydroxyl ions produced during the synthesis of ATP to escape into the right-hand or left-hand phase, respectively, and at the same time prevents protons in the left-hand phase and hydroxyl ions in the right-hand phase from reaching the active site of the enzyme. The reaction catalysed by the ATPase is given as:

$$ATP + H_2O \rightleftharpoons ADP + H_3PO_4$$

From consideration of the law of mass action it follows that

$$\frac{[ATP]}{[ADP]} = \frac{[H_2PO_4]}{K[H_2O]_{active\ site}}$$

In this equation [H_2O] is the concentration of water in equilibrium with the active site of the enzyme; this concentration will be determined by the tendency of the protons and hydroxyl ions produced to escape into the right- or left-hand phases. One way by which this tendency can be increased is by generating a large pool of protons in the left-hand phase and hydroxyl ions

Linear electron translocation

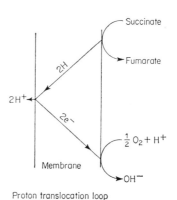

Proton translocation loop

FIG. 8 Production of a proton concentration gradient by (upper), linear electron transport or (lower), a proton translocating loop, during the transport of electrons in cellular respiration (Mitchell, 1966b).

in the right-hand phase which can then "mop up" the protons and hydroxyl ions produced as a result of ATP synthesis. Under these conditions, the concentration of water at the active site of the enzyme can be related to the concentration of protons in the left- and right-hand phases [H^+]$_L$ and [H^+]$_R$:

$$[H_2O]_{\text{active site}} = [H_2O]_{\text{aqueous}} \times \frac{[H^+]_R}{[H^+]_L}$$

and hence,

$$\frac{[ATP]}{[ADP]} = \frac{[H_3PO_4]}{K[H_2O]_{\text{aqueous}}} \times \frac{[H^+]_L}{[H^+]_R}$$

It is therefore obvious that the ratio of [ATP]/[ADP] will be dependent on the proton concentration gradient across the membrane.

In the chemiosmotic theory the proton concentration gradient across the membrane is produced by the activity of the electron transport system which must be situated in the same membrane. Figure 8 shows that the gradient may be formed either by a linear electron transporting system or by a proton translocating loop. The proton translocating loop depends on the fact that at certain points in the so-called electron transport chain, the transport of hydrogen atoms is converted into the transport of electrons. By adjusting the number of loops in the complete respiratory chain or by postulating the transport of a mixture of hydrogen atoms and electrons through parts of the chain, it is easy to obtain the correct stoichiometry necessary to produce the observed P/O ratios (Mitchell, 1966b).

Calculations of the ratio of $[H^+]_L/[H^+]_R$ necessary to produce substantial synthesis of ATP in this system indicate that it would result in a very large pH differential across the coupling membrane, greater than is actually found in practice (Chance and Mela, 1966). To overcome this problem it was necessary to consider the electrochemical activities of the ATPase equilibrium rather than the concentrations which have been considered previously. In this case the electrochemical activities are denoted by the use of curved brackets:

$$\frac{(ATP)}{(ADP)} = \frac{(H_3PO_4)}{K(H_2O)_{aqueous}} \times \frac{(H^+)_L}{(H^+)_R}$$

hence the equilibrium will depend on the electrochemical activity gradient of the protons across the membrane rather than the concentration gradient. It is possible to relate the electrochemical activity gradient of protons to the pH on either side of the membrane and the membrane potential:

$$\frac{(H^+)_R}{(H^+)_L} = pH_L - pH_R + \log \frac{EFRT}{2303}$$

where $R =$ the gas constant, $T =$ the absolute temperature, $F =$ the Faraday and $E =$ the membrane potential in mV.

The sum total of this hypothesis is that the generation of a proton concentration gradient across a membrane, or the generation of a membrane potential, facilitates the formation of an anhydride bond between ADP and H_3PO_4 resulting in the synthesis of ATP. However, this theory as it is normally presented does not take into account the sequence of events which may take place on the ATPase molecule. It would seem quite possible to visualize a series of events similar to that shown in Fig. 9; the first reaction being the removal of H^+ and OH^- from two groups X and I situated on the active site of the enzyme, resulting in the formation of X ∼ I which is then phosphory-lated to produce X ∼ P which finally interacts with ADP to produce ATP. Viewed in this manner it is obvious that the chemical coupling theory and the chemiosmotic theory are not incompatible with each other, the main discrep-ancy being in the mechanism of the initial energy conserving reaction which can now be regarded as resulting from conformational changes of the electron

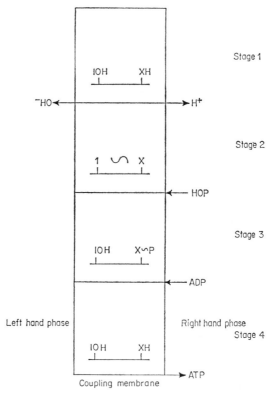

FIG. 9 Hypothetical intermediates which may participate in the synthesis of ATP by the reversal of the enzyme ATPase.

transport carriers in the chemical theory or the generation of an electro-chemical activity gradient of protons across a membrane in the chemiosmotic theory. The chemiosmotic theory offers an elegant explanation of why elec-tron transport and oxidative phosphorylation are invariably associated with membrane systems and also suggests a physiological rôle for ion uptake, in connection with the maintenance of a membrane potential, known to be associated with mitochondria.

III. ENERGY UTILIZING ACTIVITY OF THE MITOCHONDRIA

During the early stages of research when mitochondria were used in experiments to investigate respiration and oxidative phosphorylation, they came to be regarded as complex enzyme systems which were used only for the synthesis of ATP and the mitochondrion became known as the "power house" of the cell. Recently it has been shown that these organelles can carry out quite a number of energy consuming reactions which suggest that their rôle may be considerably more complex than that of a mere "power house" although this function is still of paramount importance.

The most intensively investigated energy utilizing reactions are those closely associated with the reversal of electron transport and oxidative phosphorylation namely: (a), reversal of electron transport (b), uptake of ions (c), volume changes and (d), transhydrogenation between NADH and NADP.

A. REVERSAL OF ELECTRON TRANSPORT

Chance and Hollunger (1960) were the first to show that energy supplied as ATP could be used to cause the transfer of hydrogen atoms from succinate to NAD. More recently it has been shown that electrons fed into the cytochrome chain at the level of cytochrome *c* by the ascorbate-tetramethyl phenylene-diamine system (Fig. 10) can be transferred to NAD, provided energy is available (Tager *et al.*, 1962). The energy necessary for this reaction

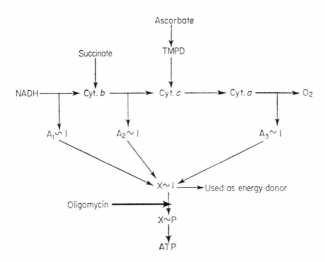

FIG. 10 Diagrammatic representation of electron transport and oxidative phosphorylation showing the point at which oligomycin is thought to inhibit energy transfer.

can be supplied by two different methods, either by adding ATP to the mito-chondria or by adding an oxidizable substrate. When ATP is added as the energy source, the energy transfer inhibitor, oligomycin, is found to inhibit the reaction. However, oligomycin has no inhibitory effect when the energy is supplied by the oxidation of a substrate. Since oligomycin is thought to inhibit energy transfer between the energy rich intermediates $X \sim I$ and $X \sim P$ (Slater, 1966a), it is apparent that a non-phosphorylated intermediate, probably $X \sim I$, is responsible for activating the reversal of electron flow (Low et al., 1963) (see Fig. 10). Work on plant mitochondria has shown that electron flow can be reversed and that only ATP can be used to supply the energy (Bonner, 1964). Reversal of electron flow has only been shown under non-phosphorylating conditions and if oxidative phosphorylation is possible this function will take preference over the reversal of electron transport (Packer et al., 1963). In the light of this observation the physiological importance of this reaction is debatable. Chance (1965b) has observed that high pressures of oxygen specifically inhibit the production of NADH by the reversal of electron transport while having no effect on the production of NADH via the more usual dehydrogenase reactions. He has also shown that under conditions of high oxygen pressure liver cells lose as much as 70% of their reduced nicotinamade adenine nucleotides suggesting that the reversal of electron transport might play an important rôle in supplying reducing power to the cell. If this is so, there is probably a complicated shuttle system, similar to the glycerophosphate cycle which is thought to transfer reducing equivalents into the mitochondria (de Duve et al., 1962), to facilitate the transfer of the reducing equivalents out of the mitochondria as the mito-chondrial membrane is rather impermeable to NADH (Greville, 1966). It should be noted, however, that mitochondria from plant sources are consider-ably more permeable to NADH (Ikuma and Bonner, 1967).

Reversal of electron transport is important in certain microorganisms which obtain all their energy from the oxidation of substrates with rather high positive redox potentials; for example *Ferrobacillus ferro-oxidons* oxi-dizes Fe^{2+} to Fe^{3+} (E'_0 $Fe^{2+}/Fe^{3+} = +0.77V$). These organisms need com-pounds such as NADH and NADPH for synthetic reactions and have been shown to be able to obtain them by using energy to reverse the electron flow in the electron transport system (Aleem et al., 1963).

B. ABSORPTION OF IONS

The entry of ions, especially calcium, into the mitochondria has been shown to be an energy requiring process which can be driven by either adding ATP or an oxidizable substrate. The use of oligomycin has again suggested that a non-phosphorylated intermediate may be the actual energy donor in both cases (Rossi et al., 1966b; Kenefick and Hanson, 1966).

The physiological significance of ion absorption by mitochondria is not clear but it could be important in establishing the membrane potential postulated in the chemiosmotic theory of oxidative phosphorylation and it is therefore possible that ion uptake is an important and integral part of the process of oxidative phosphorylation.

C. VOLUME CHANGES

Mitochondria are known to swell when suspended in media which are not conducive to energy transfer and contract when the conditions allow energy transfer to proceed. Oligomycin will inhibit the contraction normally caused by adding ATP but has no effect on the contraction caused by adding succinate as a substrate (Stoner and Hanson, 1966) and this suggests, once again, that a non-phosphorylated energy-rich intermediate is involved in causing the mitochondria to contract.

There are two schools of thought concerning the mechanism which causes the change in volume in mitochondria; one supports the theory that it is the result of an energy dependent ion translocation process occurring in the membrane which alters the osmotic pressure within the mitochondria (Slater, 1966b) and the other, that the change is directly attributable to conformational changes of components, possibly concerned with the transfer of energy, within the mitochondrial membrane (Packer et al., 1963; Harris et al., 1966). Should the latter explanation be correct it would support the suggestion that conformational changes are involved in the initial energy conserving reaction in the chemical coupling theory of oxidative phosphorylation. Kenefick and Hanson (1966) have suggested that in corn mitochondria the contracted state is a source of potential energy which can be used to absorb ions and it is therefore possible that conformation changes are an integral part of the mechanisms necessary for the formation of a non-phosphorylated energy-rich intermediate.

D. TRANSHYDROGENATION

Recently it has been shown that mitochondria are able to reduce NADP at the expense of NADH, as long as energy can be supplied in the form of either ATP or an oxidizable substrate. Again, a non-phosphorylated intermediate is thought to be intimately involved in the energy transfer process (Danielson and Ernster, 1963). This process may be regarded as being closely connected to the electron transport chain if it is considered that the hydrogen atoms are transported from NADH to NADP by a proton translocation loop similar to that already described for the chemiosmotic theory (Mitchell, 1966b). It is possible that it might be unrelated to the normal process of oxidative phosphorylation, in which case it is one of the first cases outside of the process of oxidative phosphorylation where a non-phosphorylated energy-rich intermediate is used as an energy donor to drive an energy requiring reaction. It is interesting to speculate on the significance of this reaction. It is usually considered that the NADPH, necessary for synthetic reactions within the cell, is supplied by the activity of the pentose phosphate pathway and the malic enzyme. However, estimates have shown that these systems may be capable of supplying only 50% of the NADPH required by the cell (Olson, 1966) and it is therefore possible that the mitochondria may be important in producing the NADPH required by the tissue. If this is true then there must be a special mechanism by which it is exported from the mitochondria and which probably involves the dual localization of certain tricarboxylic acid cycle enzymes (Krebs, 1967).

E. OTHER ENERGY TRANSFER FUNCTIONS ASSOCIATED WITH MITOCHONDRIA

The mitochondria are known to be the site of several energy requiring synthetic reactions; important among these are protein synthesis (Roodyn, 1965; Kroon, 1966), fatty acid synthesis (Hulsmann, 1962), phospholipid synthesis (Kahn and Hanson, 1959) and haem synthesis (Sano and Granick, 1961). A detailed discussion of these activities is really outside the scope of this paper. It is interesting, however, to point out that recent experiments have suggested that in both the synthesis of protein (Bronk, 1963; Kroon, 1966) and the activation of fatty acids (Wojtczak et al., 1966), a non-phosphorylated energy-rich intermediate is able to act as the actual energy donor.

IV. CONCLUSION

The main energy transfer function of mitochondria is the removal and subsequent oxidation of electrons from a variety of reduced carbon compounds. The energy liberated during this oxidation is conserved in the form of ATP. The mechanism of ATP synthesis in oxidative phosphorylation is unknown but is thought to occur through the participation of a series of hypothetical non-phosphorylated and phosphorylated intermediates. Recent research has shown that mitochondria are capable of carrying out a series of energy requiring reactions. Those most thoroughly investigated are associated with the reversal of the process of oxidative phosphorylation and it is now apparent that a non-phosphorylated energy donor rather than ATP is involved in bringing about these reactions. There is also evidence that other synthetic reactions such as protein and phospholipid synthesis may also involve the participation of an energy-rich non-phosphorylated intermediate. Thus it is becoming clear that reactions in the mitochondria are capable of using some of the energy they transfer and that it is used in the form of an hypothetical $X \sim I$ compound and it has been suggested (Slater, 1966a) that

ATP is the end product of oxidative phosphorylation only when the energy is exported from the mitochondria.

The reversal of electron transport and the transhydrogenase activity also raise the question of the importance of the mitochondria in supplying reducing power for the cell.

Mitochondria cannot be considered simply as complex enzyme systems the sole function of which is to produce ATP. The discovery of additional associated synthetic reactions makes it possible that the mitochondrion plays a more complex rôle than that of a mere "power house" within the economy of the cell.

REFERENCES

Aleem, M. I. H., Rees, H. and Nicholas, D. J. D. (1963). *Nature, Lond.* **200**, 759.

Barker, J., Khan, M. A. A. and Solomons, T. (1966). *Nature, Lond.* **211**, 547.

Bonner, W. D. (1964). *Pl. Physiol. Lancaster* **39**, 1x.

Bonner, W. D. (1966). *In* "Plant Biochemistry" (J. Bonner and J. E. Varner, eds), p. 89. Academic Press. New York and London.

Boyer, P. D. (1965). *In* "Oxidases and Related Redox Systems". (T. E. King, H. S. Mason and M. Morrison, eds.), p. 994. J. Wiley, New York.

Bronk, J. R. (1963). *Proc. natn. Acad. Sci. U.S.A.* **50**, 524.

Chance, B. (1965a). *In* "Control of Energy Metabolism". (B. Chance, R. W. Estabrook and J. R. Williamson, eds), p. 9. Academic Press, New York and London.

Chance, B. (1965b). *In* "Control of Energy Metabolism". (B. Chance, R. W. Estabrook and J. R. Williamson, eds), p. 274. Academic Press, New York and London.

Chance, B. and Hollunger, G. (1960). *Nature, Lond.* **185**, 666.

Chance, B. and Mela, L. (1966). *Nature, Lond.* **212**, 369, 372.

Chance, B. and Williams, G. R. (1956). *Adv. Enzymol.* **17**, 65.

Danielson, L. and Ernster, L. (1963). *In* "Energy Linked Functions of Mitochondria." (B. Chance, ed.), p. 157. Academic Press, New York and London.

Davies, D. D., Giovanelli, J. and Aprees, T. (1964). "Plant Biochemistry". Blackwell, Oxford.

de Duve, C., Wattiaux, R. and Baudhuin, P. (1962). *Adv. Enzymol.* **24**, 291.

Green, D. E. and Goldberger, R. F. (1966). "Molecular Insights into the Living Process". Academic Press, New York.

Greville, G. D. (1966). *In* "Regulation of Metabolic Processes in Mitochondria". (J. M. Tager, S. Papa, E. Quagliariello and E. C. Slater, eds), BBA library, Vol. 7. p. 86. Elsevier, Amsterdam.

Griffiths, D. (1965). *In* "Essays in Biochemistry." (P. N. Campbell and G. D. Greville, eds), p. 91. Academic Press, London and New York.

Hackett, P. D. (1959). *A. Rev. Pl. Physiol.* **10**, 113.

Harris, E. J., Cockrell, J. R. and Pressman, B. C. (1966). *Biochem. J.* **99**, 200.

Hulsmann, W. C. (1962). *Biochim. Biophys. Acta* **58**, 417.

Ikuma, H. and Bonner, W. D. (1967). *Pl. Physiol., Lancaster* **42**, 67.

Kahn, J. S. and Hanson, J. B. (1959). *Pl. Physiol., Lancaster* **34**, 621.

Kenefick, D. G. and Hanson, J. B. (1966). *Pl. Physiol., Lancaster* **41**, 1601.

136   J. M. PALMER

Krebs, H. A. (1967). *In* "Biochemistry of Mitochondria". (E. C. Slater, Z. Kaniuga and L. Wojtczak, eds) p. 105. Academic Press, London and New York.

Kroon, A. M. (1966). *In* "Regulation of Metabolic Processes in Mitochondria". (J. M. Tager, S. Papa, E. Quagliariello and E. C. Slater, eds), BBA library, Vol. 7. p. 397. Elsevier, Amsterdam.

Laties, G. G. (1957). *Survey Biol. Prog.* 3, 215.

Lehninger, A. L. (1964). "The Mitochondria". W. A. Benjamin, New York.

Lieberman, M. and Baker, J. E. (1965). *A. Rev. Pl. Physiol.* 16, 343.

Low, H., Vallin, J. and Alm, B. (1963). *In* "Energy Linked Functions of Mitochondria". (B. Chance, ed.), p. 5. Academic Press, New York and London.

Lynn, W. S. and Brown, R. H. (1965). *Biochim. biophys. Acta* 105, 15.

Mitchell, P. (1961). *Nature, Lond.* 191, 144.

Mitchell, P. (1966a). *Biol. Rev.* 41, 445.

Mitchell, P. (1966b). *In* "Regulation of Metabolic Processes in Mitochondria". (J. M. Tager, S. Papa, E. Quagliariello and E. C. Slater, eds), BBA library, Vol. 7. p. 65. Elsevier, Amsterdam.

Norman, A. W., Wedding, R. T. and Black, M. K. (1965). *Biochem. biophys. Res. Commun.* 20, 703.

Olson, J. A. (1966). *A. Rev. Biochem.* 35, 559.

Ozawa, T. (1966). *Archs. Biochem. Biophys.* 117, 201.

Packer, L., Marchant, R. H. and Mukohata, Y. (1963). *In* "Energy Linked Functions of Mitochondria". (B. Chance, ed.), p. 51. Academic Press, New York and London.

Palmer, J. M. and Wedding, R. T. (1966). *Biochim. biophys. Acta* 113, 167.

Palmer, J. M. and Kalina, M. (1967).

Roodyn, D. B. (1965). *Biochem. J.* 97, 782.

Rossi, C. R., Galzigna, L. and Gibson, D. M. (1966a). *In* "Regulation of Metabolic Processes in Mitochondria". (J. M. Tager, S. Papa, E. Quagliariello and E. C. Slater, eds), BBA library, Vol. 7. p. 143. Elsevier, Amsterdam.

Rossi, C. S., Carafoli, E., Drahota, Z. and Lehninger, A. L. (1966b). *In* "Regulation of Metabolic Processes in Mitochondria". (J. M. Tager, S. Papa, E. Quagliariello and E. C. Slater, eds), BBA library, Vol. 7, p. 317. Elsevier, Amsterdam.

Rowan, K. S. (1966). *Int. Rev. Cytol.* 19, 302.

Sano, S. and Granick, S. (1961). *J. Biol. Chem.* 236, 1178.

Slater, E. C. (1966a). *In* "Regulation of Metabolic Processes in Mitochondria", (J. M. Tager, S. Papa, E. Quagliariello and E. C. Slater, eds), BBA library, Vol. 7. p. 166. Elsevier, Amsterdam.

Slater, E. C. (1966b). *In* "Regulation of Metabolic Processes in Mitochondria". (J. M. Tager, S. Papa, E. Quagliariello and E. C. Slater, eds), BBA library, Vol. 7, p. 556. Elsevier, Amsterdam.

Stoner, C. D. and Hanson, J. B. (1966). *Pl. Physiol., Lancaster* 41, 255.

Stumpf, P. K. (1955). *Pl. Physiol., Lancaster* 30, 55.

Stumpf, P. K. and Barber, G. A. (1956). *Pl. Physiol., Lancaster* 31, 304.

Tager, J. M., Howland, J. L. and Slater, E. C. (1962). *Biochim. biophys. Acta* 58, 616.

Van den Berg, S. G. (1966). *In* "Regulation of Metabolic Processes in Mitochondria". (J. M. Tager, S. Papa, E. Quagliariello and E. C. Slater, eds), BBA library, Vol. 7, p. 533. Elsevier, Amsterdam.

Wojtczak, L., Drakota, Z., Zaluska, H. and Zborowski, J. (1966). *In* "Regulation of Metabolic Processes in Mitochondria". (J. M. Tager, S. Papa, E. Quagliariello and E. C. Slater, eds), BBA library, Vol. 7, p. 134. Elsevier, Amsterdam.

CHAPTER 8

The Chloroplast Inside and Outside the Cell

RACHEL M. LEECH

Department of Biology, University of York, Heslington, England

I. INTRODUCTION

The chloroplast is unique among cell organelles in being restricted to green plant cells. Isolated chloroplasts have been shown to be "the complete photosynthetic unit" of the cell (Arnon *et al.*, 1954; Jensen and Bassham, 1966). The ability of chloroplasts to conserve in photosynthesis the radiant energy of light in a biologically utilizable form and recent findings of DNA, RNA and ribosomal-mediated protein synthesis in chloroplasts (see Kirk and Tilney-Bassett, 1967 for a review) suggests that the mature chloroplast is, potentially at least, metabolically autonomous from the rest of the cell. There are also convincing indications that the chloroplast is to some degree autonomous genetically. In lower plants mature chloroplasts are able to replicate and in lower plants and higher plants there are now several well-authenticated examples of determinants of plastid characteristics located within the plastid and apparently outside nuclear control. Considerable discussion and experimentation at the present time is concerned with investigating the actual degree of autonomy exhibited by chloroplasts in a wide variety of organisms.

The most characteristic feature of the chloroplast is its complex pigment-bearing lipoprotein membrane system. It is here that the light-dependent

H   137

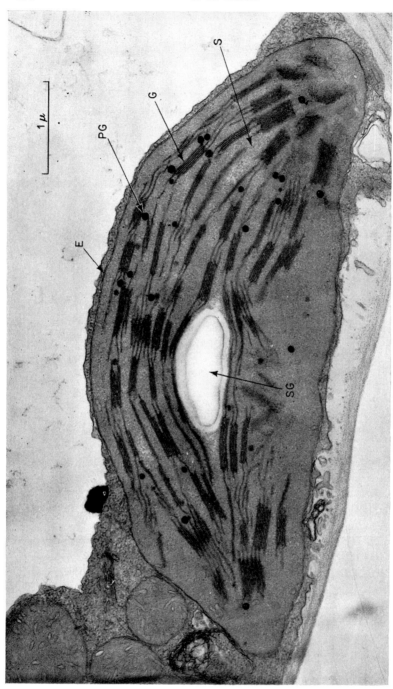

FIG. 1 Unpublished electron micrograph by A. D. Greenwood of a chloroplast in a leaf cell of *Vicia faba* L. × 29,000. Fixed with glutaraldehyde/osmium and stained with lead. Embedded in Epon. The chloroplast envelope (E), plastoglobuli (PG), grana (G) and stroma (S) are clearly seen. A starch grain (SG) is also present.

oxygen evolution and electron transport systems of photosynthesis are localized. The key to the understanding of the molecular basis of the unique properties of chloroplasts probably lies in a more detailed knowledge of its molecular structure, origin and development.

This review will be concerned with recent attempts to describe the three-dimensional molecular architecture of the chloroplast, particularly of the lipoprotein system, and to consider information about the preservation of chloroplast structure in isolation. Finally chloroplast autonomy will be discussed.

II. The Structure of the Mature Chloroplast Inside the Cell

Electron microscope studies using sections of chloroplasts from a wide range of green plants have revealed that four distinct components are characteristic of all mature algal and phanerogamic chloroplasts. The mature chloroplast consists of a lamellar (lipoprotein) system embedded in a granular stroma and surrounded by a double membrane. Within the stroma osmiophilic "plastoglobuli" are always present. These components are shown in Fig. 1.

A. THE CHLOROPLAST ENVELOPE

The chloroplast envelope is a continuous boundary of two osmiophilic unit membranes (in the sense of Robertson, 1964) and completely separates the contents of the chloroplast from the rest of the cell. Pores have never been demonstrated in this envelope. Recently Weier has suggested, from high resolution electron micrographs, that the envelope is made up of spherical subunits as are the internal chloroplast membranes (Weier *et al.*, 1965a; Weier *et al.*, 1966).

B. THE STROMA

The stroma is a hydrophilic proteinaceous continuum within the chloroplast envelope and surrounding and containing the intra-chloroplast membrane system but not penetrating within it. Within the stroma are particles heterogeneous in size and staining properties (Gunning, 1965; Gunning and Jagoe, 1967). One class of 175Å particles which stain with uranyl acetate and are completely destroyed by ribonuclease are undoubtedly ribosomes (Jacobson *et al.*, 1963; Kislev *et al.*, 1965). These are frequently seen in groups resembling polysomes (Gunning, 1965). Using glutaraldehyde (or acrolein)/osmium fixations, Gunning (1965) has discovered in chloroplasts of *Avena sativa* a "stromacentre" 1μ in diameter and consisting of aggregated fibrils 85Å in diameter and of uncertain length. The stroma centre can be seen in the light microscope and from its staining properties would appear to be proteinaceous but has so far not been reported from other plants and its significance is unknown. It is possibly regularly aggregated stroma material which is more dispersed in other species and may indeed in part be Fraction I protein. It is not known how it is related to the strikingly similar pockets of fibrils induced in the stroma of chloroplasts by treatment with either ozone or peroxylacetyl nitrate (Thomson *et al.*, 1965, 1966). Earlier, Perner (1962) described apparently crystalline structures in the stroma of isolated spinach (*Spinacia oleracea*) chloroplasts. The relationship of these structures to the stroma centre is not clear; it is possible they are different manifestations of aggregations of stroma proteins. Starch grains, when present, are localized in the stroma between but not within the elements of the membrane system.

Pyrenoids are morphologically specialized parts of the stroma found in some algae and in the Anthocerotales (Menke, 1961; Gibbs, 1962a, 1962b; Drawert and Mix, 1962; Kaja, 1966). They appear to be finely granular in the electron microscope but their composition and functions are unknown. Manton (1966) has published a series of electron micrographs showing variations in pyrenoid structure.

C. THE PLASTOGLOBULI (OSMIOPHILIC GLOBULES)

The plastoglobuli are a constant morphological feature in sections of osmium-fixed chloroplasts from all types of plant. The circular profiles of plastoglobuli vary from 100–5000Å in diameter and are embedded in the stroma between the lipoprotein membranes but never within a granum. Plastoglobuli are labile in $KMnO_4$ fixation. In the literature they have been described by a variety of names: spherical granules (Steinmann and Sjöstrand, 1955), lipid-like globules (Gibbs, 1962a, 1962c), osmiophilic granules (Murakami and Takamija, 1962), Elektronenstreuende Kugeln (Heitz, 1958), lipid droplets (Sager and Palade, 1957), magnoglobuli (Falk, 1960), osmiophilic globules (Greenwood *et al.*, 1963) and osmiophilous globules by Silaeva and Shiriaev (1966). However, the least ambiguous term would seem to be "plastoglobuli" suggested by Lichtentahler and Sprey (1966) and it is hoped that this term will be used by all future workers.

In green actively photosynthesizing leaves, the plastoglobuli contain a variety of lipidic and lipophilic compounds particularly plastoquinone-45, α-tocopherol, α-tocopherolquinone and vitamin K_1 (Bailey and Whyborn, 1963; Lichtentahler, 1964; Lichtentahler and Sprey, 1966) and polyisoprenols (Wellburn and Hemming, 1966) but are completely devoid of chlorophyll and carotenoid pigments (Greenwood *et al.*, 1963; Lichtentahler and Sprey, 1966). The plastoglobuli vary in size and staining properties in chloroplasts of different ages (and therefore presumably in chemical composition) and would seem to be a store of surplus lipid in the chloroplast in the same way as starch is a store of surplus carbohydrate material. Sprey and Lichtentahler

(1966) recently showed a decrease in plastoglobuli in greening etiolated leaves of barley seedlings during membrane formation and so suggest that the plastoglobuli, at this stage of development, are a pool from which lipids can be taken during membrane synthesis. Evidence that plastoglobuli are not artefacts of fixation is provided by their presence in freeze-etched chloroplasts (Mühletahler *et al.*, 1965). There is no evidence that plastoglobuli have enzymic activity.

D. THE LIPOPROTEIN COMPLEX

The lipoprotein fretwork system of the chloroplast contains the chlorophyll and carotenoids and is suspended in but apparently not open to the stroma. In recent years intensive studies of the three-dimensional architecture of this system have been undertaken in several laboratories using every preparative fixation and staining procedure available in the electron microscopist's armoury. The structure has been explored in a wide variety of algal and higher plant chloroplasts in sections of cells, and in whole mounts, of isolated chloroplasts and chloroplast fragments and also after freeze-etching.

It has been conclusively demonstrated by Trebst *et al.* (1958) that the light reactions and associated electron transport reactions of photosynthesis are localized in the internal chloroplast membrane system. It is now possible using modern electron microscopical techniques to preserve and resolve globular proteins of approximately 35Å in diameter and fibrous proteins 5–10Å in diameter and studies and ideas about the precise molecular arrangements responsible for the integrated metabolic activities have reached an exciting stage. However, terminology in the field of chloroplast structure is confused and confusing and makes communication difficult for in some cases apparently similar structure is described in several different ways. It would be very help-ful for those of us concerned with chloroplast function to have progress reports on current knowledge of chloroplast membrane structure but this is not easy to obtain for several apparently mutually exclusive models have been published. These ideas and the investigations from which they were derived have recently been excellently reviewed by Kirk and Tilney-Bassett (1967). In our search for an underlying pattern in the structure it may be valuable to leave the models for a moment and to look again at the pictures and to see if it is possible to suggest, even näively, alternative possible explanations for the apparent contradictions in the models.

The term "disc" was originally introduced by Steinmann and Sjöstrand in 1955 to describe the basic subunit of the chloroplast membrane system. These discs were alternatively called "membrane-bound vesicles" (Sager and Palade, 1957; Sager, 1958; Mühletahler, 1960) or "thylakoids" (saclike) (Menke, 1960, 1962). Each disc consists of two parallel membranes joined at their margins. Each membrane is about 70Å thick although dimensions vary greatly with different fixation techniques (Weier *et al.*, 1965a). Each pair of membranes surrounds an intradisc space composed of a homogeneous material of low electron opacity after fixation. There is no chemical information about this component of low electron opacity. The arrangement of the discs is different in chloroplasts from different plants (see Menke, 1966 and Manton, 1966 for summaries). In red algae (Rhodophyceae) for example, the individual discs are characteristically scattered throughout the stroma of the chloroplast while in *Euglena* (Gibbs, 1960), 2–5 closely appressed discs form a band across the chloroplast. There are about 12 bands per chloroplast. In the bands of *Euglena* the internal membranes are just less than twice as wide as the outside or terminal membranes.

The granum, a structure found in the chloroplast of higher plants and some algae, is a stack of regularly arranged discs. The width of the intradisc space in a granum is extremely variable both *in vivo* and in isolation varying from 40–700Å but the electron dense region (2 adjacent disc membranes) between the intradisc spaces is remarkably constant being just less than twice as thick as the terminal membranes.

At the edge of grana, extensions of the flattened discs penetrate into the intergranal region. Menke used the terms "large" or "stroma" thylakoids to describe the larger discs which extend into the intergranal region and "small" or "grana" thylakoids to describe the discs restricted to the grana. However, these are interpretations of three-dimensional structures derived from the appearance in a two-dimensional section. Weier and Thomson (1962) have now shown that in *Nicotiana rustica* and *Phaseolus vulgaris*, at least, the absence of projections from a granal disc in one section may be misleading as from serial sections it can be calculated that each granal disc has, in fact, 4–8 projections from its margins. Wehrmeyer (1964) has come to similar conclusions. In view of these new findings the particular distinction between large (stroma) and small (grana) thylakoids no longer seems necessary.

The pattern of the extensions into the intergranal regions is not well understood but certainly they often extend over at least two grana and possibly more (Wehrmeyer and Perner, 1962). In the intergranal regions some of the membranes may be perforated (Diers and Schötz, 1966). Wehrmeyer (1964) has shown that at the edge of a granum a lamella may bifurcate or fold back on itself thus contributing two discs to the same granum. It is quite possible that the details of disc shape vary from one species to another and at different stages in development. Using serial sections cut at right angles, attempts have been made to see whether there are perforations within the granal stack between one disc space and the next. Heslop-Harrison (1963) with *Cannabis* and Diers and Schötz (1966) with *Oenothera* have shown that such perforations do occur but are infrequent. Differences in composition between grana and granal projections have not been reported but this is technically very difficult to investigate.

A picture emerges then of a highly complex interconnected membrane system closed off from the stroma which in particular does not penetrate into the intergranal spaces. However, Weier's group in Davis, California have recently emphasized that the concept of a membrane system made up of appressed discs does not adequately describe the structures seen in their very high resolution electron micrographs. They have particularly focused attention on the electron opaque region between two intradisc spaces where, on the disc concept, two adjacent discs lie with membranes adjacent. As has already been mentioned, this region is consistently found to be less than twice as wide in section as the single outside membranes of the outer discs of the granum. Within the granum it is often difficult to resolve two distinct black lines in this region. This suggests that there is some degree of lateral fusion between adjacent intergranal membranes and the idea that the granum rather than the disc should be regarded as the unit of chloroplast structure has been evolved (Weier et al., 1963). In support of this concept Weier's group show pictures of isolated chloroplasts and chloroplasts within mineral-deficient leaves, i.e. partially damaged chloroplasts in both cases, but in which despite considerable fracture of the intergranal connections, the grana persist as compartmented structures. It is certainly remarkable that although the intergranal spaces can swell to many times their normal width in isolation the granum remains as a unit. This was first shown by Jacobi and Perner (1961) and has since been verified in several laboratories, including our own (A. D. Greenwood and R. M. Leech, 1967; unpublished results; Leech, 1964; Kahn and von Wettstein, 1961; Wehrmeyer, 1961; Nobel et al., 1966a, 1966b).

Weier's group have introduced a new set of terms to describe more appositely the membrane structures revealed in their pictures of *Aspidistra* (a monocotyledon), *Phaseolus vulgaris*, *Pisum sativum* (dicotyledons) and the green alga *Scenedesmus quadricauda* (Weier et al., 1965a; Weier et al., 1966). The thick dark membranes within the grana are termed *partitions* and are either connected at their margins or joined to other grana by frets (Fig. 2). The light space enclosed by the partition and margin is termed the *loculus* and that enclosed by the fret membrane is the *fret channel*. The outside membranes are narrower (see below) than the internal partitions and are called the end granal membranes. On Weier's interpretation the "stack of coins" pictures, obtained by shadowing OsO_4-fixed fragments of isolated, chloroplasts (Steinmann, 1952) and formerly interpreted as separated intact discs which have slid apart, would now appear to have arisen by breakage at the margin and across the loculus, leaving the partitions intact and exposing the intra-locular surfaces.

Perhaps the most exciting recent development has been the first evidence for the chloroplast membranes being composites of particulate subunits. A similar structure is currently under discussion for other biological membranes (Green and Perdue, 1966). Frey-Wyssling and Steinmann (1953) were the first to observe globular subunits in isolated and shadowed chloroplast membranes and Frey-Wyssling (1957) later pointed out how puzzling it was that they did not show up in sections of membranes. Park and Pon (1961)

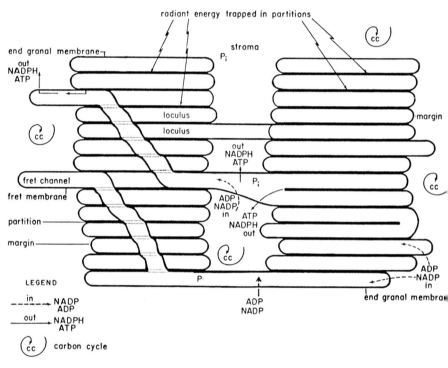

Fig. 2 Diagram showing the relationship between membranes and stroma within a higher plant chloroplast (reproduced with permission from Weier et al., 1967). Possible relationships of components involved in photosynthetic reactions are also shown. The carbon cycle is located in the stroma and the light reactions in the membranes. Weier et al. (1967) postulate that energy transfer from the membranes occurs by movement of ATP, ADP, NADP and NADPH in the directions shown in the diagram.

and Park and Biggins (1964) extended these studies and obtained pictures showing layers of particles 160–185Å long, 155Å wide and 100Å thick within the granal membranes. The name "quantasome" was coined for these sub-units; this was perhaps a rather unfortunate term as the relationship of this structural unit to the photosynthetic unit or to the physiological quantum conversion unit is still obscure. The particles were originally (1961) conceived of as being partially embedded in and forming one component of the membrane but also filling the intradisc space. More recently, Bamberger and Park (1966) have suggested the particles are actually part of the membrane and do not occupy the intradisc space. The 175Å particles are often in highly organized arrays. In addition, other granal surfaces have been shown to bear more scattered 90Å particles. The particles can also be visualized in negatively-stained preparations. Using the technique of freeze-etching introduced by Moor *et al.* (1961), Mühletahler and his associates have again shown particles of two size categories but of smaller dimensions than those observed by Park and his colleagues. Mühletahler (1966) describes particles 120Å wide, each probably of 4 subunits 60Å deep, and a second class of single 60Å particles. Recently, Bamberger and Park (1966) have also shown their 90Å and 175Å particles in freeze-etched preparations. This technique of freeze-etching involves "sectioning" frozen specimens followed by surface replication and would be expected to minimize fixation artefacts. However there is presently considerable disagreement between Mühletahler's group and Park's group concerning the location of the particles within the granal structure. The decision as to whether the particles lie outside but partially embedded in the membranes (Mühletahler) or actually constitute the membrane itself (Park) rests on knowledge of the plane of fracture along or within the membrane. This is extremely difficult to determine with certainty and neither group seems to have published convincing pictorial evidence that their interpretation of the plane of sectioning is the correct one. Branton (1966) has, however, published evidence supporting the contention that fracture is within the membrane and not along the surface. The pictures produced by the two groups by similar techniques are very similar (Mühletahler *et al.*, 1965; Bamberger and Park, 1966), both showing two categories of particles and differences in size which may reflect preparative rather than real differences in the particle sizes *in vivo*.

Whatever the location of these particular particles it seems possible that we may very well be observing several chemically different particles in chloroplasts both within the membranes and also lying superficially on the membranes but originating in the stroma. Mühletahler (1966) himself suggests the possibility that one class of particles that he observes may be ribosomes. Alternatively, some of the superficial 120Å particles may be Fraction I protein which has been shown by Haselkorn *et al.* (1965) to measure 120Å along its edge.

In sections of membranes, too, apparently spherical subunits have now been visualized, using sophisticated fixation procedures and high resolution electron microscopy (Weier *et al.*, 1963, 1965a, b, 1966). In micrographs, these

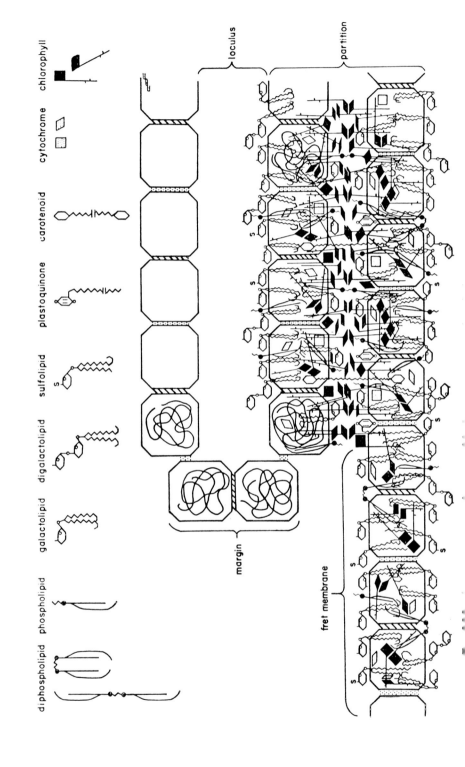

diphospholipid phospholipid galactolipid digalactolipid sulfolipid plastoquinone carotenoid cytochrome chlorophyll

margin

fret membrane

loculus

partition

subunits in glutaraldehyde and permanganate fixations appear to consist of a light core about 37Å in diameter with a dark rim about 28Å wide. Partitions apparently consist of two rows of particles and fret membranes of a single row of subunits. However, again differences in interpretation exist; Bamberger and Park (1966) would interpret their lipoprotein particles as being enclosed top and bottom by a continuous galactolipid layer but Weier (see Weier and Benson, 1966) would apparently conceive of the whole membrane consisting of mixed protein and lipid components. Again from X-ray scattering studies Kreutz (1966) has suggested that the lipid and protein components are separate.

The membrane proteins presumably include the protein isolated by Criddle (1966), plastocyanin (a copper-containing protein) and the cytochromes f, b_6 and b_{559}. The lipids, apart from chlorophylls a and b and the carotenoids, include the phytoquinones, plastoquinones A, B, C, D, plastochromanol, tocopherols and tocopherolquinones, vitamins K and phospholipids and glycolipids (see Kirk and Tilney-Bassett, 1967 for a summary).

It is of considerable interest to try fitting this variety of chemical molecules into positions within the three-dimensional membrane structure visualized by the electron microscope. Weier and Benson (1966) published the first detailed suggestions along these lines. They do not take into account the relative proportions of the different molecules but suggest that the molecules of protein are relatively hydrophobic in nature and that the hydrocarbon chains of chlorophyll, carotenoids and lipids are buried within the protein molecular band in hydrophilic association. This interesting formulation is shown in Fig. 3 and suggests further experimentation.

Another approach to structure/function relationships at the molecular level is to search for methods of altering specifically the morphological and biochemical properties of the membranes. Detergents have been used for this purpose. More recently solvents have also been used but microscopical resolution does not appear sufficient to identify specific changes in morphological structures. Ninety-three per cent of plastoquinones A and C can be removed from isolated chloroplasts using heptane and petroleum ether and only 18% chlorophyll but only minor modification in membrane structure (Magree et al., 1966) can be detected. Chloroplasts isolated from leaves prefixed in glutaraldehyde appear to be little changed morphologically but retain only 25% of their Hill reaction activity. Acetone also destroys Hill reaction activity but no change in structure has yet been detected. By studying membrane structure after protease and lipase treatment, Bamberger and Park (1966) deduced that chlorophyll is located in the membrane particles.

There is no evidence that chemical differences exist between fret membranes and partitions and indeed this would be very difficult to explore.

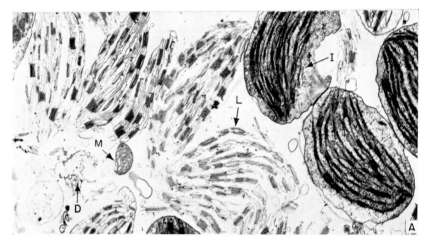

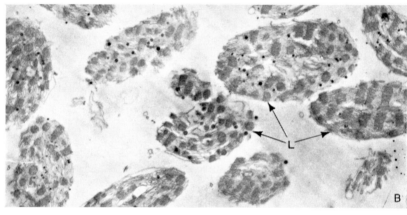

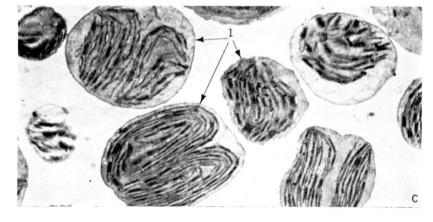

III. THE CHLOROPLAST OUTSIDE THE CELL

To study quantitatively the chemical composition and biochemical capabilities of the parts of the chloroplast, isolation from the cell is necessary. Electron microscope studies have shown that many isolated chloroplasts used in biochemical studies are considerably altered morphologically from their state in the cell. Two general types of isolation method are available, either (a), grinding the fresh material in an osmotically adjusted, buffered aqueous medium or (b), grinding lyophilized material in non-aqueous solvents, for example, petroleum ether/carbon tetrachloride mixtures (Thalacker and Behrens, 1959; Heber, 1957) or hexane/carbon tetrachloride mixtures (Stocking, 1959). By neither the aqueous nor the non-aqueous technique is it possible to separate the chloroplast cleanly from the other components of the cell using only differential centrifugation; density gradient centrifugation is always required (Leech *et al.*, 1964). Retention of soluble proteins is good in *non-aqueous* preparations notably of the enzymes NADP-triose-phosphate de hydrogenase (1.2.1.13) and ribulose-1-5-diphosphate carboxylase (4.1.1.39.,1) essential in the first stages of photosynthetic carbon reduction (Smillie and Fuller, 1959; Heber *et al.*, 1963) but Hill reaction activity is totally lost (Heber and Tyszkiewitz, 1962). In contrast, in chloroplasts isolated by *aqueous* techniques, the soluble enzyme systems are the most vulnerable. Electron micrographs have shown that the loss is due to fracture of the envelope and physical washing out of the stroma. Perner (1965) has shown that free spinach chloroplast membranes devoid of stroma can only be maintained in isolation in a state equivalent to that *in vivo* in hypertonic sucrose with pyrophosphate and not in 0·2% NaCl.

In *Vicia faba* loss of the stroma itself is considerably greater if the chloroplasts are isolated in buffered 0·35M NaCl than if they are isolated in 0·3–0·8M buffered sucrose (compare Figs 4 and 6). Even if the envelope is still intact its properties may change in isolation. Isolated spinach (*Spinacia oleracea*) chloroplasts have been studied by light and electron microscopy by Kahn and von Wettstein (1961) who distinguished two types of chloroplast in their suspensions and suggested that the chloroplasts appearing opaque in the

FIG. 4 Electron micrographs of chloroplasts isolated from *Vicia fabia* L. × 8000. Fixed in buffered (pH 7·0) 0s0$_4$: A and C embedded in Epon; B embedded in araldite. (R. M. Leech and A. D. Greenwood, unpublished results).
A. A section of a 1000 × *g* pellet showing intact membrane-bound chloroplasts (I) free lamella systems (L) mitochondria (M) and cell debris (D).
B. A section of a "chloroplast" pellet prepared according to James and Das (1957). Only free lamella systems (L) are present.
C. A section of a chloroplast pellet prepared according to Leech (1964). Almost all the profiles are of intact membrane-bound chloroplasts.

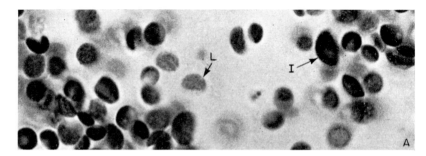

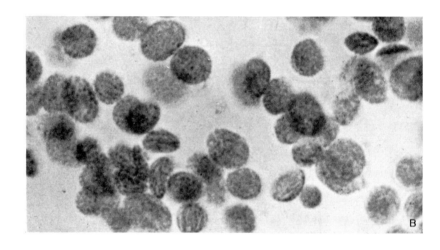

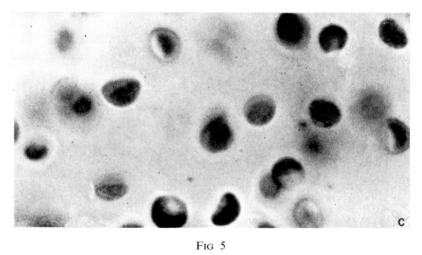

FIG 5

light microscope corresponded to those in the electron micrographs with intact envelopes and stroma. Chloroplasts, granular in appearance in the light microscope, would be those shown in the electron micrographs to be stripped of their bounding envelopes and a considerable portion of their stroma. However, the suggestion could not be vindicated until suspensions of chloroplasts consisting exclusively of one morphological category only could be prepared and examined. Using the method of James and Das, (1957), suspensions can be prepared containing only chloroplasts stripped of their outer membranes (James and Leech, 1964). By selecting a fraction from a sucrose density gradient, a suspension consisting virtually entirely of intact chloroplasts can be prepared (Leech, 1964). The latter method has recently been adopted for the Zonal centrifuge (C. A. Price, private communication). In Figs 4 and 5 are shown the appearances of the preparations containing only one type of chloroplast in both light and electron micrographs. A preparation containing both chloroplast types is also shown. It can be seen that at least for *Vicia faba* the suggestion of Kahn and von Wettstein is vindicated. A note of caution should be added here. A biochemist wishes to know the state of preservation of the chloroplast in the actual suspension he used for his biochemical assay. Any gross subsequent changes during fixation and embedding for electron microscopy will lead to a more pessimistic view than is warranted. Isolated cell organelles appear to be very much less resilient to osmotic shock than are intact cells and osmotic adjustment of not only the fixative but also the dehydration stages is necessary (Leech, 1964).

Despite their respective limitations, aqueous and non-aqueous techniques have been used with considerable success in the study of chloroplast enzymology. Hall and Whatley (1967) have reviewed the information to date. The state of integrity of the chloroplasts clearly affects their biochemical attributes *in vitro*. Walker (1965, 1967) obtained higher CO_2 fixation rates and lower rates of ATP synthesis in suspensions containing a large proportion of intact chloroplasts than in suspensions of broken chloroplasts. Jeffrey *et al.* (1966) using intact chloroplasts from the chrysomonad *Hymenomonas* obtained rates of CO_2 fixations equivalent to 25% of the rate of fixation by the intact organism. This was the highest rate expressed as a percentage of whole plant fixation published at that time. The recent achievement of Jensen and Bassham (1966) in obtaining *in vitro* rates of CO_2 fixation (248 μmoles CO_2/mg chlorophyll/hr) actually in excess of *in vivo* rates, can also

---

FIG. 5 Light micrographs ($\times$ 1750) of the same material as shown in Fig. 4.
A. A 1000 $\times$ g "chloroplast" fraction. Both intact (opaque) (I) and envelope-free chloroplasts (L) (showing grana) are present.
B. A section of a "chloroplast" pellet prepared according to James and Das (1957). Only free lamella systems (L) are present.
C. A section of a chloroplast pellet prepared according to Leech (1964). Almost all the profiles are of intact membrane-bound chloroplasts.

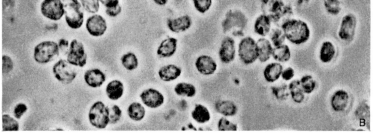

FIG 6

be attributed in part to their use of suspensions containing a high proportion of intact chloroplasts. The activity of multi-enzyme systems localized within the pigment-containing membrane system may be lower when assayed in intact chloroplasts than when using free membrane systems. This is presumably because of the impermeability of the chloroplast envelope and has been clearly shown for cyclic photophosphorylation in intact and broken pea chloroplasts by Walker (1967).

Much attention has been devoted to obtaining reliable quantitative values for the chemical composition of the chloroplast but this has proved very difficult. Clearly these values can only have significance if they are referred to chloroplasts in a particular morphological state isolated from one species of plant at one developmental stage (Smillie and Krotkov, 1961). Many of the earlier estimates, obtained before the considerable damage attendant on

TABLE I

Total protein and total lipid content of chloroplasts
from *Vicia faba* leaves (3 weeks old).

†Chloroplast preparation	$\mu g/\mu g$ Chlorophyll		Lipid: Protein
	*Total lipid	†Total protein	
‡Intact	15·0 ⎫ 15·9 ⎬ 15·8 16·5 ⎭	3·2 ⎫ 3·7 ⎬ 3·4 3·2 ⎭	4·65
1000 × *g* fraction	3·9 ⎫ 3·85 3·8 ⎭	2·3 ⎫ 2·6 ⎬ 2·3 2·0 ⎭	1·67

* Lipid values Jarvis *et al.*, 1967.
† Protein values and methods of chloroplast isolation from Leech, 1966.
   Chlorophyll determined in 80% acetone (Arnon, 1949).
   Protein determined by the method of Lowry *et al.* (1951).
   Lipid determined gravimetrically after 3 extractions in 80% acetone.
‡ The bacterial count for this chloroplast preparation was 5×10^3–10^3/ml.

isolation was discovered, are almost certainly too low. Protein loss from chloroplasts during aqueous isolation is more often allowed for (e.g. Kirk and Tilney-Bassett, 1967) and indeed can be correlated with the degree of integrity of the chloroplasts (Leech, 1966 and Table I.) For chloroplasts which are intact under the electron microscope from three-week-old *Vicia faba* plants the protein/chlorophyll value is 3 : 1 and about 35% of the protein

FIG. 6 1000 × *g* chloroplast fraction prepared in buffered 0·35 M NaCl (R. M. Leech and A. D. Greenwood, unpublished results).
A. Electron micrograph of a section of the chloroplast pellet fixed in buffered OsO_4 and embedded in Araldite.
B. Light micrograph of the same suspension.

I

is in the membrane fraction. Loss of lipid during aqueous isolation had previously been suspected (Leech, 1966) but L. Jarvis, H. M. Hallaway and R. M. Leech (1967, unpublished results) have shown this can be very considerable and cannot be ignored. Since chlorophyll is restricted to the chloroplast lamellae, measurement of the lipid to chlorophyll ratio provides an index of the relative amount of lipid in the different types of preparation. Jarvis has clearly shown (Table II) that using a 1000 × *g* fraction the ratio is affected considerably according to the species used, the isolation media and the type of homogenization. In the comparison of intact chloroplasts and a 1000 × *g* preparation which contains a mixture of whole and broken chloroplasts, mitochondria etc., it can be seen that about 70% of the chloroplast lipids have already been lost (Table I). Increasing the molarity of the sucrose in the

TABLE II

The lipid/chlorophyll (μg/μg) ratios in 1000 × *g* fraction from leaves using different extraction techniques (data of Jarvis *et al.*, 1967).

		Lipid/chlorophyll (μg/μg)	
		0·3M buffered sucrose	0·6M buffered sucrose
Vicia faba	A	2·9	8·9
	B	10·0	10·0
Nasturtium	A	10·6	28·5
officinale	B	19·6	19·8
Lactuca	A	16·7	25·3
sativa			

A. Initial homogenization using a pestle and mortar.
B. Initial homogenization using a liquidizer.

isolation media increases the proportion of intact chloroplasts and, as would be expected, also the lipid/chlorophyll ratio. Intact chloroplasts have a ratio lipid/chlorophyll of 15·8 ± 0·7 compared with 3·4 ± 0·3 for protein/chlorophyll and this would suggest a lipid/protein ratio of between 4 and 5 in the intact chloroplast. These chloroplasts contained only a very few small plastoglobuli and they could not have accounted for the high values of stroma lipid. To obtain quantitative values per chloroplast, an accurate method for determining the proportion of intact and envelope-free chloroplasts is necessary. Haemocytometer counting is tedious and not very precise but differences in resistance may be sufficient to enable the two classes of chloroplasts to be distinguished on the Coulter Counter (Ridley *et al.*, 1967).

IV. THE CHLOROPLAST AS AN AUTONOMOUS UNIT

The mature chloroplast of the higher plant is the primary site of the whole complex of reactions leading to the capture of light and its eventual storage in chemical form in carbohydrates. Isolated chloroplasts from a variety of plants fix CO_2 and synthesize ATP and $NADPH_2$ and recent work has demonstrated they are also able to synthesize sucrose (Bird et al., 1965), lipids (Stumpf and James, 1962; Stumpf, et al., 1963) and proteins (Spencer, 1965; Sissakian et al., 1965). They are also able to reduce nitrate and nitrite photochemically (Ramirez et al., 1964; Paneque et al., 1964; Losada and Paneque, 1966) and can probably carry out the complete biosynthesis of chlorophylls and carotenoids. Evidence for this wide range of synthetic reactions, taken together with very good evidence that higher plant chloroplasts contain DNA (see Gibor and Granick, 1964) and RNA (see Kirk and Tilney-Bassett, 1967 for a critical assessment of the evidence) and are also able to synthesize their own RNA (Kirk, 1964), demonstrates very clearly that chloroplasts have a high degree of biochemical autonomy. It is pertinent to ask just how independent is the chloroplast of the rest of the cell not only biochemically but also genetically as a self-determining self-duplicating structure. Gibor and Granick published a very comprehensive review of the subject in 1964 and Kirk and Tilney-Bassett (1967) have reviewed the additional information up to 1966.

In studies of this kind the green algae *Euglena* and *Acetabularia* have been used with considerable success as experimental material. It is not difficult to see why the biological characteristics of these organisms made them such valuable experimental objects. In *Euglena gracilis* var. *bacillaris* formation of the chloroplast is light-dependent and by keeping dark grown cells on "resting" medium and exposing them to the light it is possible to study chloroplast development uncomplicated by cell division. *Acetabularia* is a giant cell with only a single nucleus and if the nucleus is removed the rest of the cell is able to survive for about three months in the light. Using this organism one has the unique possibility of studying the behaviour of chloroplasts *in vivo* in the presence and in the absence of the nucleus. When assessing the degree of autonomy of the chloroplast, observations on *Euglena* and *Acetabularia* are usually taken in conjunction with evidence derived from studies of higher plants. This could be misleading for a highly determinate heterogeneous organ such as a leaf is very different biologically from a haploid organism such as *Euglena* reproducing by binary fission and different again from the vegetative stage of a diploid giant unicell such as *Acetabularia*. In the leaf the immature chloroplasts can be regarded as the end-products of differentiation from proplastids of the meristem and there is no evidence that these chloroplasts are able to divide in the mature state. In many algae, on the other hand, chloroplasts have frequently been seen in division (e.g. the recent cine film of chloroplast division in *Nitella* by Green, 1964) and the products of the division are the first chloroplasts of the next cell generation. Recent evidence from algae and from higher plants will, therefore, be considered separately here.

Gibor (1967) has pointed out that the perpetuation of a genetic system requires the presence of DNA and RNA and of enzymes for DNA synthesis, for RNA synthesis and for protein synthesis. These attributes will be considered in turn.

A. ALGAE

1. *Acetabularia*

Gibor and Izawa (1963) and Balthus and Brachet (1963) demonstrated that in bacteria-free enucleate *Acetabularia* extranuclear DNA is present to the extent of 1×10^{-16} g/chloroplast (Gibor and Granick, 1964). This DNA is localized in the chloroplast and has a buoyant density of 1·695 in a CsCl gradient (Gibor, 1965). Gibor (1967) has fed $^{14}CO_2$ to enucleated *Acetabularia* in the light and has shown clearly that synthesis of deoxynucleosides, their phosphorylation and polymerization can proceed in the absence of the nucleus. The location of these synthetic reactions is not known but may be in the chloroplast. Actinomycin D-sensitive RNA synthesis has been demonstrated in isolated *Acetabularia* chloroplasts and Janowski (1965) has shown ^{32}P incorporation into RNA of more than one kind in the chloroplast fraction isolated from enucleated *Acetabularia*. Shepherd (1965) has used autoradiographic techniques to show that chloroplast RNA and protein synthesis proceeds at the same rate and DNA synthesis at half the rate in the absence of the nucleus as in its presence. Protein synthesis can indeed continue for up to four weeks after enucleation (Hämmerling, 1963). Synthesis of an enzyme thought to be localized exclusively in the chloroplast of green cells, namely NADPH-triose phosphate dehydrogenase (1.2.1.13), has been shown by Ziegler *et al.* (1967) to occur in the absence of the nucleus in the light, rising from no activity one day after enucleation to the same level of activity as in the nucleated control after 5 days. Shepherd (1965) has clearly shown that *Acetabularia* chloroplasts can replicate in the absence of the nucleus. There seems to be little information about ribosomes from *Acetabularia*; the difficulties of isolation in sufficient quantities for analysis are formidable.

Enucleate fragments of *Acetabularia* would therefore appear to have a complete functional genetic apparatus which enables survival for several weeks but no longer and we can agree with Shepherd who suggests that in this organism growth, replication and biosynthetic activity of the chloroplast can apparently proceed without coded information of nuclear origin. There is good evidence that many of the elements of the genetic apparatus reside in the chloroplast. Few studies have been made on the genetics of the organism and there is no evidence about the interaction between nuclear genes and chloroplast genes during development or even that the chloroplast genetic apparatus is inherited. The studies on isolated chloroplasts from enucleated cytoplasts of *Acetabularia* initiated by Gibor (1965) are awaited with considerable interest.

2. *Euglena*

In *Euglena gracilis* var. *bacillaris* there is no doubt that the chloroplast divides (Schiff and Epstein, 1965, have published a beautiful picture which clearly demonstrates this). There is also no doubt that the chloroplast is inherited. The DNA of the whole *Euglena* cell shows three peaks in CsCl gradient centrifugation (Edelman *et al.*, 1965; Ray and Hannawalt, 1965), one major peak and two minor satellite peaks. One satellite, of buoyant density 1·686, is enriched in the chloroplast fraction from green *Euglena* cells and absent from mutants incapable of forming proplastids or chloroplasts (Schiff and Epstein, 1965). This satellite DNA would, therefore, appear to be localized within the chloroplast. Gibor and Granick (1964) have calculated that the *Euglena* chloroplast contains 4×10^{-15} g DNA. *Euglena* chloroplast ribosomes have a sedimentation coefficient of 60S (with a minor 36S component) compared with cytoplasmic ribosomes of 70S (Eisenstadt and Brawerman, 1964a). Cytoplasmic and chloroplast ribosomes present in non-dividing cells with developing chloroplasts differ in the base ratios of their RNA; the adenine/cytosine ratio for chloroplast ribosomes is 1·8, for cytoplasmic ribosomes 0·87 (Brawerman *et al.*, 1962). A 14S and a 19S component of RNA were found in cytoplasmic ribosomes (Brawerman and Eisenstadt, 1964). Template RNA has been shown to be present in the *Euglena* chloroplast (Eisenstadt and Brawerman, 1964a) and isolated *Euglena* chloroplasts are able to incorporate amino-acids into proteins (Eisenstadt and Brawerman, 1964b). Several chloroplast enzymes have been shown to appear in the development in the light of chloroplasts in dark-grown cells (see Schiff and Epstein, 1965, for a review). On the basis of their evidence, Schiff and Epstein reached the conclusion that in *Euglena gracilis* var. *bacillaris* chloroplast replication and development involves the replication and reading of an autonomous code.

B. LEAVES OF HIGHER PLANTS

The mature leaf as an organ for studying chloroplast autonomy is not ideal but it is very valuable as a source of isolated fully differentiated chloroplasts in sufficient quantity for biochemical assay.

Satellite DNAs have also been detected in leaf material with buoyant densities of 1·705 and 1·719 compared with the major nuclear DNA of

1·695 (Chun et al., 1963). In contrast to Euglena and Acetabularia, in leaves cytoplasmic DNA would appear to have a lower buoyant density than nuclear DNA. DNA synthesis has not been demonstrated in chloroplasts in leaves in vivo and Wollgiehn and Mothes (1964), using mature leaves of tobacco, could get no evidence for DNase-sensitive ³H-thymidine incorporation into chloroplasts. Kirk (1964), however, has demonstrated a DNA-dependent polymerase in Vicia faba chloroplasts. When ribosomes are examined there are also differences between the algae and higher plants. In leaves from several species two classes of ribosomes are found with sedimentation coefficients of 72–80S and 62–70S, the smaller category of particles apparently being restricted to the chloroplast. The actual S values vary in the different reports and this may reflect technical differences or differences in S values in different species. Lyttleton (1962) was the first to isolate two classes of ribosomes from Spinacia leaves and Spencer (1965) confirmed that there were 70S and 80S ribosomes in these leaves. The corresponding values for Brassica pekinensis are 68S and 83S (Clark et al., 1964) and for tobacco 70S and 80S (Boardman et al., 1965). It may be that chloroplast and cytoplasmic ribosomes are more similar in higher plants than in the algae. There is a possibility, however, that real differences are concealed because of the presence of chloroplast ribosomes in the "cytoplasmic" ribosomal fraction. Pollard et al. (1966) have isolated RNA from "cytoplasmic" and chloroplast ribosomes of Romaine lettuce and found an 18S and 28S component in both types of ribosome. From our own unpublished results we have found both light and heavy RNA components in both cytoplasmic and chloroplast ribosomal fractions from Vicia faba leaves (T. A. Dyer and R. M. Leech, unpublished results). Spencer and Whitfield (1966) however, were only able to isolate one component sedimenting at 16S from the RNA of spinach chloroplast ribosomes but 16S and 23S fractions could be isolated from cytoplasmic ribosomes. The reason for the disparity is not clear but might reflect specific properties of spinach leaves. Again the demonstration by Boardman (1966) that both 70S and 80S ribosomes are present in etiolated Phaseolus leaves and that no more ribosomes can be isolated from a mature than from an etiolated leaf is also in sharp contrast to the position in Euglena. Thirdly, although they have been sought, no differences in the base ratios of the magnitude of those found in Euglena have yet been found between chloroplast ribosomal and cytoplasmic ribosomal fractions from leaves. Even if considerable care is taken it is impossible to avoid some chloroplast breakage during the initial homogenization of the leaves. However, the low molecular weight RNA components of chloroplasts from Vicia leaves certainly have physical properties distinct from those of the cytoplasmic RNA (Dyer and Leech, 1967). As was mentioned previously, protein synthesis has also been demonstrated in higher plant chloroplasts (Spencer, 1965).

In phanerogams much genetic evidence points to plastid genome continuity from one generation to the next (Kirk and Tilney-Bassett, 1967) and inheritance of mutant plastome genes via both male and female gametes has been demonstrated notably in *Oenothera*, *Pelargonium* and *Epilobium*.

Thus the information concerning the chloroplast genetic system is uneven from algae and from higher plants. There seems good evidence that the basic biochemical systems responsible for genetic continuity are present in the chloroplast but the study of their function and control are only just beginning. It is the study of the interactions of the nuclear and plastid genomes during the development and functional life of the chloroplast in the different organisms which will provide interest and excitement in the years to come.

ACKNOWLEDGEMENTS

I should like to thank Mr. A. D. Greenwood for his generous help in stimulating discussions and also for permission to use the photographs in Figs 1, 4 and 6. I also wish to thank Professor T. E. Weier, Professor C. R. Stocking and Dr. Shumway for permission to reproduce the diagrams in Figs 2 and 3.

REFERENCES

Arnon, D. I. (1949). *Pl. Physiol., Lancaster* **24**, 1.
Arnon, D. I., Allen, M. B. and Whatley, F. R. (1954). *Nature, Lond.* **174**, 394.
Bailey, J. L. and Whyborn, A. G. (1963). *Biochim. biophys. Acta* **78**, 163.
Balthus, E. and Brachet, J. (1963). *Biochim. biophys. Acta* **76**, 490.
Bamberger, E. S. and Park, R. B. (1966). *Pl. Physiol., Lancaster* **41**, 1591.
Bird, I. F., Porter, H. K. and Stocking, C. R. (1965). *Biochim. biophys. Acta* **79**, 746.
Boardman, N. K. (1966). *Expl Cell Res.* **43**, 474.
Boardman, N. K., Francki, R. I. B. and Wildman, S. G. (1965). *Biochemistry, N.Y.* **4**, 872.
Branton, D. (1966). *Proc. natn. Acad. Sci., U.S.A.* **55**, 1048.
Brawerman, G. and Eisenstadt, J. M. (1964). *J. molec. Biol.* **10**, 403.
Brawerman, G., Pogo, A. O. and Chargaff, E. (1962). *Biochim. biophys. Acta* **55**, 326.
Chun, E. H. L., Vaughan, M. H. and Rich, A. (1963). *J. molec. Biol.* **7**, 130.
Clark, M. F., Matthews, R. E. F. and Ralph, R. K. (1964). *Biochim. biophys. Acta* **27**, 145.
Criddle, R. S. (1966). NATO Symposium, "Biochemistry of Chloroplasts". Vol. I, p. 203. (T. W. Goodwin, ed.), Academic Press, London and New York.
Diers, L. and Schötz, F. (1966). *Planta* **70**, 322.
Drawert, H. and Mix, M. (1962). *Planta* **58**, 50.
Dyer, T. A. and Leech, R. M. (1967). *Biochem. J.* **102**, 6P.
Edelman, M., Schiff, J. A. and Epstein, H. T. (1965). *J. molec. Biol.* **11**, 769.
Eisenstadt, J. M. and Brawerman, G. (1964a). *J. molec. Biol.* **10**, 392.
Eisenstadt, J. M. and Brawerman, G. (1964b). *Biochim. biophys. Acta* **80**, 463.

R. M. LEECH

Falk, H. (1960). *Planta* **55**, 525.

Frey-Wyssling, A. (1957). "Macromolecules in Cell Structure". Harvard University Press, Cambridge, Mass., U.S.A.

Frey-Wyssling, A. and Steinmann, E. (1953). *Naturforsch. Ges. Zuerich* **98**, 20.

Gibbs, S. P. (1960). *J. Ultrastruct. Res.* **4**, 127.

Gibbs, S. P. (1962a). *J. Ultrastruct. Res.* **7**, 247.

Gibbs, S. P. (1962b). *J. Ultrastruct. Res.* **7**, 262.

Gibbs, S. P. (1962c). *J. Ultrastruct. Res.* **7**, 418.

Gibor, A. (1965). *Proc. natn. Acad. Sci., U.S.A.* **54**, 1527.

Gibor, A. (1967). NATO Symposium, "Biochemistry of Chloroplasts". Vol. 2, p. 321. (T. W. Goodwin, ed.), Academic Press, London and New York.

Gibor, A., and Izawa, M. (1963). *Proc. natn. Acad. Sci., U.S.A.* **50**, 1164.

Gibor, A. and Granick, S. (1964). *Science, N.Y.* **145**, 890.

Green, D. E. and Perdue, J. F. (1966). *Proc. natn. Acad. Sci., U.S.A.* **55**, 1295.

Green, P. B. (1964). *Am. J. Bot.* **51**, 334.

Greenwood, A. D., Leech, R. M. and Williams, J. P. (1963). *Biochim. biophys. Acta* **78**, 148.

Gunning, B. E. S. (1965). *J. Cell Biol.* **24**, 79.

Gunning, B. E. S. and Jagoe, M. P. (1967). NATO Symposium, "Biochemistry of Chloroplasts". Vol. 2, p. 655. (T. W. Goodwin, ed.), Academic Press, London and New York.

Hall, D. O. and Whatley, F. R. (1967). *In* "Enzyme Cytology". p. 181. (D. B. Roodyn, ed.), Academic Press, London and New York.

Hämmerling, J. (1963). *A. Rev. Pl. Physiol.* **14**, 65.

Haselkorn, R., Fernandez-Moran, H., Kieras, F. J. and van Bruggen, E. F. J. (1965). *Science, N.Y.* **150**, 1598.

Heber, U. (1957). *Ber. dt. bot. Ges.* **70**, 371.

Heber, U. and Tyszkiewiez, E. (1962). *J. exp. Bot.* **13**, 185.

Heber, U., Pon, N. G. and Heber, M. (1963). *Pl. Physiol., Lancaster.* **38**, 355.

Heitz, E. (1958). *In* "4th International Congress of Electron Microscopy". Vol. 2, p. 501. Springer-Verlag, Berlin.

Heslop-Harrison, J. (1963). *Planta* **60**, 243.

Jacobi, G. and Perner, E. (1961). *Flora* **150**, 209.

Jacobson, A. B., Swift, H. and Bogorad, L. (1963). *J. Cell Biol.* **17**, 557.

James, W. O. and Das, V. S. R. (1957). *New Phytol.* **56**, 325.

James, W. O. and Leech, R. M. (1964). *Proc. R. Soc.* B. **160**, 13.

Janowski, M. (1965). *Biochim. biophys. Acta* **103**, 399.

Jeffrey, S. W., Ulrich, J. and Allen, M. B. (1966). *Biochim. biophys. Acta* **112**, 35.

Jensen, R. G. and Bassham, J. A. (1966). *Proc. natn. Acad. Sci., U.S.A.* **56**, 1095.

Kahn, A. and von Wettstein, D. (1961). *J. Ultrastruct. Res.* **5**, 557.

Kaja, H. (1966). *Z. Naturf.* **21b**, 379.

Kirk, J. T. O. (1964). *Biochim. biophys. Res. Commun.* **16**, 233.

Kirk, J. T. O. and Tilney-Bassett, R. A. E. (1967). "The Plastids". Freeman, London and San Francisco.

Kislev, N., Swift, H. and Bogorad, L. (1965). *J. Cell Biol.* **25**, 327.

Kreutz, W. (1966). NATO Symposium, "Biochemistry of Chloroplasts". Vol. 1, p. 83. (T. W. Goodwin, ed.), Academic Press, New York and London.

Leech, R. M. (1964). *Biochim. biophys. Acta* **79**, 637.

Leech, R. M. (1966). NATO Symposium, "Biochemistry of Chloroplasts". Vol. 1, p. 65, (T. W. Goodwin, ed.), Academic Press, London and New York.

Leech, R. M., Stocking, C. R. and Greenwood, A. D. (1964). *Abstracts 1st Meeting Federation European Biochemical Soc.* BI, 109.

Lichtentahler, H. K. (1964). *Ber. dt. bot. Ges.* **74**, 398.

Lichtentahler, H. K. and Sprey, B. (1966). *Z. Naturf.* **21b**, 690.

Lowry, O. H., Rosenborough, N. J., Farr, A. L. and Randall, R. J. (1951). *J. biol. Chem.* **193**, 265.

Losada, M. and Paneque, A. (1966). *Biochim. biophys. Acta* **126**, 578.

Lyttleton, J. W. (1962). *Expl Cell Res.* **26**, 312.

Magree, L., Henninger, M. D. and Crane, F. L. (1966). *J. biol. Chem.* **241**, 5197.

Manton, I. (1966). NATO Symposium, "Biochemistry of Chloroplasts". Vol. 1, p. 23. (Goodwin, T. W., ed), Academic Press, London and New York.

Menke, W. (1960). *Z. Naturf.* **15b**, 479.

Menke, W. (1961). *Z. Naturf.* **16b**, 334.

Menke, W. (1962). *A. Rev. Pl. Physiol.* **13**, 27.

Menke, W. (1966). NATO Symposium, "Biochemistry of Chloroplasts". Vol. 1, p. 3. (T. W. Goodwin ed.), Academic Press, New York.

Moor, H., Mühletahler, K., Waldner, H. and Frey-Wyssling, A. (1961). *J. Cell Biol.* **10**, 1.

Mühletahler, K. (1960). *Z. wiss. Mikroskop.* **64**, 444.

Mühletahler, K. (1966). NATO Symposium, "Biochemistry of Chloroplasts". Vol. 1, p. 49. (T. W. Goodwin, ed.), Academic Press, London and New York.

Mühletahler, K., Moor, H. and Szarkowski, J. W. (1965). *Planta* **67**, 305.

Murakami, S. and Takamiya, A. (1962). In "Electron Microscopy". (S. Breeze, ed.), Vol. 2, XX, p. 12. Saunders, Philadelphia, U.S.A.

Nobel, P. S., Murakami, S. and Takamiya, A. (1966a). 6th International Congress for Electronmicroscopy, Kyoto.

Nobel, P. S., Murakami, S. and Taharnija, A. (1966b). *Plant and Cell Physiol.* **7**, 263.

Paneque, A., Ramirez, J. M., Del Campo, F. F. and Losada, M. (1964). *J. biol. Chem.* **239**, 1737.

Park, R. B. and Pon, N. G. (1961). *J. molec. Biol.* **3**, 1.

Park, R. B. and Biggins, J. (1964). *Science, N.Y.* **144**, 1009.

Perner, E. (1962). *Port. Acta biol.* **6**, 359.

Perner, E. (1965). *Planta* **66**, 44.

Pollard, C. J., Stemler, A. and Blaydes, D. F. (1966). *Pl. Physiol., Lancaster* **41**, 1323.

Ramirez, J. M., Del Campo, F. F., Paneque, A. and Losada, M. (1964). *Biochem. biophys. Res. Commun.* **15**, 297.

Ray, D. S. and Hannawalt, P. C. (1965). *J. molec. Biol.* **11**, 760.

Robertson, R. D. (1964). In "22nd Symposium of Soc. for Development and Growth". (M. Locke, ed.), p. 31, Academic Press, New York and London.

Sager, R. (1958). *Brookhaven Symp. Biol.* **11**, 101.

Sager, R. and Palade, G. E. (1957). *J. biophys. biochem. Cytol.* **3**, 463.

Schweiger, H. G. and Berger, S. (1964). *Biochim. biophys. Acta* **87**, 533.

Schiff, J. A. and Epstein, H. T. (1965). In "Reproduction, Molecular, Subcellular and Cellular". (M. Locke, ed.), p. 131. Academic Press, New York and London.

Schiff, J. A. and Epstein, H. T. (1966). NATO Symposium "Biochemistry of Chloroplasts". Vol. 1, p. 341. (T. W. Goodwin, ed.), Academic Press, London and New York.

Shepherd, D. C. (1965). *Expl Cell Res.* **37**, 93.

Silaevia, A. M. and Shiriaev, A. I. (1966). *Dokl. Akad. Nauk SSSR* **170**, No. 2.

Sissakian, N. M., Filipovich, I. I., Svetailo, E. N. and Aliyev, K. A. (1965). *Biochim. biophys. Acta* **95**, 474.

Smillie, R. M. and Fuller, R. C. (1959). *Pl. Physiol.*, *Lancaster* **37**, 716.

Smillie, R. M. and Krotkov, G. (1961). *Can. J. Bot.* **39**, 891.

Spencer, D. (1965). *Archs Biochem. Biophys.* **111**, 381.

Spencer, D. and Whitfield, P. R. (1966). *Archs Biochem. Biophys.* **117**, 337.

Sprey, B. and Lichtentahler, H. K. (1966). *Z. Naturf.* **21b**, 697.

Steinmann, E. (1952). *Expl Cell Res.* **3**, 367.

Steinmann, E. and Sjöstrand, F. S. (1955). *Expl Cell Res.* **8**, 15.

Stocking, C. R. (1959). *Pl. Physiol.*, *Lancaster* **34**, 56.

Stumpf, P. K. and James, A. T. (1962). *Biochim. biophys. Acta* **57**, 400.

Stumpf, P. K., Bové, J. M. and Goffeau, A. (1963). *Biochim. biophys. Acta* **70**, 260.

Thalacker, R. and Behrens, M. (1959). *Z. Naturf.* **14b**, 443.

Thomson, W. W., Dugger, W. M. and Palmer, R. L. (1965). *Bot. Gaz.* **126**, 62.

Thomson, W. W., Dugger, W. M. and Palmer, R. L. (1966). *Can. J. Bot.* **44**, 1677.

Trebst, A. V., Tsujimoto, H. Y. and Arnon, D. I. (1958). *Nature, Lond.* **182**, 351.

Walker, D. A. (1965). *Pl. Physiol.*, *Lancaster* **40**, 1157.

Walker, D. A. (1967). NATO Symposium, "Biochemistry of Chloroplasts". Vol. II, (T. W. Goodwin, ed.), p. 53. Academic Press, London and New York.

Wehrmeyer, W. (1961). *Ber. dt. bot. Ges.* **74**, 209.

Wehrmeyer, W. (1964). *Planta* **62**, 272.

Wehrmeyer, W. and Perner, E. (1962). *Protoplasma* **54**, 573.

Weier, T. E. and Benson, A. A. (1966). NATO Symposium, "Biochemistry of Chloroplasts". Vol. 1, p. 91. (T. W. Goodwin, ed), Academic Press, London and New York.

Weier, T. E. and Thomson, W. W. (1962) *Am. J. Bot.* **49**, 807.

Weier, T. E., Bisalputra, T. and Harrison, A. (1966). *J. Ultrastruct. Res.* **15**, 38.

Weier, T. E., Englebrecht, A. H. P., Harrison, A. and Risley, E. B. (1965a). *J. Ultrastruct. Res.* **13**, 92.

Weier, T. E., Stocking, C. R., Bracker, C. E., Risley, E. B. (1965b). *Am. J. Bot.* **52**, 339.

Weier, T. E., Stocking, C. R., Thomson, W. W. and Drever, H. (1963). *J. Ultrastruct. Res.* **8**, 122.

Weier, T. E., Stocking, C. R. and Shumway, L. K. (1967). *Brookhaven Symp. Biol.* **19**, 353.

Wellburn, A. R. and Hemming, F. W. (1966). NATO Symposium, "Biochemistry of Chloroplasts". Vol. 1, p. 173. (T. W. Goodwin, ed.), Academic Press, London and New York.

Wollgiehn, R., Ruess, M. and Munsche, D. (1966). *Flora*, **157**, 92.

Wollgiehn, R. and Mothes, K. (1964). *Expl Cell Res.* **35**, 52.

Ziegler, H., Ziegler, I. and Beth, K. (1967). *Planta* **72**, 247.

CHAPTER 9

The Function and Metabolism of Fatty Acids and Acyl Lipids in Chloroplasts

B. W. NICHOLS AND A. T. JAMES

Unilever Research Laboratory, Sharnbrook, Bedfordshire, England

I. INTRODUCTION

Although recent years have seen major advances in our knowledge of the lipid chemistry and biochemistry of photosynthetic tissues, much of the work has been performed on intact cell preparations rather than on isolated chloroplasts. To a large extent this is a reflection of the difficulty experienced in isolating plastids with their full metabolic capacities unimpaired but metabolic studies on whole cells can give data which, carefully interpreted, may yield much useful information regarding plastid metabolism.

II. ACYL LIPIDS OF CHLOROPLASTS

The photosynthetic tissues of plants contain a complex variety of neutral glycerides, phospholipids and glycolipids (Fig. 1). The higher algae possess similar lipids but lack both sterol glycosides and cerebrosides. Several groups of workers, however, (Benson and Maruo, 1958; Nichols,

1963) have shown that leaf chloroplasts possess a much simpler acyl lipid composition than the whole cell and that they contain only four acyl lipids in major proportions. These comprise three glycolipids (mono- and di-galactosyl diglyceride and sulphoquinovosyl diglyceride) and one phospholipid (phosphatidyl glycerol), the structures of which are depicted in Fig. 2.

The presence of only these four acyl lipids in chloroplasts has now been established for a variety of plants and the generalization would seem to be valid. To our knowledge, the lipid compositions of isolated algal chloroplasts have not been studied and data for whole cells is usually assumed to

---

Phospholipids	
Phosphatidyl glycerol	Phosphatidyl inositol
Phosphatidyl choline (lecithin)	Cardiolipin
Phosphatidyl ethanolamine	Phosphatidic acid
Phosphatidyl serine	

Glycolipids

Monogalactosyl diglyceride	Cerebroside
Digalactosyl diglyceride	Sterol glycoside ester
Sulphoquinovosyl diglyceride (Sulpholipid)	

Other lipids

Diglyceride   Triglyceride   Sterol ester

FIG. 1 The acyl lipids of plant leaves.

be sufficient. An indication that this assumption is acceptable comes from our own studies on the lipid composition of the blue-green algae where the major sub-cellular particles are chloroplast lamellae. The major acyl lipids of these blue-green algae have been shown to be the same four lipids found in leaf chloroplasts which are known to be primarily concentrated in the lamellae (Nichols et al., 1965a; Allen et al., 1966; Nichols and Wood, 1968).

The question of whether lecithin is present in chloroplasts is an interesting one and arises from the difficulty experienced in isolating uncontaminated chloroplasts from leaves using aqueous media. The proportion of lecithin in such preparations is relatively small compared with that of the major chloroplast lipids and the purer the preparation, the smaller does this proportion become. So far, there have been no reports of leaf chloroplast preparations which are free from lecithin and Allen and co-workers have even detected its presence in preparations of spinach chloroplast lamellae (Allen et al., 1966). Indirect evidence for the presence of lecithin in chloroplasts is the reported relationship in photosynthetic tissue between lecithin and the synthesis of linoleic acid and the latter is known to be associated with the plastid fractions (Harris et al., 1967).

The major portion of the lecithin fraction from leaves, however, undoubtedly originates from the mitochondrial-microsomal fractions and one might presume that its function in these particles would be different from that in the chloroplast. The lecithin fraction from these different classes of particle might, therefore, be expected to have differing fatty acid compositions and to be synthesized and metabolized at different rates. Such differences have yet to be established. We have studied the lecithin fractions from chloroplast and "mitochondrial" preparations from a variety of leaf tissues which had been incubated with ^{14}C-labelled acetate. At all times the fatty acid composition and the specific activities of these different fractions from the same plant were found to be identical. The lecithins are thus either freely exchangeable between cellular organelles or are synthesized in a single site and then transferred to other sites. Other evidence that lecithin is not always essential for normal photosynthetic function is provided by the blue-green algae which, although apparently photosynthesizing in a manner similar to that of green algae and higher plants, contain only the four "chloroplast lipids" and no lecithin (Nichols et al., 1965a; Allen et al., 1966; Nichols and Wood, 1968).

The proplastid bodies present in etiolated leaves are even more difficult to prepare than the chloroplasts. There is consequently little published information regarding their lipid composition although studies involving whole etiolated leaves indicate that they contain the same lipid classes but in different relative proportions (B. W. Nichols, unpublished results).

III. Fatty Acids of Chloroplasts

Leaf chloroplasts contain a high proportion of polyenoic acids, particularly those of the C_{18} series (James and Nichols, 1966) (Table I). There are greater variations in fatty acid composition of chloroplasts from different plant species than in the corresponding acyl lipid compositions. Thus, some chloroplasts such as those from spinach (Allen et al., 1966) and tobacco (B. W. Nichols, unpublished results) contain significant quantities of the corresponding C_{16} polyenoic acids, while the chloroplasts of marine algae (Kates and Volcani, 1966; Klenk et al., 1963) and the pteridophyta (Schlenk and Gellerman, 1965; Wolf et al., 1966; Nichols, 1965a; Radunz, 1967) frequently contain polyenoic acids of the C_{20} series, including arachidonic acid. The major C_{16} monoenoic acids of leaves and the higher algae are of the Δ^9 and Δ^7 varieties (e.g. Klenk et al., 1963; Schlenk and Gellerman, 1965) and these tissues also always contain small yet significant quantities of a unique C_{16} acid which contains a trans double bond in the 3-position (e.g. Nichols et al., 1965b). The proplastid bodies of dark-grown leaves also contain relatively large proportions of polyenoic acids, although rather less than in chloroplasts, but the trans-3-hexadecenoic acid is absent from etiolated tissues (Nichols et al., 1965c; Nichols, 1965b).

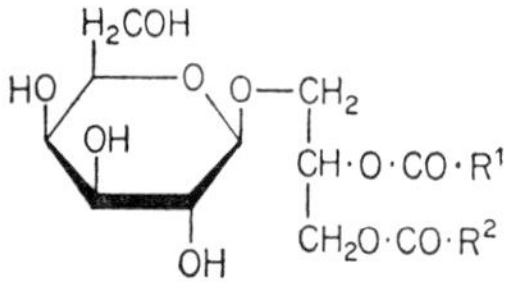

Monogalactosyl diglyceride
[β–D–galactosyl–(1 →1′)–2′, 3′–
diacyl–D–glycerol]

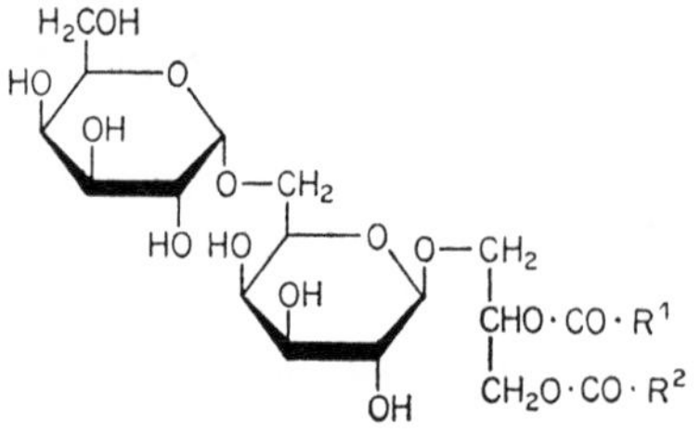

Digalactosyl diglyceride [α–D–galactosyl–(1–6)–β–D–galactosyl–(1–1′)–
2′, 3′–diâcyl–D–glycerol]

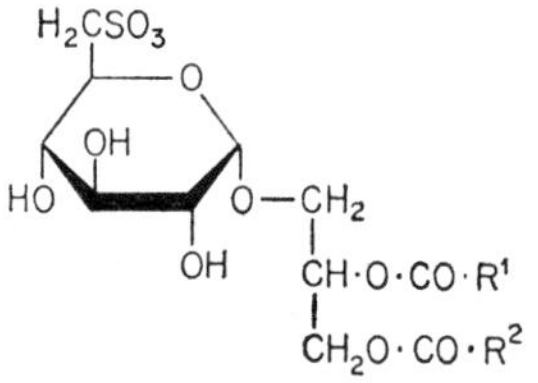

Sulphoquinovosyl diglyceride
[6–Sulpho–α–D–quinovosyl–
(1–1′)–2′, 3′–diacyl–D–glycerol]

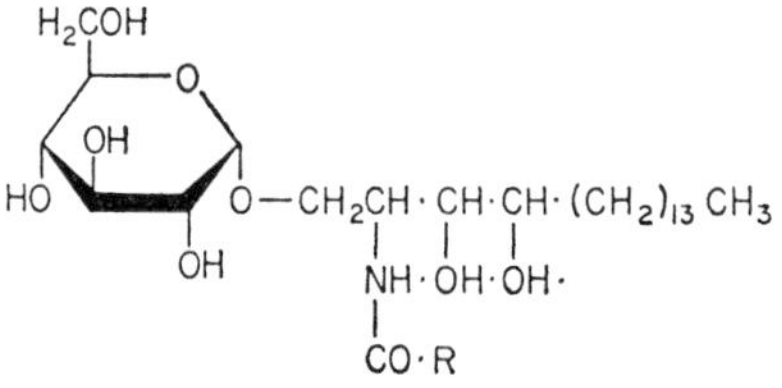

Glucocerebroside
N–Acyl–α–D–glucosyl–(1–1′)–
phytosphingosine

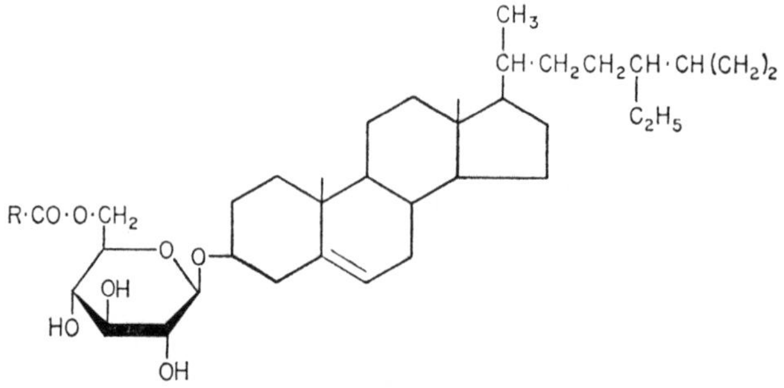

6–Acyl–β–D–glucopyranosyl (1–3′)–β–sitosterol

Fig. 2

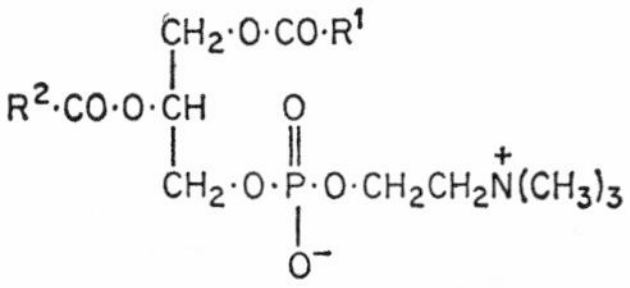

$CH_2 \cdot O \cdot CO \cdot R^1$
$R^2 \cdot CO \cdot O \cdot CH$
$CH_2 \cdot O \cdot P \cdot O \cdot CH_2CH_2 \overset{+}{N}(CH_3)_3$

Phosphatidyl choline (Lecithin)

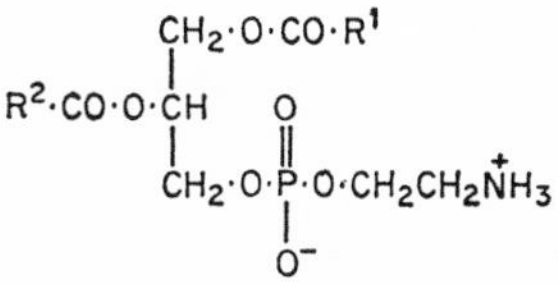

$CH_2 \cdot O \cdot CO \cdot R^1$
$R^2 \cdot CO \cdot O \cdot CH$
$CH_2 \cdot O \cdot P \cdot O \cdot CH_2CH_2 \overset{+}{N}H_3$

Phosphatidyl ethanolamine

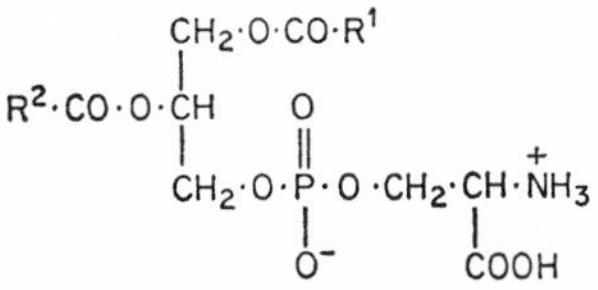

$CH_2 \cdot O \cdot CO \cdot R^1$
$R^2 \cdot CO \cdot O \cdot CH$
$CH_2 \cdot O \cdot P \cdot O \cdot CH_2 \cdot CH \cdot \overset{+}{N}H_3$
$COOH$

Phosphatidyl serine

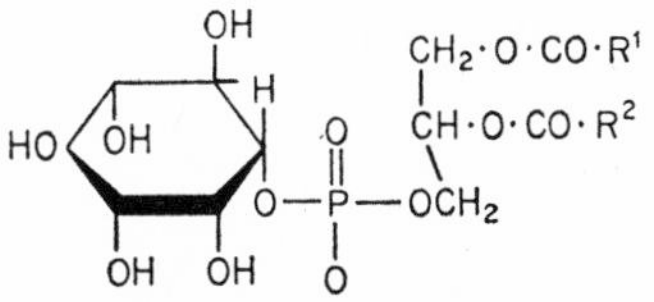

Phosphatidyl inositol

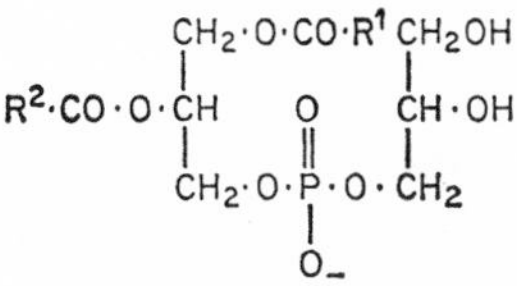

$CH_2 \cdot O \cdot CO \cdot R^1 \quad CH_2OH$
$R^2 \cdot CO \cdot O \cdot CH \qquad CH \cdot OH$
$CH_2 \cdot O \cdot P \cdot O \cdot CH_2$

Phosphatidyl glycerol

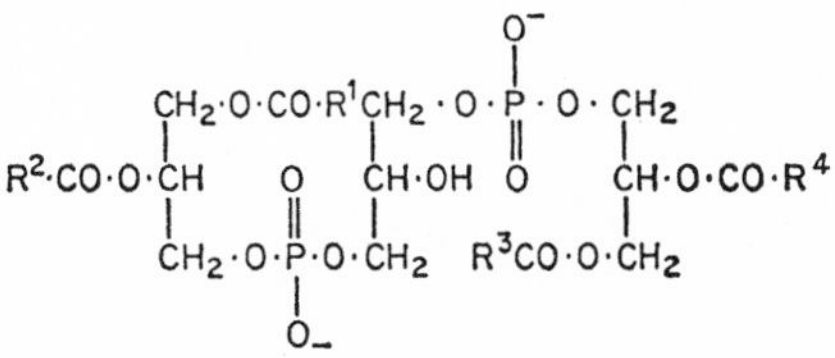

Diphosphatidyl glycerol (Cardiolipin)

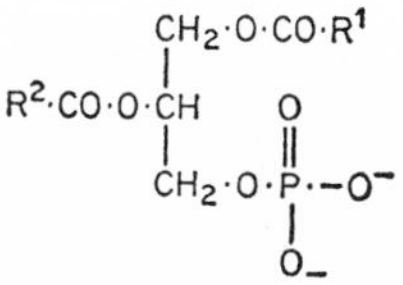

$CH_2 \cdot O \cdot CO \cdot R^1$
$R^2 \cdot CO \cdot O \cdot CH$
$CH_2 \cdot O \cdot P \cdot -O^-$

Phosphatidic acid

FIG. 2

TABLE I

Fatty acids of some leaf tissue.

Tissue	16:0[a]	Δ^{7+9} 16:1	Δ^3 16:1	16:3	18:0	18:1	18:2	18:3	22:0
Broad bean[1] (Etiolated leaf)	16·7	—	—	—	4·7	—	33·5	39·4	4·6
Broad bean[1] (Green leaf)	11·7	6·9		—	3·7	3·4	14·3	56·4	4·0
Broad bean[1] (Chloroplasts)	7·4	9·2		—	1·2	5·2	2·6	72·0	1·2
Spinach leaf[2]	12·9	—	2·6	4·6	t	6·6	16·3	56·2	
Holly leaf[3]	22·0	t	t	—	t	2·5	13·8	60·2	

[a] The figure before the colon denotes the number of carbon atoms; that after the colon, the number of double bonds.

[1] Crombie, 1958; [2] Debuch, 1961; [3] Nichols, 1965a; t = trace quantity.

The fatty acids of chloroplasts are not randomly distributed between the different acyl lipids but show a very high degree of specificity for certain lipids (Allen *et al.*, 1966; Nichols, 1965b). These specificities are common to all the photosynthetic tissues of higher plants and algae which have been examined in detail and are typified by the date presented in Table II. The

TABLE II

% Fatty acid composition of the major chloroplast lipids of *Chlorella vulgaris* (Nichols, 1965b).

	16:0	Δ^9 16:1	Δ^3 16:1	16:2	18:1	18:2	18:3
Partially etiolate							
Monogalactosyl diglyceride	3	11	—	28	17	33	5
Digalactosyl diglyceride	10	7	—	4	17	56	4
Sulphoquinovosyl diglyceride	33	11	—	4	16	28	3
Phosphatidyl glycerol	57	5	t	t	16	14	t
Photosynthetic							
Monogalactosyl diglyceride	5	2	—	19	3	17	45
Digalactosyl diglyceride	8	3	—	6	3	35	37
Sulphoquinovosyl diglyceride	32	5	—	3	10	25	15
Phosphatidyl glycerol	31	5	16	—	10	25	5

t = Trace quantity.

trienoic acids are commonly found in combination with the galactosyl diglycerides, especially in the monogalactosyl diglyceride. Palmitic acid is mainly found in both the phosphatidyl glycerol and sulpholipid fractions whereas *trans*-3-hexadecenoic acid is found only in the phosphatidyl glycerol. In those tissues where the C_{20} polyunsaturated acids occur, they are particularly associated with the plastidic galactosyl diglycerides (Nichols, 1965a).

While the tendencies we have just described appear to be fairly general for the chloroplasts of the higher plants and algae, they do not always hold for the blue-green algae which do not synthesize *trans*-3-hexadecenoic acid (Nichols *et al.*, 1965a; Nichols and Wood, 1968) nor in some cases polyenoic acids (Holton *et al.*, 1964; Parker *et al.*, 1967).

IV. BIOSYNTHESIS OF THE ACYL LIPIDS

A. GALACTOSYL DIGLYCERIDES

Ferrari and Benson (1961) observed a rapid incorporation of ^{14}C into monogalactosyl diglyceride and a slower entry into digalactosyl diglyceride during the growth of *Chlorella pyrenoidosa* in $^{14}CO_2$ and concluded that the digalactosyl diglyceride was synthesized by galactosylation of the monogalactosyl diglyceride. These authors proposed the following mechanism for biosynthesis of the galactosyl diglycerides:

D-2, 3-diglyceride $+$ UDP-galactose $\longrightarrow$ monogalactosyl diglyceride

$\Big\downarrow$ UDP-galactose

digalactosyl diglyceride

Neufeld and Hall (1964) have demonstrated that spinach chloroplasts catalyse the transfer of galactose from UDP-galactose to an uncharacterized endogenous acceptor with the apparent formation of mono-, di-, tri- and possibly tetra-galactosyl diglyceride.

Although this and other kinetic data is consistent with the formation of digalactosyl diglyceride by galactosylation of monogalactosyl diglyceride, the fact that these two lipids almost invariably possess somewhat different fatty acid compositions when isolated from the same tissue or chloroplast preparation remains to be explained. If the pathway suggested by Ferrari and Benson (1961) is correct then there must be either a highly specific galactosylation mechanism for monogalactosyl diglyceride of a particular fatty acid composition or some degree of deacylation-reacylation *in vivo* of either, or both, of these lipids. The latter type of mechanism would require lipases capable of removing one or both acyl moieties from the galactosyl diglycerides and the

K

presence of such enzymes in the leaves of runner bean has been demonstrated by Sastry and Kates (1964).

B. SULPHOQUINOVOSYL DIGLYCERIDE

By analogy with the biosynthesis of monogalactosyl diglyceride from UDP-galactose, Benson (1963) has suggested that the sulpholipid might be synthesized by transfer of the sulphoquinovose group from a nucleoside diphosphosulphoquinovose (identified in extracts of *Chlorella*) to a diglyceride:

nucleoside diphosphosulphoquinovose   sulphoquinovosyl diglyceride

$+$ $\longrightarrow$ $+$

diglyceride   nucleoside diphosphate

C. PHOSPHATIDYL GLYCEROL

Haverkate and van Deenen (1964, 1965) demonstrated that the phosphatidyl glycerol fraction from spinach leaves has the same stereo-chemical configuration as the phosphatidyl glycerol from animals and bacteria and suggested that its synthesis might proceed by the same pathway, namely the reaction of CDP-diglyceride with glycerol-3-phosphate:

CDP-diglyceride + glycerol-3-phosphate

$\longrightarrow$ phosphatidyl glycerophosphate + CMP

phosphatidyl glycerophosphate $\longrightarrow$ phosphatidyl glycerol + P_i

An alternative route for the synthesis of this lipid in chloroplasts has been suggested by two groups of workers (Benson *et al.*, 1967; Dawson, 1967) who found that plant tissues containing phospholipase D can catalyse the transfer of a phosphatidyl unit from lecithin to various alcohols such as glycerol, ethanolamine, methanol and ethylene glycol with the formation of the equivalent phospholipid. Thus phosphatidyl glycerol could be synthesized as follows:

phosphatidyl choline + glycerol $\longrightarrow$ phosphatidyl glycerol + choline

As we have already indicated, all four chloroplast lipids show such different fatty acid compositions that it seems inconceivable that they could arise from a common diglyceride "pool", the two galactosyl diglycerides being a probable exception.

V. BIOSYNTHESIS OF FATTY ACIDS

In early work we showed that acetate, octanoate, decanoate and tetra-decanoate were utilized by chopped leaves to form longer chain saturated and unsaturated fatty acids and that the major site of such synthesis was the chloroplast (James, 1963; Stumpf and James, 1963). Although both acetyl-CoA and malonyl-CoA are effectively utilized, it is now known that acetyl-S-ACP and malonyl-S-ACP are the true substrates (Brooks and Stumpf, 1966). Isolated chloroplasts require ATP, Mg^{++}, CO_2, inorganic phosphate and CoA when synthesis is started from acetate.

The effects of light on fatty acid synthesis in chloroplasts are still unclear. Stumpf and James (1963) found that synthesis in isolated chloroplasts was greatly diminished in the dark and inhibited in the light by both NH_3 and PCMU. Such inhibitions could be explained by repression of the photo-synthetic production of $NADPH_2$ and ATP. However Stumpf et al. (1963) also showed a coupling between non-photosynthetic production of $NADPH_2$, O_2 and ATP and lipid synthesis and was unable to replace light by addition of ATP, $NADPH_2$ and O_2 (Stumpf et al., 1967). On the other hand, Mudd and McManus (1962) showed that two fractions could be obtained from dis-rupted spinach chloroplasts one of which was soluble and was able to incor-porate acetyl-CoA into long chain fatty acids in the dark provided that

$$\text{Malonyl-S-CoA} + \text{ACP-SH} \underset{\text{transacylase}}{\overset{\text{malonyl}}{\rightleftharpoons}} \text{malonyl-S-ACP} + \text{CoA-SH}$$

$$\text{Acetyl-S-CoA} + \text{ACP-SH} \underset{\text{transacylase}}{\overset{\text{acetyl}}{\rightleftharpoons}} \text{acetyl-S-ACP} + \text{CoA-SH}$$

$$\text{Acetyl-S-ACP} + \text{malonyl-S-ACP} \underset{\text{synthetase}}{\overset{\beta\text{-ketoacyl-ACP}}{\rightleftharpoons}} \text{acetoacetyl-S-ACP} + CO_2 + \text{ACP-SH}$$

$$\text{Acetoacetyl-S-ACP} + \text{NADPH} + H^+ \underset{\text{reductase}}{\overset{\beta\text{-ketoacyl-ACP}}{\rightleftharpoons}} \text{D(-)-}\beta\text{-hydroxybutyryl-S-ACP} + \text{NADP}^+$$

$$\text{D(-)-}\beta\text{-hydroxybutyryl-S-ACP} \underset{\text{dehydrase}}{\overset{\beta\text{-hydroxyacyl-ACP}}{\rightleftharpoons}} \text{crotonyl-S-ACP} + H_2O$$

$$\text{Crotonyl-S-ACP} + \text{NADPH} \underset{\text{reductase}}{\overset{\text{enoyl-ACP}}{\rightleftharpoons}} \text{butyryl-S-ACP} + \text{NADP}^+ \quad \text{etc., etc.}$$

FIG. 3

$NADPH_2$ and ATP were present. The apparent contradictions in these results have yet to be explained.

Brooks and Stumpf (1966) have shown that synthesis of long chain fatty acids in chloroplasts involves malonyl-S-ACP rather than malonyl-S-CoA and it is probable that the fatty acid synthetase system of chloroplasts is essentially similar to that originally described by Vagelos and co-workers (e.g. Alberts *et al.*, 1963) for bacteria (Fig. 3).

A. MONOENOIC ACIDS

Despite earlier work which in some cases gave apparently contradictory results, it now seems reasonably certain that oleic acid is synthesized in both leaf and algal tissues by direct desaturation of stearic acid, probably in the form of its ACP thiol ester (Harris *et al.*, 1965; Nagai and Bloch, 1965). A similar mechanism has been established for the synthesis of 9-hexadecenoic acid in algae by desaturation of palmitic acid (Harris *et al.*, 1965) but this route has yet to be established in leaves. The *trans*-3-hexadecenoic acid has been shown to be derived by direct dehydrogenation of palmitic acid (Nichols *et al.*, 1965b).

There is as yet no clear evidence that the 7-hexadecenoic and 11-octadecenoic acid of leaves and algae are synthesized by the direct desaturation of palmitic and stearic acids, respectively, and Bloch and his associates (Nagai and Bloch, 1965; Bloch *et al.*, 1967) regard their presence as being indicative of a route involving chain elongation of β, γ-unsaturated C_{10} or C_{12} acids produced by an oxygen-requiring desaturation:

$$C_{10} \xrightarrow{O_2} \Delta^3\text{--}C_{10} \longrightarrow \Delta^5\text{--}C_{12} \dashrightarrow \Delta^7\text{--}C_{14} \longrightarrow \Delta^9\text{--}C_{16} \longrightarrow \Delta^{11}\text{--}C_{18}$$

$$C_{12} \xrightarrow{O_2} \Delta^3\text{--}C_{12} \longrightarrow \Delta^5\text{--}C_{14} \longrightarrow \Delta^7\text{--}C_{16} \longrightarrow \Delta^9\text{--}C_{18}$$

Such steps have yet to be verified experimentally.

B. POLYUNSATURATED ACIDS

The polyunsaturated fatty acids such as linoleic acid and linolenic acid are produced by the stepwise oxygen-requiring dehydrogenation of the corresponding monoenoic acids (James, 1962; Harris and James, 1965), e.g.:

$$\text{Oleic acid} \xrightarrow{O_2} \text{linoleic acid} \xrightarrow{O_2} \text{linolenic acid}$$

This desaturation system is very sensitive to disruption of the tissue and functional cell-free systems have been produced only from *Chlorella vulgaris* and safflower seeds. The system is particle bound, presumably to the plastid. Pathways leading to the formation of the C_{16}, C_{18}, C_{20} and C_{22} tetraenoic acids observed in some chloroplast preparations have not been investigated.

VI. FUNCTION OF LIPIDS IN CHLOROPLASTS

Although the structure and relative stoichimetry of the lipids present in chloroplasts are now fairly well understood, their functions have yet to be clearly defined. That these compounds contribute some essential function in photochemical processes has been recently demonstrated by Shibuya and Maruo (1966) who succeeded in restoring much of the electron transport activity of delipidized chloroplast lipoprotein by recombining aqueous suspensions of the lipid and the protein. These lipids could function as either chemical or structural components of the photochemical apparatus and might serve a dual purpose.

The difficulties experienced in the isolation and study of the different units of the photosynthetic apparatus has meant that any data relevant to lipid function in these systems has usually been of an indirect nature.

A. STRUCTURAL FUNCTION

We shall consider first the possible structural rôle of the chloroplast lamella lipids. These lipids could have two types of structural rôle in the protein-pigment-lipid complex of the chloroplast.

The first possibility is that they might represent specific structural components which could maintain the pigments in correct steric orientation with one another and their associated enzymes. In such a case there would be fairly specific requirements for lipid structure and ionic charge and one might consequently expect similar lipids or groups of lipids to occur in all photosynthetic systems of a given type.

Alternatively, they could provide an organized micellar medium of low dielectric constant in which the pigment-protein complexes could be embedded and in which the electron transport sequences could operate. Such a medium could be provided by a variety of ampiphatic substances and highly specific structures and charge distributions would not be involved. Thus, similar photosynthetic processes could be operated by complexes in which the nature of the lipid components *could* be fairly variable.

As we have already indicated, the evidence available shows that all photosynthetic apparatus which perform the Hill reaction have the same acyl lipid composition, even although the relative stoicheiometry and individual fatty acid composition may show slight variations. Thus, this similarity is either of evolutionary significance or else these lipids are acting as specific structural components. Recently Weier and Benson (1966) and Mühlethaler (1966) have suggested how these compounds and other components of the photo-chemical apparatus could be arranged in the chloroplast lamellae. It is proposed that those lipids which are devoid of charged groups, i.e. the galactosyl diglycerides may participate in hydrophobic interactions with structural protein of the chloroplast while the negatively charged lipids (phosphatidyl glycerol and sulpholipid) may play a prominent part in attaining charge-charge interactions between lipid micelles and proteins (van Deenen and Haverkate, 1966).

Whether or not the lipids may be partially responsible for the ultrastructural geometry of an organelle is not clear. Changes in ultrastructure are usually accompanied by changes only in the relative concentrations of the chloroplast lipids. Thus the conversion of proplastids to chloroplasts is accompanied by the rapid synthesis of phosphatidyl glycerol (Miller, 1963), monogalactosyl diglyceride (Bloch et al., 1967) and sulpholipid (Rosenberg and Pecker, 1964) in addition, of course, to that of chlorophyll. Synthesis of digalactosyl diglyceride is not appreciably accelerated during this process (Bloch et al., 1967). We also know that the major subcellular particles of some yellow petals are derived from chloroplasts, such as the polymembranous particle of narcissus trumpet (Nichols et al., 1967). During this transition the relative proportions of the mono- and di-galactosyl diglycerides change significantly. On the other hand, maturation of the buttercup petal involves the breakdown of the chloroplast lamellae into large globuli (Frey-Wyssling and Kreutzer, 1958) quite unlike the particles of daffodil trumpet and in buttercup tissue the relative proportions of the two galactosyl diglycerides are entirely reversed. It is thus unlikely that the lipids control the ultrastructure of any of these organelles.

B. METABOLIC FUNCTION

We might now consider the possibility that lipids could be chemically involved in the various metabolic processes carried out within the chloroplast.

One suggestion made in the past is that part of the acyl lipids might be involved in the electron transport chain of photosynthesis. This would require a readily oxidizable component such as a highly unsaturated fatty acid and since high levels of polyenoic acids are characteristic of the chloroplasts of higher plants and algae it was frequently speculated that these acids might have such a function (Erwin et al., 1964). However, the observation by Holton and co-workers (1964), and subsequently by others (Nichols and Wood, 1968; Parker et al., 1967), that some blue-green algae contain no polyenoic acids and yet seem to function photosynthetically in a perfectly normal manner would seem to invalidate this proposal.

As an alternative explanation for the wide distribution of polyunsaturated fatty acids it might be pointed out that leaves and, to a lesser extent, algae, must sometimes be able to function at low ambient temperatures and a high proportion of unsaturated fatty acids might ensure that their lipoprotein structures were fully mobile over a wide temperature range.

The observation that in leaves and green algae *trans*-3-hexadecenoic acid is specifically located on phosphatidyl glycerol (Allen *et al.*, 1964; Weenink and Shorland, 1964; Haverkate *et al.*, 1964), metabolically the most active chloroplast lipid, and that it is absent from the corresponding etiolated tissue (Nichols *et al.*, 1965c; Nichols, 1965b), led us to suggest that this acid might have some specific active rôle in photosynthesis. However, we found subsequently that this acid does not occur in the blue-green algae (Nichols *et al.*, 1965a; Nichols and Wood, 1968) so that unless there is some discrete difference between the mechanisms of photosynthesis in green algae and leaves and that in blue-green algae, involvement of this acid cannot be obligatory for photosynthesis.

The chloroplast lipids might also function as required substrates or co-factors for the enzymes synthesizing fatty acids and they could also be involved in the mobilization of fatty acids in an analogous manner to CoA and ACP derivatives. The former class of function seems particularly plausible in the formation of *trans*-3-hexadecenoic acid from palmitic acid. Haverkate and van Deenen (1965) have shown that in spinach leaves this acid is specifically bound to the β-hydroxyl group of the glyceride moiety of phosphatidyl glycerol, which is otherwise most usually occupied by palmitic acid. Thus it is possible that the desaturation occurs either on the molecule or in its immediate environment. Support for this hypothesis has recently been found in our laboratory (Bartels *et al.*, 1967) where it was shown that added free *trans*-3-hexadecenoic acid was very rapidly reduced to palmitic acid by algal and leaf tissue but that before this reduction was complete, some of the *trans*-acid was incorporated into all the other lipid classes. Thus the specific association of the *trans*-3-hexadecenoic acid with the phosphatidyl glycerol fraction of photosynthetic tissue is most convincingly explained by invoking the palmityl phospholipid as the required substrate for the dehydrogenation. Any tendency for the acid to be split from the phosphatidyl glycerol molecule by lipase action would presumably result in a rapid hydrogenation of the *trans*-acid before it could be incorporated into the other lipid classes.

We have also obtained evidence which suggests that, in particular, phosphatidyl glycerol and monogalactosyl diglyceride might be similarly involved in the synthesis and metabolism of other fatty acids in the chloroplast. In studies involving the incorporation of ^{14}C-labelled acetate into the lipids of *Chlorella vulgaris*, we noted that the uptake and turnover of certain fatty acids in these lipids was faster than one would normally expect from that due to *de novo* synthesis of these lipids during cell growth and division (Nichols and James, 1967). Thus it appears that certain fatty acids are continually

TABLE III

Classification of possible lipid function based on metabolic studies.

Lipid	Metabolic function	Structural function
Monogalactosyl diglyceride	(a) Involved in fatty acid biosynthesis of the C_{14}, C_{16} and C_{18} saturated acids, and the C_{16} and C_{18} unsaturated acids. (b) Involved in galactose metabolism.	Major component of chloroplast lamellae.
Digalactosyl diglyceride	Involved in galactose metabolism.	Major component of chloroplast lamellae.
Sulpholipid	Involved in hexose metabolism. Suggested function as a sulphur and carbon reserve material.	Major component of chloroplast lamellae.
Phosphatidyl glycerol	(a) Involved in fatty acid biosynthesis of the C_{14}, C_{16} and C_{18} saturated acids, and the *trans*-3-hexadecenoic acid, as well as the C_{18} mono- and dienoic acids. (b) Involved in phosphate metabolism.	Major component of chloroplast lamellae.
Phosphatidyl choline	(a) Involved in the biosynthesis of the C_{18} unsaturated fatty acids. (b) Involved in phosphate metabolism.	Possibly a minor component of chloroplasts.

fluxing through these lipids suggesting that they might be required "carriers" or substrates in certain fatty acid conversions. On this basis, the lipids would not be merely acceptors of the end-products from a fatty acid synthetase but an integral part of the system.

Ferrari and Benson (1961) have also noted that the fatty acids of monogalactosyl diglyceride and phosphatidyl glycerol were rapidly labelled when *Chlorella pyrenoidosa* was incubated with $^{14}CO_2$. These authors also observed a rapid turnover of label in the sugar moieties of the three plastid glycolipids which, in the case of the digalactosyl diglyceride and the sulpholipid, was considerably faster than that in the fatty acid portion of the molecule. They therefore concluded that these lipids, particularly the galactosyl diglycerides, might be intimately involved in sugar metabolism and transport.

Miyachi and Miyachi (1966) have observed that starving cells of *Chlorella* utilize the carbon and sulphur of the sulpholipid which therefore serves as an emergency reserve for these elements but it is debatable whether this observation is indicative of the main function of the lipid in the healthy cell.

Thus the available evidence is that the acyl lipids of chloroplasts have both a metabolic and structural rôle and these possible functions are summarized in Table III.

REFERENCES

Alberts, A. W., Goldman, P. and Vagelos, P. R. (1963). *J. biol. Chem.* **238**, 557.
Allen, C. F., Good, P., Davis, H. F. and Fowler, S. D. (1964). *Biochem. biophys. Res. Commun.* **15**, 424.
Allen, C. F., Hirayama, O. and Good, P. (1966). *In* "Biochemistry of Chloroplasts". (T. W. Goodwin, ed), Vol. I, p. 165. Academic Press, London and New York.
Bartels, C. T., James, A. T. and Nichols, B. W. (1967). *Eur. J. Biochem.*, **3**, 7
Benson, A. A. (1963). *In* "Advances in Lipid Research". Vol. 1, p. 387.
Benson, A. A. and Maruo, B. (1958). *Biochim. biophys. Acta* **27**, 189.
Benson, A. A., Freer, S. and Yang, S. F. (1967). *J. biol. Chem.* **242**, 477.
Bloch, K., Constantopoulos, G., Kenyon, C. and Nagai, J. (1967). *In* "Biochemistry of Chloroplasts". (T. W. Goodwin, ed.), Vol. II, p. 197. Academic Press, London and New York.
Brooks, J. L. and Stumpf, P. K. (1966). *Archs Biochem. Biophys.* **116**, 108.
Crombie, W. M. (1958). *J. Expl Bot.* **9**, 254.
Dawson, R. M. C. (1967). *Biochem. J.* **102**, 205.
Debuch, H. (1961). *Z. Naturforsch.* **9**, 561.
Erwin, J., Hulanicka, D. and Bloch, K. (1964). *Comp. Biochem. Physiol.* **12**, 191.
Ferrari, R. A. and Benson, A. A. (1961). *Archs Biochem. Biophys.* **93**, 185.
Frey-Wyssling, A. and Kreutzer, E. (1958). *Planta* **51**, 104.
Harris, R. V. and James, A. T. (1965). *Biochim. biophys. Acta* **106**, 456.
Harris, R. V., Harris, P. and James, A. T. (1965). *Biochim. biophys. Acta* **106**, 465.
Harris, R. V., James, A. T. and Harris, P. (1967). *In* "Biochemistry of Chloroplasts". (T. W. Goodwin, ed.), Vol. II, p. 241. Academic Press, London and New York.
Haverkate, F. and van Deenen, L. L. M. (1964). *Biochim. biophys. Acta* **84**, 106.

Haverkate, F. and van Deenen, L. L. M. (1965). *Biochim. biophys. Acta* **106**, 78.
Haverkate, F., de Gier, J. and van Deenen, L. L. M. (1964). *Experientia* **20**, 511.
Holton, R. W., Blecker, H. H. and Onore, M. (1964). *Phytochemistry* **3**, 595.
James, A. T. (1962). *Biochim. biophys. Acta* **57**, 167.
James, A. T. (1963). *Biochim. biophys. Acta* **70**, 20.
James, A. T. and Nichols, B. W. (1966). *Nature, Lond.* **210**, 372.
Kates, M. and Volcani, B. E. (1966). *Biochim. biophys. Acta* **116**, 264.
Klenk, E., Knipprath, W., Eberhagen, D. and Koof, H. D. (1963). *Z. phys. Chem.* **234**, 44.
Miller, J. A., quoted by Benson, A. A. (1963). *In* "Mechanism of Photosynthesis". (H. Tamiya, ed.), p. 340. Pergamon Press, London.
Miyachi, S. and Miyachi, S. (1966). *Pl. Physiol., Lancaster* **41**, 479.
Mudd, J. B. and McManus, T. T. (1962). *J. biol. Chem.* **237**, 2057.
Mühlethaler, K. (1966). *In* "Biochemistry of Chloroplasts". (T. W. Goodwin, ed.), Vol. I, p. 117. Academic Press, London and New York.
Nagai, J. and Bloch, K. (1965). *J. biol. Chem.* **240**, 3702.
Neufeld, E. F. and Hall, E. W., (1964). *Biochem. biophys. Res. Commun.* **14**, 503.
Nichols, B. W. (1963). *Biochim. biophys. Acta* **40**, 417.
Nichols, B. W. (1965a). *Phytochem.* **4**, 769.
Nichols, B. W. (1965b). *Biochim. biophys. Acta* **106**, 274.
Nichols, B. W. and James, A. T. (1967). *Biochem. J.* **104**, 486.
Nichols, B. W. and Wood, B. J. B. (1968). *Lipids.* **3**, 46.
Nichols, B. W., Harris, R. V. and James, A. T. (1965a). *Biochem. biophys. Res. Commun.* **20**, 256.
Nichols, B. W., Harris, P. and James, A. T. (1965b). *Biochem. biophys. Res. Commun.* **21**, 473.
Nichols, B. W., Wood, B. J. B. and James, A. T. (1965c). *Biochem. J.* **95**, 6.
Nichols, B. W., Stubbs, J. M. and James, A. T. (1967). *In* "Biochemistry of Chloroplasts". (T. W. Goodwin, ed.), Vol. II, p. 677. Academic Press, London and New York.
Parker, P. L., van Baalen, C. and Maurer, L. (1967). *Science, N. Y.* **155**, 708.
Radunz, A. (1967). *Phytochem.* **6**, 399.
Rosenberg, A. and Pecker, M. (1964). *Biochemistry* **3**, 254.
Sastry, P. S. and Kates, M. (1964). *Biochemistry* **3**, 1280.
Schlenk, H. and Gellerman, J. L. (1965). *J. Am. Oil Chem. Soc.* **42**, 504.
Shibuya, I. and Maruo, B., quoted by Benson, A. A. (1966). *J. Am. Oil Chem. Soc.* **43**, 265.
Stumpf, P. K. and James, A. T. (1963). *Biochim. biophys. Acta* **70**, 20.
Stumpf, P. K., Bove, J. M. and Goffeau, A. (1963). *Biochim. biophys. Acta* **70**, 260.
Stumpf, P. K., Brooks, J., Galliard, T., Hawke, J. C. and Simoni, R. (1967). *In* "Biochemistry of Chloroplasts". (T. W. Goodwin, ed.), Vol. II, p. 214. Academic Press, London and New York.
van Deenen, L. L. M. and Haverkate, F. (1966). *In* "Biochemistry of Chloroplasts". (T. W. Goodwin, ed.), Vol. I, p. 117. Academic Press, London and New York.
Weenink, R. O. and Shorland, F. B. (1964). *Biochim. biophys. Acta* **84**, 613.
Weier, T. and Benson, A. A. (1966). *In* "Biochemistry of Chloroplasts". (T. W. Goodwin, ed.), Vol. I, p. 49. Academic Press, London and New York.
Wolf, F. T., Coniglio, J. G. and Bridges, R. B. (1966). *In* "Biochemistry of Chloroplasts". (T. W. Goodwin, ed.), Vol. I, p. 187. Academic Press, London and New York.

CHAPTER 10

The Organization of the Endoplasmic Reticulum, the Golgi Bodies and Microtubules during Cell Division and Subsequent Growth

D. H. NORTHCOTE

Department of Biochemistry, The University, Cambridge, England

I. Introduction

The deposition of the material in a cell wall of a plant represents a programmed sequence of synthetic events and a complex organizational system for the transport and incorporation of the material in a definite manner in the complex texture of the wall. After the formation of the cell plate it can develop, for example, into the spiral or reticulate thickened secondary wall of the xylem vessel, the pattern of specialized pores of the sieve plate of the phloem or the highly mucilaginous wall of the outer root cap cells.

The growth of a plant tissue depends on the relative disposition of the cells within the tissue and their individual growth into distinct shapes and types. The arrangement of the cells is determined to a great extent by the plane of division of the cells and any fine structural study of the differentiation mechanisms within the cells is concerned with the spatial organization of the organelles of the cell during mitosis, cytokinesis and the subsequent growth. Fine structural studies of plant cells have been made using ultra thin stained sections and replicas of freeze-etched material.

Most of the work into the fine structure of fixed specimens which I shall discuss here has been published previously with the pictorial evidence for the conclusions that are made so that only references to the relevant papers will be given and the figures will not be duplicated. However, some freeze-etch studies and previously unpublished pictures of thin sections which support and extend the previous investigations will be presented.

II. Mitosis and Cytokinesis

Usually in the plant cell no centrioles are found at the polar regions of the mitotic spindle during the process of cell division. Nevertheless the poles can be defined as the regions in the cytoplasm to which the microfibrils form-ing the birefringent bands of the spindle converge (Bajer and Mole-Bajer, 1963; Harris and Bajer, 1965). The cell plate is usually formed at the centre

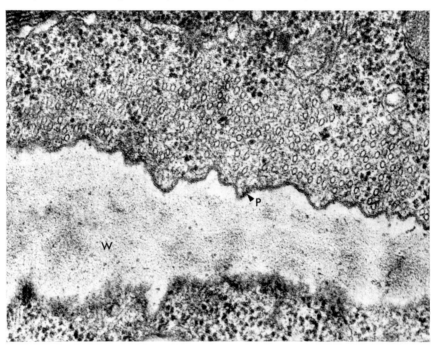

Fig. 1 Longitudinal section of the root tip of Timothy grass. The upper cell is at preprophase and the preprophase band of microtubules can be seen cut in transverse section. × 58,000. W = wall, P = plasmalemma. (Photograph taken by J. Burgess).

of the spindle and thus the initial orientation of the spindle at its formation influences the final plane of division. Furthermore, in a vacuolated cell the position of the nucleus and the cytoplasm in the cell, relative to the vacuole, prior to the division, will also serve to determine the subsequent position of the cell plate.

If a cell is examined just before prophase, a transient band of microtubules

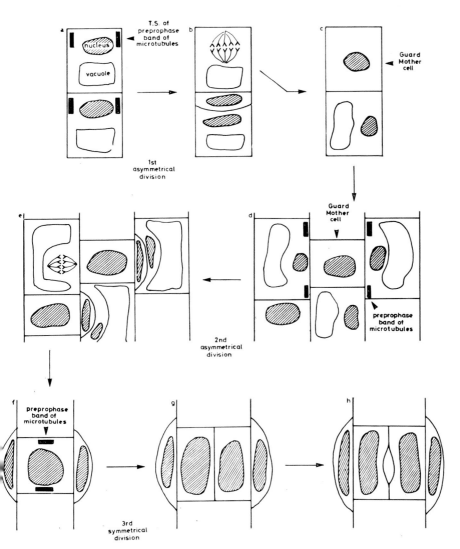

FIG. 2 Diagrammatic representation of the formation of the stomatal complex in young wheat leaves. Epidermal cells (a), which have become polarized by the positioning of the nucleus and vacuole undergo asymmetric division (b). The cell plate joins the mother cell wall at the position indicated by the preprophase band shown in (a). After the first division a small, compact guard mother cell is formed and a larger vacuolated cell (c). During the next preprophase stage the nucleus in each epidermal cell adjacent to the guard mother cell takes up a position at the common wall between it and the guard mother cell (d). These epidermal cells then divide independently. This is the second asymmetric division d——>e; note the position of the preprophase bands of microtubules and the subsequent position of the cell plates. The guard mother cell, which now has two small subsidiary cells on each side of it (f), divides symmetrically f——>g to give two equal guard cells (g). The guard cells grow and the wall between them splits to form the pore (h).

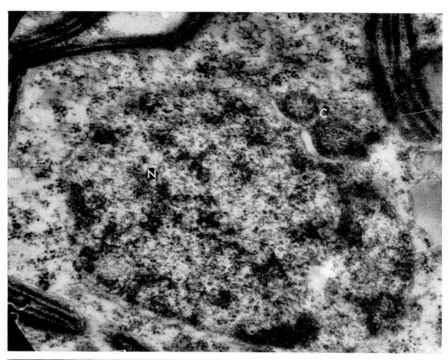

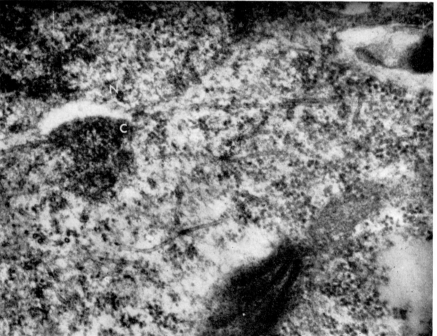

Figs 3 and 4

encircling the nucleus can be found (Pickett-Heaps and Northcote, 1966a, b; Burgess and Northcote, 1967). The band is usually adjacent to the wall of the cell and it contains approximately 200 microtubules arranged in rows 5 or 6 deep. It extends about $0·25\mu$ in from the plasmalemma and about $2·0\mu$ along the wall (Fig. 1). In cambial cells this band lies along the mother cell wall at the position at which the cell plate will meet it at cytokinesis. In the development of the stomatal complex of the leaves of wheat, the relation of this band to the plane of division is seen in an even more striking manner (Pickett-Heaps and Northcote, 1966b). During the formation of the stomata, the epidermal cells which give rise to the guard mother cell and the subsidiary cells are polarized so that the nuclei and surrounding cytoplasm of the cells come to take up definite positions within the cells. The preprophase band is located at the positions where the cell plates will divide the mother cells at the asymmetric divisions (Fig. 2). The function of the preprophase band of microtubules appears to be that of orienting and aligning the nucleus within the cell prior to division so that the direction of the mitotic spindle is determined.

If cells are examined at various times during the onset of prophase and the development of the mitotic spindle, that is at times when numerous microtubules are being formed either along the preprophase band or within the spindle, then smooth elements of the endoplasmic reticulum are found in close association with the microtubules at both locations and the endoplasmic reticulum could thus be important for the function or formation of these structures (Pickett-Heaps and Northcote, 1966a; Burgess and Northcote, 1967).

In some plant cells where mitosis does not result in cell division and where no cell plate is formed, centrioles are found. These appear at the nuclear membrane at the beginning of prophase. Such a condition is seen in the coenobium of *Hydrodictyon africanum*. In this plant, microtubules can be seen which at first radiate from the two centrioles which are disposed at right angles to one another. Some of the microtubules extend into the cytoplasm around the nucleus and some appear very close to the nuclear membrane (Figs 3, 4). At metaphase microtubules penetrate the nucleoplasm and form the mitotic spindle (Figs 5, 6); in the spindle some are attached to the chromatids. In the area where the tubules are attached to the chromatids, a distinct kinetochore plate is found which is not normally seen in the spindle of higher plants (Fig. 5). Kinetochores and centrioles are also found in animal cells and it is probably significant that these mitotic structures are found in cells

---

Figs 3 and 4 (facing page) Nuclei (N) in the coenobium of *Hydrodictyon africanum* at prophase. The centrioles (C) and microtubules radiating from them can be clearly seen. The nuclear membrane at the position where the centrioles appear is considerably modified (Fig. 4). Figure 3 $\times$ 33,000, Fig. 4 $\times$ 62,000.

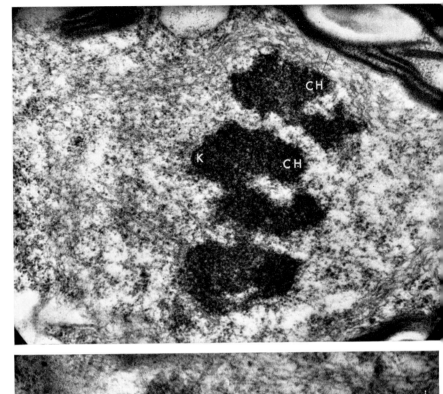

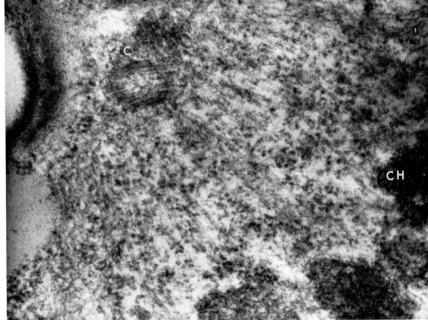

Figs 5 and 6

where no definite arrangement of the spindle is needed to fix the position of the new cells relative to their neighbours by the formation of a rigid cell wall at cytokinesis.

The formation of the cell plate at cytokinesis results from a fusion of material carried in vesicles up to the site of its construction (Bajer, 1965). The vesicles are probably derived from the Golgi bodies which enter the region of the mitotic spindle at telophase (Whaley et al., 1960; Whaley and Mollenhauer, 1963; Frey-Wyssling et al., 1964; Whaley et al., 1966). The small vesicles pass, sometimes in rows, between the radiating microtubules up to the cell plate area (Esau and Gill, 1965; Bajer and Allen, 1966; Pickett-Heaps and Northcote, 1966a, b). The plate extends outwards towards the mother cell. At its edge there is a concentration of vesicles and microtubules; the latter persist in this region and radiate back towards the vanished poles of the spindle on each side of the plate.

III. XYLEM VESSELS

The secondary thickening of the cell wall is accompanied by a changing pattern in the distribution of the organelles (Wooding and Northcote, 1964; Esau et al., 1966a; Pickett-Heaps and Northcote, 1966c), a change in the type of polysaccharide laid down in the matrix material and a deposition of lignin which begins at this time in the middle lamella and primary wall over the top of the thickenings (Thornber and Northcote, 1961a, b; 1962; Northcote, 1963a, b). Microtubules, which are normally scattered and randomly distributed along the wall of the young cells during primary growth (Ledbetter and Porter, 1963; Srivastava, 1966), become grouped over the top of the secondary thickenings (Wooding and Northcote, 1964; Esau et al., 1966b; Pickett-Heaps and Northcote, 1966c). In the fast developing cells of the vascular tissue of wheat coleoptiles the endoplasmic reticulum is arranged in a definite way so that profiles of sheets of the reticulum can be seen at right angles to the wall between each thickening when longitudinal sections are examined (Pickett-Heaps and Northcote, 1966c). Lignin is deposited in the wall at a very early stage and can be detected in the walls of cells about three rows in from the active cambium (Wooding and Northcote, 1964). During this development the Golgi bodies also produce material in vesicles which is incorporated into the thickening wall by reverse pinocytosis. The microtubules lying along the top of the thickening have the same orientation as the direction of the microfibrils in the wall. This could mean that they are concerned with

FIGS 5 and 6 (facing page) Nuclei in the coenobium of *Hydrodictyon africanum* at metaphase. The microtubules are present in the nucleoplasm and are attached to the chromatids (CH). A kinetochore plate (K) can be seen in Fig. 5. The polar regions of the spindle are established by the position of the centrioles (C) (Fig. 6). Figure 5 × 30,000, Fig. 6 × 65,000.

L

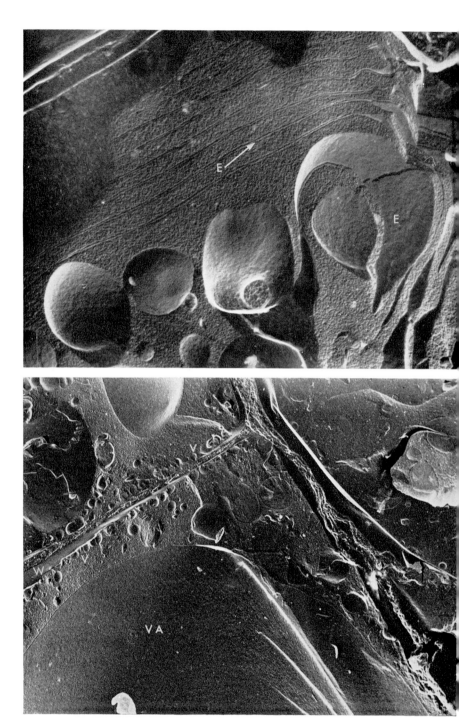

Figs 7 and 8

the laying down of the α-cellulose microfibrils of the wall or that they direct matrix material into the wall in a definite direction which imposes a definite orientation on the developing microfibrils which are being formed within it.

IV. PHLOEM SIEVE TUBES AND COMPANION CELLS

The development of the walls of the phloem tissue are characterized by the formation of the sieve plate pores and the pores between the companion cells and sieve tubes. In angiosperms both types of pore are found to be closely associated with the pattern of distribution of the endoplasmic reticulum and with the deposition of the polysaccharide, callose (Esau *et al.*, 1962; Northcote and Wooding, 1966).

The sieve plate is marked out on the end walls of the sieve tube at a very early stage by elements of the endoplasmic reticulum which run as profiles parallel to the plasmalemma on each side of the end wall at the positions where the pores will be formed. The endoplasmic reticulum lies close to the plasmalemma and where the two membranes are adjacent the endoplasmic reticulum membrane carries no ribosomes although these are found on the corresponding opposite membrane of the profile (Northcote and Wooding, 1966; Pickett-Heaps and Northcote, 1966c). These profiles of the endoplasmic reticulum lie one on each side of a plasmadesma of the wall and the plasmadesma is lined by the plasmalemma and carries a thin strand of endoplasmic reticulum in its lumen. As the wall develops the areas under the endoplasmic reticulum grow by the deposition of callose while the other regions of the wall thicken by the incorporation of the normal wall polysaccharides. The pads of callose are formed as two cones joined at their apexes, which meet at the centre of the wall, and their bases are located underneath the endoplasmic reticulum profiles at the surfaces of the wall. The bases initially bulge out from the general surface of the wall but the callose is then eroded from the wall at the centre where the endoplasmic reticulum in the middle of the plasmadesma proliferates and the pore consequently widens at this point. Presumably the endoplasmic reticulum supplies enzymes for the breakdown of the callose and/or assists with the transport of material away from the centre of the wall to make the wide pore of the sieve plate. By a continuation of this process the pore widens from the centre outwards

---

FIG. 7 (facing page) Freeze-etch preparation of the root tip of a pea, longitudinal section. The sheets of endoplasmic reticulum (E) surrounding various cell organelles can be seen. × 17,500. Reversed print.

FIG. 8 (facing page) Vesicles (V) at the surface of a growing cell wall (W) in a cell of the root tip of pea. Freeze-etch preparation, longitudinal section. × 12,500. Reversed print. VA, vacuole.

towards both surfaces of the wall (Northcote and Wooding, 1966; Tamulevich and Evert, 1966) and at all times it is lined with callose. Since callose is deposited at sites in the plant where wounding occurs and since during the preparation of the specimens for microscopical examination the tension in the mature phloem sieve tubes is released when the stem or root is cut and put in the fixative, it is possible that some of the callose seen at the sieve plate pore could be formed as a result of the specimen preparation technique. This is indicated by autoradiographic studies when tritiated glucose is fed to a cut stem because radioactive material is then incorporated into the callose around the sieve pores but is not found at any other position on the wall of mature sieve tubes (Northcote and Wooding, 1966; Wooding, 1966).

The pores between the sieve tubes and companion cells are also developed in a characteristic manner (Wooding and Northcote, 1965a; Wooding, 1966). Once again a close association with the endoplasmic reticulum is found on both sides of the pore and callose is deposited on the sieve tube side. At the centre of the pore there is a proliferation of the lumen of the pore to the companion cell so that the mature pore is connected to the sieve tube by a single relatively large channel which at the centre fans out into 4 or 5 smaller pores which connect with the companion cell over a relatively large area of the wall. Covering this area of the wall on the companion cell side is a profile of endoplasmic reticulum and this element of the endoplasmic reticulum is connected with the large nucleus of the cell and with sheets of the reticulum system which encircle the plastids (Wooding and Northcote, 1965a, b). This pattern of the endoplasmic system is obviously of importance to the complex transport of material between the sieve tubes and the rest of the tissues of the plant via the companion cells. In many types of plant cells a close sheathing of various organelles by the endoplasmic reticulum can sometimes be seen (Fig. 7) but, unlike that found around the plastids in the companion cells, it is usually transitory (Wooding and Northcote, 1965b).

V. Outer Root Cap Cells

In the outer root cap cells of wheat, maize and onion fine structural studies have shown that a function of the Golgi apparatus is to transport material, in the form of vesicles, across the plasmalemma by reverse pinocytosis into the cell wall (Whaley et al., 1960; Mollenhauer et al., 1961; Branton and Moor, 1964). This process has been investigated by radioautographic studies of electron microscope sections of roots which have been fed D-[U-³H]-glucose before they are fixed and embedded (Northcote and Pickett-Heaps, 1965). The glucose metabolism of these cells is directed towards the production of high molecular weight material which is found within 5 min exposure of the cells to the radioactivity within the Golgi bodies. In the outer cap cells very little of the supplied radioactive glucose is incorporated into the starch grains which are present. If the roots before fixation are first given a pulse of radioactive glucose by incubation in a solution of tritiated glucose for 15 min and then if this is "chased" by subsequent incubation in a solution of non-radioactive glucose for varying lengths of time (10, 30 and 60 min), the radioactive high molecular weight material first found in the Golgi bodies is seen to be transferred to the Golgi vesicles and then across the plasmalemma and into the wall. After about 60 min "chase", all the original material synthesized within the cell has been transported to the outside.

VI. POLYSACCHARIDE SYNTHESIS

Since the material which is formed within the Golgi bodies and which is transported is radioactive in the experiments described above, it can be extracted from the cell and identified. It is found to be polysaccharide and upon hydrolysis it gives galacturonic acid, galactose and arabinose (Northcote and Pickett-Heaps, 1965; Jones and Morré, 1967). Thus it resembles the pectic substances of the cell wall polysaccharides.

In this system there is an analogy for a general hypothesis for the formation of some of the matrix polysaccharides of the wall. The Golgi body probably transports material into the cell plate (middle lamella), the cambial cell wall (primary wall) and the secondary thickening of the xylem and phloem (secondary wall) (Sievers, 1963; 1965a, b; Wooding and Northcote, 1964; Esau et al., 1966a; Mollenhauer and Morré, 1966; Northcote and Wooding, 1966; Pickett-Heaps, 1966; Pickett-Heaps and Northcote, 1966c; Schnepf and Koch, 1966; Srivastava and O'Brien, 1966) (Fig. 8). Different polysaccharides are formed in the matrix of the wall at these different stages of its development (Northcote, 1963a). Hence, one of the metabolic processes which is changed during differentiation is the synthesis of polysaccharides which are transported by the Golgi apparatus. Since polysaccharide formed from supplied radioactive glucose to the root cap cells of wheat can be found within 5 min in the Golgi apparatus, it is reasonable to think that some of these syntheses occur in the Golgi body itself. Hassid and his colleagues (Neufeld and Hassid, 1963; Barber, 1965; Neufeld and Ginsburg, 1966) have made detailed studies of enzyme systems extracted from plant cells which are capable of bringing about the synthesis of polysaccharides with the appropriate nucleotide phosphate-sugar precursor. These enzyme systems are usually bound to membranes or cell particles when isolated from the cell and therefore they might well be contained within a vesicular system such as the Golgi body in situ (Northcote, 1964).

The changes in polysaccharide synthesis during differentiation are represented in Fig. 9. The epimerase activities, which are also isolated bound to

cell particles, control the interconversion of the monosaccharide precursors
of the different polysaccharides (Feingold *et al.*, 1960; Kessler *et al.*, 1961;
Barber, 1965) and it is possible that the varying sequence of polysaccharides
formed during the growth cycle of the plant cell could be brought about by a
control of the epimerase activity of the cell (Zetsche, 1966). This could be
achieved either by the control of the production of the individual enzymes
or by the formation of inhibitors and activators.

Chemical and metabolic studies of the pectic substances of higher plants
have shown that these substances continually change in type during the initial

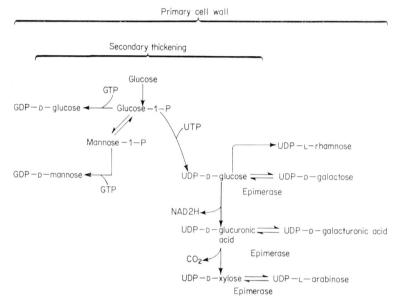

FIG. 9 Some sugar interconversions in plants which give rise to the possible precursors of the polysaccharides found in the cell wall. Polysaccharides composed of
the glycosyl radicals of the galactose series of monomers, shown on the right of the
diagram, are found mainly in the primary cell wall. (UTP, uridine triphosphate;
UDP, uridine diphosphate; GTP, guanosine triphosphate; GDP, guanosine
diphosphate; NAD, nicotinamide adenine dinucleotide).

growth phase of the plant cell (Barrett and Northcote, 1966; Stoddart *et al.*,
1967). Part of this change occurs between the arabinan-galactan fraction and
the weakly acidic pectinic acid fraction and involves a transfer of neutral
sugar residues from the arabinan-galactan to the pectinic acid material
(Stoddart and Northcote, 1967). The changes and transfer of sugar residues
from one fraction to another appears to involve material which has already
been deposited within the structure of the wall. These changes could account
for the differing physical nature of the wall made apparent by differences in

its plasticity and elasticity during its growth and which are effected by indolyl acetic acid. Throughout the growth of the cell wall the polysaccharides deposited in the wall become progressively more neutral and the acidic pectinic acids laid down during the initial phase of growth become more neutral by the transfer on to them of neutral residues. This transfer of sugars from one

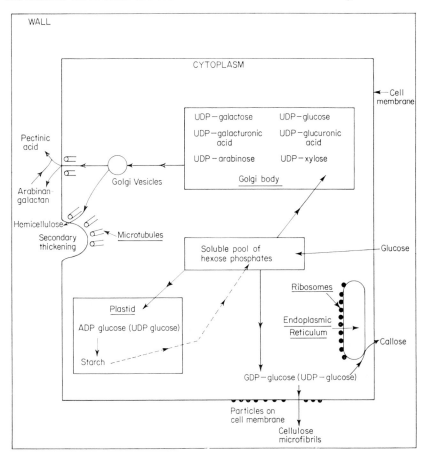

FIG. 10 Diagram to represent possible sites of synthesis and transport of various polysaccharides of a growing plant cell.

polysaccharide to another can take place by transglycosylation and trans-glycosylases of this type could be another point in the metabolism at which the control of the differentiation of the cell could be applied.

A scheme for the possible sites of polysaccharide synthesis, transport and deposition is shown in Fig. 10.

The wall is composed of two phases, an organized, α-cellulose microfibrillar structure embedded in a continuous matrix. During differentiation there are distinct changes in the orientation and sites of deposition of the α-cellulose microfibrils but no apparent change in its chemical composition although there is a definite change in the chemical composition of the matrix material (Northcote, 1958; 1963b). During secondary thickening some of the substances making up the matrix are organized so that they are transported from the cytoplasm and deposited into definite regions of the wall. The corresponding organization of the microtubules around the developing wall during primary and secondary growth suggests that these tubules might be concerned with directing this material from the Golgi bodies into the wall.

The way in which the microfibrils of α-cellulose are formed into the complex interwoven layers of oriented fibres is much more difficult to envisage. Recently freeze-etch studies, which reveal the membrane surfaces of cells and organelles, have directed attention to the presence of fine particles approximately 80Å in diameter which are found on the outer surface of the plasmalemma. Staehelin (1966), in a study of the developing wall of *Chlorella*, has shown that these particles can migrate from the plasmalemma surface and accumulate in the middle zone of the wall where microfibrils seem to be formed from them. It is therefore assumed that the secreted plasmalemma particles are enzyme complexes capable of synthesizing cellulose microfibrils. Similar particles can be found on the surface of the plasmalemma of higher plants and some indication of microfibrils growing from them can be seen (Figs 11–16).

Although these particles could account for the synthetic system for α-cellulose microfibrillar formation, the control of their definite orientation within the wall texture still has to be considered. This might be brought about by the incorporation around them in the growing wall of the material of the continuous matrix which is directed into the wall in a definite direction by the microtubules of the cytoplasm.

VII. CONTROL OF DIFFERENTIATION

Within the intact plant there is an ordered sequence of cell division and growth which builds the individual tissues of the plant. This sequence of

FIGS 11–16 Surfaces of plasmalemma (P) and cell wall (W) revealed by freeze-etch technique applied to the cells of the root tip of pea. Reversed prints.
FIGS 11 and 12 Plasmalemma surfaces and pit fields. Figure 11 × 32,000, Fig. 12 × 49,000.
FIGS 13–16 Relationship of particles seen at the surface of the plasmalemma to the microfibrils (M) in the cell wall. Figure 15 also shows vesicles (V) closely applied or breaking through the cell surface into the wall. Figure 13 × 47,000; Fig. 14 × 42,000; Fig. 15 × 34,000; Fig. 16 × 50,000.

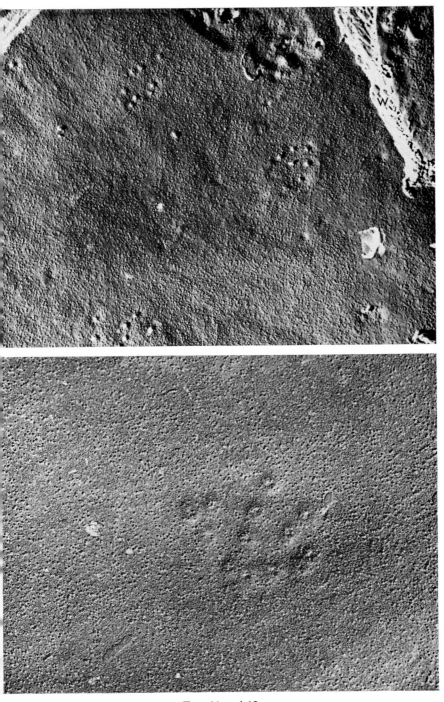

Figs 11 and 12

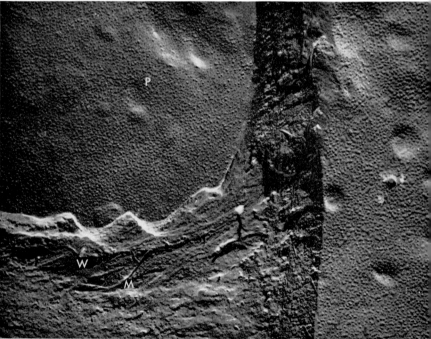

Figs 13 and 14

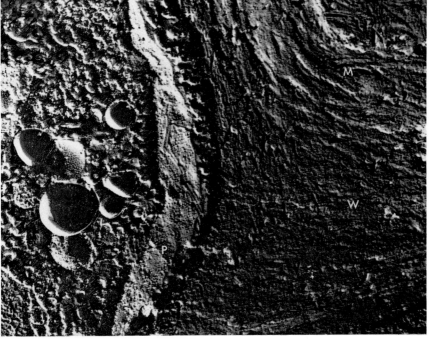

FIGS 15 and 16

events depends on the ordered use of information available in the DNA of the nuclei of the cells. Experimentally, differentiation can be induced in an undifferentiated plant tissue, such as tissue culture callus, by the application of gradients of concentration of growth factors such as auxin, kinetin and sucrose (Wetmore and Rier, 1963; Wetmore *et al.*, 1964; Jeffs and Northcote, 1966; 1967) and these factors could therefore act as part of the control mechanism of the synthetic processes which are switched on and off during the differentiation of the cell. It has been possible to induce xylem vessel formation in an undifferentiated bean tissue callus. The induced tissue is very similar in its chemical nature and microscopical appearance to the vessels of the intact plant (Jeffs and Northcote, 1966). The formation of callose in sieve plates of phloem-like tissue can also be experimentally induced in tissue cultures by using gradients of indolyl acetic acid and sucrose (Jeffs and Northcote, 1967). These experiments present a model system whereby the organized growth of a plant can be explained in terms of the nutritional supply of growth factors and other materials to each cell of the plant tissue. The supply of these nutrients to any cell depends on the metabolic activity of other cells and the transport of materials to it by the environmental cells. This nutritional supply brings about the differentiation of the cell which is itself part of the environment of other cells and influences their growth and development. Thus there is a biostatic interrelationship between the cell pattern of the tissue and the development of the individual cells which go to make up this pattern.

ACKNOWLEDGEMENT

The work on the freeze-etch preparations reported in this paper was carried out in collaboration with Mrs. D. Lewis.

REFERENCES

Bajer, A. (1965). *Expl Cell Res.* **37**, 376.
Bajer, A. and Mole-Bajer, J. (1963). *In* "Cinematography in Cell Biology". (G. G. Rose, ed.), p. 357. Academic Press, London and New York.
Bajer, A. and Allen, R. D. (1966). *J. Cell Sci.* **1**, 455.
Barber, G. A. (1965). *In* "Biosynthetic Pathways in Higher Plants". (J. B. Pridham and T. Swain, eds), p. 117. Academic Press, London and New York.
Barrett, A. J. and Northcote, D. H. (1966). *Biochem. J.* **94**, 617.
Branton, D. and Moor, H. (1964). *J. Ultrastruct. Res.* **11**, 401.
Burgess, J. and Northcote, D. H. (1967). *Planta* **75**, 319.
Esau, K. and Gill, R. H. (1965). *Planta* **67**, 168.
Esau, K., Cheadle, V. I. and Risley, E. B. (1962). *Bot. Gaz.* **123**, 233.
Esau, K., Cheadle, V. I. and Gill, R. H. (1966a). *Am. J. Bot.* **53**, 756.
Esau, K., Cheadle, V. I. and Gill, R. H. (1966b). *Am. J. Bot.* **53**, 765.
Feingold, D. S., Neufeld, E. F. and Hassid, W. Z. (1960). *J. biol. Chem.* **235**, 910.

Frey-Wyssling, A., Lopez-Saez, J. F. and Mühlethaler, K. (1964). *J. Ultrastruct. Res.* **10**, 422.

Harris, P. and Bajer, A. (1965). *Chromosoma* **16**, 624.

Jeffs, R. A. and Northcote, D. H. (1966). *Biochem. J.* **101**, 146.

Jeffs, R. A. and Northcote, D. H. (1967). *J. Cell Sci.* **2**, 77.

Jones, D. D. and Morré, D. J. (1967). *Z. Pflanzenphys.* **56**, 166.

Kessler, G., Neufeld, E. F., Feingold, D. S. and Hassid, W. Z. (1961). *J. biol. Chem.* **236**, 308.

Ledbetter, M. C. and Porter, K. R. (1963). *J. Cell Biol.* **19**, 239.

Mollenhauer, H. H. and Morré, D. J. (1966). *A. Rev. Pl. Physiol.* **17**, 27.

Mollenhauer, H. H., Whaley, W. G. and Leech, J. H. (1961). *J. Ultrastruct. Res.* **5**, 193.

Neufeld, E. F. and Hassid, W. Z. (1963). *Adv. Carbohydrate Chem.* **18**, 309.

Neufeld, E. F. and Ginsburg, V. (1966). In "Methods in Enzymology," (Colowick, S. P. and N. O. Kaplan, eds) Vol. 8, Academic Press, New York.

Northcote, D. H. (1958). *Biol. Rev.* **33**, 53.

Northcote, D. H. (1963a). *Symp. Soc. exp. Biol.* **17**, 158.

Northcote, D. H. (1963b). *Int. rev. Cytol.* **11**, 223.

Northcote, D. H. (1964). *A. Rev. Biochem.* **33**, 51.

Northcote, D. H. and Pickett-Heaps, J. D. (1965). *Biochem. J.* **98**, 159.

Northcote, D. H. and Wooding, F. B. P. (1966). *Proc. R. Soc.* **163B**, 524.

Pickett-Heaps, J. D. (1966). *Planta* **71**, 1.

Pickett-Heaps, J. D. and Northcote, D. H. (1966a). *J. Cell Sci.* **1**, 109.

Pickett-Heaps, J. D. and Northcote, D. H. (1966b). *J. Cell. Sci.* **1**, 121.

Pickett-Heaps, J. D. and Northcote, D. H. (1966c). *J. exp. Bot.* **17**, 20.

Schnepf, E. and Koch, W. (1966). *Z. Pflanzenphys.* **55**, 97.

Sievers, A. (1963). *Protoplasma* **56**, 188.

Sievers, A. (1965a). *Funkt. morph. Organization Zelle.* **2**, 89.

Sievers, A. (1965b). *Z. Pflanzenphys.* **53**, 193.

Staehelin, T. (1966). *Z. Zellforsch. mikrosk. Anal.* **74**, 325.

Stoddart, R. W. and Northcote, D. H. (1967). *Biochem. J.* **105**, 45.

Stoddart, R. W., Barrett, A. J. and Northcote, D. H. (1967). *Biochem. J.* **102**, 194.

Srivastava, L. M. (1966). *J. Cell Biol.* **31**, 79.

Srivastava, L. M. and O'Brien, T. O. (1966). *Protoplasma* **61**, 257.

Tamulevich, S. R. and Evert, R. F. (1966). *Planta* **69**, 319.

Thornber, J. P. and Northcote, D. H. (1961a). *Biochem. J.* **81**, 449.

Thornber, J. P. and Northcote, D. H. (1961b). *Biochem. J.* **81**, 445.

Thornber, J. P. and Northcote, D. H. (1962). *Biochem. J.* **82**, 340.

Wetmore, R. H. and Rier, J. P. (1963). *Am. J. Bot.* **50**, 418.

Wetmore, R. H., De Maggio, A. E. and Rier, J. P. (1964). *Phytomorphology* **14**, 203.

Whaley, W. G. and Mollenhauer, H. H. (1963). *J. Cell Biol.* **17**, 216.

Whaley, W. G., Mollenhauer, H. H. and Leech, J. H. (1960). *Am. J. Bot.* **47**, 401.

Whaley, W. G., Dauwalder, M. and Kephart, J. E. (1966). *J. Ultrastruct. Res.* **15**, 169.

Wooding, F. B. P. (1966). *Planta* **69**, 230.

Wooding, F. B. P. and Northcote, D. H. (1964). *J. Cell Biol.* **23**, 327.

Wooding, F. B. P. and Northcote, D. H. (1965a). *J. Cell Biol.* **24**, 117.

Wooding, F. B. P. and Northcote, D. H. (1965b). *Am. J. Bot.* **52**, 526.

Zetsche, K. (1966). *Biochim. biophys. Acta* **124**, 332.

CHAPTER 11

Protein Synthesis in Cell Organelles

E. C. COCKING

Department of Botany
University of Nottingham, Nottinghamshire, England

I. INTRODUCTION

In any discussion of protein synthesis in plants there is nearly always present the desire to concentrate attention on the genetic code and to assess to what extent the mechanism of protein synthesis in plants parallels that in bacterial and animal cells. Often the special structural and organizational problems posed by plant cells are largely ignored and an experimental approach modelled on that of the bacterial system is adopted. Certain other difficulties were encountered in the earlier studies on the synthesis of protein in cell-free systems from plants. The work of Webster (1959) and Raacke (1959) in which pea ribosomes were claimed to synthesize protein *in vitro* in milligramme quantities was found to be non-reproducible (Lett and Takahashi, 1962) and only recently has it become generally realized that meaningful studies using plant cell organelles for *in vitro* investigations need to be carried out under aseptic conditions and that this is also probably the case when tissue slices are used in protein synthesis studies (Bamji and Jagendorf, 1966; Hall and Cocking, 1966b). For studies on the photosynthetic activity of isolated pea chloroplasts it is clear from the recent comments of Walker (1967) that pride of place would go to spinach (*Spinacea oleracea* L.). Not only does this species have a soft leaf and cell sap near to neutrality but it is readily available in local markets, at least throughout North America. From the point of view of bacterial contamination this ready availability is a major hazard if these chloroplasts are to be used for studies on *in vitro* protein synthesis.

Recently, several excellent, comprehensive reviews of protein synthesis in plants and in various plant organelles have been published. Steward and Durzan (1965) have discoursed at great length on proteins and protein metabolism while various aspects of protein synthesis, particularly of protein synthesis by chloroplasts *in vitro* together with the ultrastructural aspects of these organelles, have been described (Goodwin, 1966; 1967). Kirk and Tilney-Bassett (1967) have fully documented the now extensive literature on protein synthesis by plastids in general. Often in reviewing various aspects of protein synthesis in plant cell organelles insufficient attention is given to the experimental basis from which the results and conclusions are obtained. Results are frequently expressed in a variety of different forms which makes comparison between one organelle and another difficult and sometimes impossible. It is also becoming clear that not only is there a very close connection between photosynthesis and protein synthesis but that plant cells may contain two protein synthesizing systems. One, the cytoplasmic ribosome system containing 80 S-type ribosomes which is largely unaffected by inhibitors of bacterial protein synthesis and the other, the chloroplast ribosome and yeast mitochondrial ribosome systems containing 70 S-type ribosomes similar to those found in bacteria (Clark-Walker and Linnane, 1966).

II. Incorporating Systems

Chemical methods for the detection of newly formed protein are precluded since relatively gross amounts of protein fractions are required for activity in comparison with the small amount of amino acid which is fixed into newly formed protein. Mans (1967) has calculated that in an average incorporation experiment using maize ribosomes after incubation at 37° for 30 min less than 2µg of new protein is synthesized from the added amino acids and that this extra 2µg of new protein is associated with each milligramme of ribosomal protein in the incubation mixture; he stressed that such a 0·2% change is beyond the sensitivity of the colorimetric protein determination of Lowry *et al.* (1951). A characteristic feature of the *in vitro* systems using various plant organelles is that the rate of incorporation rapidly decreases after about 30 min incubation so that prolonged incubation does not result in a progressive increase in the amount of protein formed. Indeed the opposite is sometimes the case. Both of the difficulties arising from these two considerations have been largely circumvented by the availability of ^{14}C-labelled amino acids of high specific activity allowing use to be made of the extreme sensitivity of radioactive isotope detection devices. The autotrophic nature of plants means that other simpler sources of carbon must be considered in relation to protein synthesis and also more complex forms such as sugars because of the possible more ready utilization of substrates other than amino acids for protein synthesis in plants (Steward and Bidwell, 1966). For animal and bacterial cell-free systems it is now appreciated that results of amino acid incorporation into ribosomal protein are better expressed as $\mu\mu$moles of the ^{14}C-labelled amino acid incorporated/mg of protein (or mg of ribosomal RNA/min) and not as cts/mg of protein/min. However, the use of mixtures of labelled amino acids, of labelled sugars and of labelled carbon dioxide in protein synthesis studies in plants has resulted in real difficulty in the presentation of the results in a form which allows ready comparison of the protein synthesis using these different substrates both between themselves and with the incorporation activities in bacterial and animal cells. Davies and Cocking (1967a) have given particular attention to the form in which results of both *in vivo* and *in vitro* incorporation are expressed and have presented their data as $\mu\mu$g of carbon incorporated/mg of protein/min, thereby enabling a ready comparison to be made between the incorporation of amino acid mixtures, pyruvate, glucose and carbon dioxide into the protein of illuminated plastids. It is of importance when comparing, say, the activity of ribosomes isolated from chloroplasts with the activity of the chloroplasts themselves to express the results, if possible, on a mg/ribosomal RNA basis. Eisenstadt (1967) is quite clear in this respect in his presentation of his studies of leucine incorporation into various organelles of *Euglena gracilis*. He showed that ribosomes isolated from chloroplasts exhibited an amino acid incorporating activity appreciably lower than that of isolated chloroplasts or cytoplasmic ribosomes but that the chloroplasts themselves and the cytoplasmic ribosomes had similar specific incorporation activities. All results were expressed in terms of RNA content since, as Eisenstadt points out, there is an excessively large protein to RNA ratio in the chloroplasts and most of the RNA which is associated with the chloroplasts sediments with the ribosomes. In contrast, Sissakian *et al.* (1965) in their studies of amino acid incorporation into the protein of pea seedling chloroplasts expressed their results as cts/min/mg of protein obtaining an incorporation by chloroplasts of 39 (^{14}C glycine supplied) and by ribosomes of 9554 (^{14}C glycine supplied). This led Kirk and Tilney-Bassett (1967) to conclude that according to Sissakian *et al.* (1965) the ribosomes isolated from pea chloroplasts were very much more active than the chloroplasts in incorporating ^{14}C-labelled glycine into protein. The importance of expressing results of incorporation experiments on a sound comparative basis is also evident when comparing the activity of plant cell organelles with the bacterial ribosome system. Hall and Cocking (1966b) have pointed out that, on the basis of protein content, the *E. coli* system appears to possess an activity an order higher than that obtained using plant organelles but that this can be explained by the fact that organelles, such as chloroplasts and mitochondria, contain much protein not concerned directly with protein synthesis and hence the specific activity appears to be low.

Following incubation of reaction mixtures of cell-free systems, it is customary to precipitate both unlabelled and any labelled protein with trichloroacetic acid. The precipitated material is then usually subjected to a fairly extensive procedure which also removes lipid-soluble substances; it is a method based on that of Siekevitz (1952) and routinely used in studies on bacterial and animal ribosome systems. Parisi and Ciferri (1966), in their study of amino acid incorporation by the ribosomal system of castor bean embryos, deduced that the incorporation of L-[^{14}C] lysine was probably the result of the binding of the amino acid to a growing peptide chain rather than some other phenomena such as an exchange of amino acids in the terminal positions of protein. This conclusion was based on the fact that addition of an excess of unlabelled lysine did not decrease the amount of labelled amino acid rendered trichloroacetic acid insoluble at the time of addition of the unlabelled lysine (Table I; cf. also Goffeau and Brachet, 1965, p. 308).

TABLE I

The effect of an excess of unlabelled amino acid, added at
various time intervals, on the incorporation of
L–[^{14}C] lysine by castor bean ribosomes.

Time of addition (min)	[^{14}C] lysine incorporation*	
	Addition of trichloroacetic acid	Addition of an excess of L-[^{12}C] lysine
0	2·60	—
5	11·70	16·61
10	16·98	18·55
15	19·07	22·07
20	19·68	20·59
30	21·94	24·03
40	23·79	—

* Values are $\mu\mu$-moles of L-[^{14}C] lysine (specific activity 180μC/μmole) per mg of ribosomes. Incubations were for 30 min at 37°.
(Modified from Parisi and Ciferri, 1966).

They also showed that the incorporation of L-[^{14}C] lysine at 0° for 30 min was identical with that of the controls in which trichloroacetic acid was added at zero time. When algal ^{14}C-labelled hydrolysate is employed as a source of labelled amino acids, high zero time control values of up to 1000 cts/min are encountered. Although these values can be reduced by initially precipitating the radioactive TCA-insoluble material present in the algal protein hydrolysate (Spencer, 1965), synthetic mixtures of suitably labelled amino acids which give much lower zero time values are to be preferred (Davies and Cocking, 1967a). The problem of binding of labelled material to precipitated

M

protein, which is therefore misleading in the final incorporation activity recorded, has long been appreciated in studies on protein synthesis *in vitro* and this problem is often even more pronounced when plant cell organelles, particularly chloroplasts, are being investigated, using protein precursors such as carbon dioxide and various sugars. Only four years ago Smillie (1963) was able to state quite definitely that experiments with photosynthesizing isolated chloroplasts had shown that glucose polymers were the only acid-insoluble products formed from $C^{14}O_2$. Contamination of slightly labelled chloroplast proteins by highly labelled starch is a very real problem in both *in vitro* and *in vivo* experiments on protein synthesis in these organelles. Davies and Cocking (1967b), in their studies of protein synthesis in tomato fruit locule tissue in which many of the plastids contain large quantities of starch, have developed a washing procedure which consists of prolonged washes with TCA (20%) and unlabelled amino acids followed by various washes with 95% v/v ethanol containing 1% potassium acetate, ethanol-chloroform, ethanol-ether, ether and perchloric acid. This effectively removes any labelled starch.

Steward and Durzan (1965) have clearly summarized the current views on the pathway of protein synthesis in molecular terms utilizing ideas drawn from the study of bacteria and of cell-free systems. The main steps involved are ". . . amino acid activation and recognition by specific enzymes, the transfer of amino acids by sRNA and their location at specified points on a ribosome template surface, the genetic (DNA) control over the nature of the template surface via mRNA and the carrying by mRNA, by a linear sequence of bases in triplets, of the information to arrange the protein amino acids in the linear order in which they are bound." In cell-free studies incubation mixtures are designed to contain all the enzymes, nucleic acids and cofactors required for this multi-stage process. The organelles, crude amino acid activating enzymes and sRNA preparations used are often unavoidably contaminated by enzymes such as ribonuclease, ATPase and proteases, in addition to those actually required for protein synthesis. All of these contaminating enzymes can be detrimental to the demonstration of activity although the extent to which they are in fact detrimental varies with the nature of the cell-free system being investigated. Spencer and Whitfield (1966) have noted that although the RNA components of their chloroplast protein-synthesizing system were spared from the action of endogenous nucleases the system was extremely sensitive to added pancreatic ribonuclease. Isolated ribosome systems are much more sensitive to the action of endogenous nucleases. ATPase activity in incubation mixture can largely be circumvented by the use of an ATP-generating system. Indeed, ribonuclease activity can also be largely eliminated by adding low levels of Cu^{++} ions to incubation mixtures (Hall and Cocking, 1966a). Amino acid activation is not inhibited but with plastid the presence of Cu^{++} ions may cause high zero time values (Davies and Cocking 1967a). Polyvinyl sulphate, which has also been shown to inhibit ribonuclease, has been found to induce dissociation of purified 80S ribosomes from plant leaves into subunits (Vanyushin and Dunn 1967) and therefore its use in cell-free incubation mixtures is beset with difficulties. The refinements of the incubation mixtures used in cell-free studies of protein synthesis by plant biochemists, as well as the characterization of the system (Table II), have paralleled those introduced for the bacterial system.

TABLE II

Characteristics of L-[^{14}C] lysine incorporation into protein by the cell-free ribosome system from castor bean seedlings.

Additions or omissions	[^{14}C] lysine incorporation*	% Inhib.
Complete system	16·01	0
− sRNA	11·15	30
− 105,000g supernatant	0·66	95
− Ribosomes	0·07	99
− 105,000g supernatant and sRNA	0·76	95
− Ribosomes and sRNA	0·09	99
− ATP, PEP, pyruvate kinase and GTP	0·41	97
− ATP, PEP and pyruvate kinase	0·46	97
− ATP	2·45	84
− GTP	12·23	23
− 19[^{12}C] amino acids	10·98	31
+ RNase (30 μg)	0·17	99
+ DNase (5 μg)	13·80	13
Complete, deproteinized at 0 time	0·04	—

* Values are μμ-moles of L-[^{14}C] lysine (Specific activity 180μC/μmoles) per assay. (Modified from Parisi and Ciferri, 1966).

Ammonium ions have been included, as well as mercaptoethanol, as the rôle of SH groups in the activity and stability of the bacterial system has become more fully understood (Stern et al., 1966). Perhaps the refinement of the cell-free plant protein synthesizing system which is most lacking is the appreciation of the effect that the *concentrations* of the labelled amino acids, bicarbonate or sugars—as distinct from their specific activities—can have, and do have, on the rate of incorporation of ^{14}C into protein. There are few if any instances in the literature where the optimum concentration of the labelled precursor has been established. Certain workers (Spencer and Wildman, 1964) have noted the importance of the concentration of the labelled amino acid. Attwood and Cocking (1965) found that the L-alanine activating enzyme of tomato roots possessed a higher Michaelis constant than most bacterial amino acid activating enzymes and it would seem likely that higher concentrations of amino acids are required *in vitro* in the plant system than are required in the bacterial system for maximum reaction rates. Even if higher rates of incorporation of ^{14}C from glucose or bicarbonate than from amino acids are obtained *in vitro* these results should be interpreted with caution unless it has been shown that the *in vitro* conditions, both with respect to the concentration of the labelled precursor and with respect to the various cofactors, are such as to give the maximum possible rate (cf. Davies and Cocking, 1967b).

III. COMPARISON OF *In Vivo* AND *In Vitro* PROTEIN SYNTHESIS RATES

Nisman and Pelmont (1964) have made it clear that *de novo* protein synthesis means, "... the sequence of reactions starting with the formation of messenger RNA and the transcription of its nucleotide sequences into polypeptide chains possessing specific biological activity". Most of the systems used for *in vitro* synthesis, generally, and probably all the higher plant systems do not fulfil the above requirements. Moreover even when only incorporation of carbon from protein precursors into growing peptide chains can be demonstrated this incorporation usually ceases after about 30 min *in vitro*. These inherent difficulties in studying protein synthesis using isolated plant cell organelles have served to emphasize the apparently greater synthesizing efficiency of the whole cell (Steward and Durzan, 1965). Direct comparison of *in vitro* incorporation rates with *in vivo* incorporation rates is, however, difficult. Problems of uptake of labelled precursors, while often a problem using *in vitro* studies with organelles such as membrane-bounded chloroplasts and mitochondria, are even greater in the case of *in vivo* studies in which dilution effects due to endogenous levels of the unlabelled precursors may also arise. The rate of uptake of the supplied protein precursor may change during the development of a tissue so that careful comparative studies of the *in vitro* and *in vivo* system at the same stage of development are required. The isolation of labelled plant cell organelles also presents certain difficulties since redistribution of labelled protein between the various organelles is likely to occur even if great care is taken to obtain a clean separation of the various organelles. The isolation of structurally intact chloroplasts by Leech (1964) illustrates the extreme difficulty in obtaining intact chloroplasts. Most preparations of chloroplasts used for *in vitro* studies have broken bounding membranes around the chloroplasts but fortunately it appears that the amino acid incorporating activity of isolated chloroplasts is firmly bound to the lamellar system (Spencer and Whitfield, 1966). Polyvinylpyrrolidone added to fractionation media greatly reduces the loss of protein from the various organelles (Davies and Cocking, 1967a; cf. also Loomis and Battaile, 1966).

In view of these difficulties it might be thought to be better to sum the incorporation rates of the various cell organelles obtained *in vitro* and then to deduce from this a rate of protein synthesis. The rate of protein synthesis could then be compared with that calculated from the observable rate of protein synthesis of the whole tissue as judged by its growth. This approach is complicated by the fact that the amount of protein present in any cell organelle at one particular moment is a reflection of the balance between the rate of synthesis and the rate of breakdown. As discussed by Hall and Cocking (1966c), studies involving isotopes can only record protein containing the isotope label and, providing that the synthesis of protein takes place by a stepwise addition of amino acids and not by random incorporation, labelled protein must either be *de novo* synthesis or completion of previously started protein. Therefore incorporation *in vivo* over a given period of time can be equated to the rate of synthesis as it is also likely that amino acids used in synthesis and formed in breakdown are not the same. Heber (1962) exposed spinach leaves to $^{14}CO_2$ in the dark and following this treatment he illuminated the leaves. He was able to show that radioactivity appeared in the chloroplast protein sooner than it did in the cytoplasmic protein. This experiment not only indicated that the chloroplasts became labelled *in vivo* from supplied CO_2 but also that chloroplast protein is probably synthesized in the chloroplast rather than in the cytoplasm. Spencer and Wildman (1964) showed that the amino acid-incorporating activity of a crude cell-free extract of tobacco leaves was greatest in the 1000-*g* fraction (Table III). The relatively

TABLE III

Distribution of amino acid-incorporating activity in
cell-free extracts of tobacco leaves.

Cell fraction	$[^{14}C]$ valine incorporation*
Cell-free extract	99
1000*g* fraction	1010
12,000*g* fraction	31
144,000*g* fraction	181
144,000*g* supernatant	1

* The amino acid incorporation into protein is expressed as the extent of labelling of material insoluble in hot trichloroacetic acid (cts/min/assay).
(Modified from Spencer and Wildman, 1964).

low activity of the original cell-free extract was thought to be due to the presence of an endogenous inhibitor or to large pools of $[^{12}C]$ valine in the unfractionated extracts. The major component of this 1000-*g* fraction was chloroplasts. The findings of Heber (1962) suggested that there was an active synthesis of protein from photosynthetically fixed CO_2 and the studies by

Rhodes and Yemm (1966) of the changes of proteins and nucleic acids occurring during the development of the first blade of barley seedlings, in which they were able to show that the synthesis of proteins associated with the development of chloroplasts appeared to be closely dependent upon prolonged exposure to light and photosynthesis, serve to confirm this supposition. The results of Parthier (1964) which suggest that mitochondria are the primary sites of protein synthesis in leaves of *Nicotiana rustica* utilizing $^{14}CO_2$ for the synthesis of protein should be interpreted with due consideration to the possibility of redistribution of labelled proteins between the various organelles during the fractionation procedures.

There have been various suggestions that difficulties in obtaining active cell-free incorporating systems from algal, yeast and higher plant cells arise

TABLE IV

Incorporation of carbon from bicarbonate into protein by
disrupted protoplasts compared with whole protoplasts
both from tomato fruit locule tissue.

Preparation	Incubation time (min)	cts/min/ mg protein	$\mu\mu$g carbon/ mg protein	Incorporation rate $\mu\mu$gC/mg/min
whole protoplasts	10	0	0	0
	30	395	7746	258·2
disrupted protoplasts	10	0	0	0
	30	285	5599	186·6

The incubation mixture contained 50 μmoles Tris-HCL pH 7·8, 10 μmoles magnesium acetate, 10 μmoles KCL, 300 μmoles sucrose, 5 μmoles ATP and 2·8 μmoles (1μC) ^{14}C–bicarbonate per ml of incubation mixture (whole protoplasts in 1 ml final, disrupted protoplasts in 0·5 ml). The complete washing procedure was used. Bacterial contamination nil. Results corrected for zero time control.
(From Davies and Cocking, 1967b).

mainly from the difficulties in rupturing the relatively tough cell wall. A procedure was used by Lucas *et al.* (1964) which yielded active ribosomal preparations from *S. cerevisiae* which involved enzymatic digestion of the cell wall and subsequent disruption of the resulting protoplasts. It was later shown, however, that a cell-disruption procedure based on grinding with alumina under special conditions gave active ribosomes more rapidly and in better yield than did the protoplast procedure. The increasing appreciation of the important rôle of plastids in the protein metabolism of the plant prompted Davies and Cocking (1967b) to re-appraise the possibility of obtaining plastids from isolated higher plant protoplasts and to compare their protein synthetic capabilities. Isolated protoplasts are readily obtained from tomato fruit locule tissue (Cocking, 1966) by digestion of the highly pectinaceous cell wall with polygalacturonase. It was found that when the incorporation of carbon from bicarbonate into the protein of disrupted protoplasts was compared with that of whole protoplasts, the incorporation rate of the disrupted protoplasts was only a little less than that of the intact organelles (Table IV). Light and electron microscopic examination revealed that little structural disorganization had occurred with the disrupted protoplasts apart from the rupture of the plasmalemma and tonoplast of the main vacuole. Plant cells are characterized by extensive development of membranous material during cell expansion and, as noted by Chrispeels (1964), as much as 50% of the protein synthesized during the expansive growth of corn root is membranous. This membranous material is recovered after normal disruption of plant cells as strands and fragments of the endoplasmic reticulum. The studies by Fukuhara (1967) of protein synthesis in nongrowing yeast in which the synthesizing capacity of several classes of ribosomes were characterized *in vivo* are pertinent. In only one class, i.e. those firmly attached to lipoprotein particles, was there activity. It is clear, however, that isolated ribosomes from plants are active at incorporation but continued incorporation and *de novo* synthesis of proteins may be dependent on the maintenance of general structural integrity of the cell system. Provided plastids were isolated from tomato fruit locule tissue by a very gentle teasing method using card clothing, they appeared to be no less active at incorporation than plastids isolated from protoplasts. The plastids isolated by the former procedure incorporated carbon from bicarbonate into protein much more readily than they did from added amino acids (Table V). Tissue

TABLE V

Incorporation of carbon from bicarbonate and amino acids
by isolated plastids from tomato fruit locule tissue.

Time (min)	Bicarbonate			Protein hydrolysate		
	cts/min/mg protein	$\mu\mu$gC/mg protein	$\mu\mu$gC/mg per min	cts/min/mg protein	$\mu\mu$gC/mg protein	$\mu\mu$gC/mg per min
10	116	2193	219	377	176	17·6
20	474	8956	447	639	299	15·0
30	137	2590	86	416	195	6·7

The incubation mixture contained 25 μmoles Tris–HCL pH 7·8, 5 μmoles magnesium acetate, 5 μmoles KCL, 150 μmoles sucrose, 2·5 μmoles ATP and 1·4 μmoles (0·5μC) ^{14}C–bicarbonate or 2·08μg (1·25μc) ^{14}C–protein hydrolysate in a final volume of 0·5 ml; complete washing procedure used. Bacterial contamination nil. The protein hydrolysate tubes gave 878–1699 counts/min above background and the bicarbonate tubes 9–16 counts/min above background. Results are corrected for zero time control.
(From Davies and Cocking, 1967b).

slices of this locule tissue (age from pollination of fruit 4 weeks) were incubated with ^{14}C-labelled amino acids and protein synthesis estimated in the various organelles after fractionation and counting. It was found that the incorporation rate of the plastid fraction was 28 μμg carbon/mg of protein/min which compares favourably with the incorporation rate of the cell-free plastid system which was 16 μμg of carbon/mg of protein/min (calculated from Table V). With single labelled amino acids such as glutamic acid rates of up to 108 μμg of carbon were obtained with the cell-free plastid system which increased to over 200 μμg of carbon/mg of protein/min in the presence of growth substances (Davies and Cocking, 1967a). Davies and Cocking (1966) have therefore concluded that protein syntheses with this cell-free plastid system are often equivalent to intact cell rates but can vary and be only one-tenth of the intact cell rate. They have also calculated that *in vitro* the initial incorporation rates are equivalent to a synthesis of the order of 10^6 protein molecules/min. This initial rate lasted for only about 10 min and they suggest that messenger RNA, peptide chain initiation or release of peptides from ribosomes may become limiting. It is of interest that the high initial rate lasted longer in the presence of growth substances.

IV. Sites and Control of Protein Synthesis

Boulter (1965) has adequately reviewed the situation regarding the sites and control of protein synthesis in plants. Work since 1965 with chloramphenicol and actinomycin D and the studies of protein synthesis in anucleate *Acetabularia* require some comment. In addition the very recent demonstration of a differential effect of chloramphenicol on the induction of nitrate and nitrite reductase in green leaf tissue needs to be viewed against the general background of protein synthesis by cell-free extracts from leaves and the relative protein synthesizing activities of the 70S chloroplast and 80S cytoplasmic ribosomes. Boardman *et al.* (1966) have carefully compared the properties of these two classes of ribosomes. The initial suggestion that there might be two ribosome systems in the leaves seems to have originated from experiments to elucidate the finding referred to earlier that more than 80% of the protein-synthesizing activity was associated with particles which sedimented at 1000g. Analysis of extracts of chloroplasts in the ultracentrifuge and by density gradient centrifugation served to show that amino acid-incorporating activity was associated with ribosome menomers and later it was shown that two classes of ribosomes, 70S and 80S, were present in the proportion of 4 to 1 in these chloroplast extracts. Incorporation studies using [^{14}C]-labelled valine were carried out to compare the relative activities of the cytoplasmic ribosomes (present in large amounts in the cytoplasmic extract) with the chloroplast ribosomes (present in large amounts in the

TABLE VI

[^{14}C] valine-incorporating activity and ribosome content
of cytoplasmic extract and chloroplast supernatant.

| | Experiment I | | Experiment II | |
	Cytoplasmic extract	Chloroplast supernatant	Cytoplasmic extract	Chloroplast supernatant
70S ribosome concentration (mg/ml)	0·03	0·11	0·03	0·09
80S ribosome concentration (mg/ml)	0·13	0·04	0·12	0·02
[^{14}C] Valine incorporation (cts/min/ml)	272	5320	330	4280
Cts/min/mg ribosomes (70S + 80S)	1700	35,000	2200	39,000
$\mu\mu$moles/mg ribosomes (70S + 80S)	12	240	15	260
Cts/min/mg 70S ribosomes	9100	48,000	7300	48,000
Cts/min/mg 80S ribosomes	2100	—	2800	—

(From Boardman et al., 1966).

chloroplast supernatant) (Table VI). It was concluded that most of the activity of cell-free preparations from tobacco leaves is associated with the 70S class of ribosomes which remains inside the chloroplast during normal extraction. The greater activity of the tobacco leaf chloroplast ribosomes in comparison with the cytoplasmic ribosomes (Table VI) contrasts with the reverse situation

TABLE VII

The effect of TMV–RNA and polyuridylic acid on amino
acid incorporation by the 1000-g fraction of tobacco leaves.

| | [^{14}C] Amino Acid Incorporation | |
Condition	Experiment 1*	Experiment 2†
[^{14}C] valine	1824	
[^{14}C] valine + poly U (200 μg/ml)	1674	
[^{14}C] valine + TMV–RNA (250 μg/ml)	1692	
[^{14}C] phenylalanine	2418	1289
[^{14}C] phenylalanine + poly U (200 μg/ml)	2703	3079

* The amino acid incorporation is expressed as the extent of labelling of material insoluble in cold trichloroacetic acid (cts/min/assay).
† The amino acid incorporation is expressed as the extent of labelling of material insoluble in hot trichloroacetic acid (cts/min/assay).
(Modified from Spencer and Wildman, 1964).
*

in *Euglena gracilis* referred to earlier in which ribosomes from the cytoplasm are much more active in amino acid incorporation than ribosomes derived from the chloroplasts. The differences are difficult to explain. Earlier, Spencer and Wildman (1964) had reported that there was no effect of TMV-RNA, and only a slight effect of polyuridylic acid, on amino acid incorporation by the 1000-*g* fraction of tobacco leaves (Table VII) and Hall and Cocking (1966b) obtained somewhat comparable results using tomato leaf chloroplasts. At that time it was suggested that the lack of stimulation was related to difficulties of penetration of TMV-RNA and poly U into the chloroplasts, since cytoplasmic ribosome preparations do respond markedly to poly U giving great increases in the incorporation of L-[^{14}C] phenylalanine (Table VIII). Boardman *et al.* state that their 70S and 80S ribosomes of

TABLE VIII

Effect of polynucleotides on the incorporation of
L-[^{14}C] amino acids by castor bean ribosomes.

Amino acid	Addition	[^{14}C] Amino Acid incorp.*	Stimulation-fold
L-[^{14}C] phenylalanine	—	6·96	1
	Poly U	292·52	42
	Poly U + streptomycin	282·44	40·6
	Poly U + chloramphenicol	324·04	46·5
	Poly U + puromycin	63·80	9·2
	Poly C	8·66	1·2
	Poly A	9·13	1·3
L-[^{14}C] isoleucine	—	8·83	1
	Poly U	8·37	0·9
	Poly U + streptomycin	9·54	1·1
L-[^{14}C] proline	—	14·25	1
	Poly C	61·45	4·3

* Values are $\mu\mu$moles of L-[^{14}C] phenylalanine, of L-[^{14}C] isoleucine or of L-[^{14}C] proline per mg of ribosomal RNA.
(From Parisi and Ciferri, 1966).

tobacco leaves do not respond significantly to the vital equivalent of template RNA (i.e. TMV-RNA). It would be of interest to know if they respond to differing extents in the presence of poly U since adequate responses to TMV-RNA may be more difficult to initiate than with poly U (cf. Stanley *et al.*, 1966). Stimulation by poly U does not require an additional factor (cf. Eisenstadt and Brawerman, 1966). The amino acid-incorporating activity of *Euglena* chloroplast ribosomes is markedly stimulated by the addition of template RNA in the form of F$_2$ RNA and the coat protein of the F$_2$ coliphage is synthesized (Schwartz *et al.*, 1965) so that it would appear that lack of endogenous messenger RNA is responsible for the lower activity of these chloroplast ribosomes. Eisenstadt has suggested that each *Euglena* plastid contains enough DNA for the specification of chloroplast proteins and that messenger RNA is synthesized within the chloroplasts and utilized in the formation of proteins.

Studies of the effect of chloramphenicol on cytoplasmic and chloroplast ribosomes in *Euglena* have shown that cytoplasmic ribosomes are unaffected in their leucine incorporation abilities by concentrations of chloramphenicol greatly in excess of these which completely block protein synthesis in bacteria. Chloroplast ribosomes in contrast are markedly inhibited in their incorporation activity (Eisenstadt, 1967). It has been suggested that the apparent resistance of cytoplasmic ribosomes to chloramphenicol is related to their high affinity for template RNA. Graebe and Novelli (1966) have observed a similar insensitivity of maize endosperm ribosomes to chloramphenicol. Endogenous ribonuclease activity was low in their preparations and the system was not dependent on messenger RNA synthesis since there was no inhibiting action of DNase; this suggests that protein synthesis due to endogenous messenger is unaffected by chloramphenicol. When cytoplasmic castor bean ribosomes are treated with chloramphenicol together with poly U, no inhibition of the stimulation is observed (Table VIII). Spencer and Wildman (1964) noted, however, a marked inhibiting effect of chloramphenicol on amino acid incorporation by the 1000-*g* fraction of tobacco leaves (Table IX) and somewhat similar results have been recorded by Davies and Cocking (1967b) and Hall and Cocking (1966b) with cell-free plastid and chloroplast systems under aseptic conditions. The report by James and Richens (1962) that 0·002M chloramphenicol inhibited almost completely synthesis of "precipitable-N" by isolated wheat nuclei may be a similar example of marked inhibition by chloramphenicol but it should be noted that incubations were probably not bacteria free. Macdonald *et al.* (1966) have recently reported on the differences in activity between the D- and L-threo isomers of chloramphenicol and care should be taken to use the correct isomer in these studies and to note that the chloramphenicols are inhibitors of oxidative phosphorylation. Many workers do not report which isomer they use (but see Rendi and Ochoa, 1962) and normally it is assumed to be the D-threo isomer. Margulies (1964) has reported that the synthesis of chloroplast proteins in intact plants is inhibited by chloramphenicol while Beevers *et al.* (1965) noted that chloramphenicol was not very effective in inhibiting substrate induction of nitrate reductase in radish cotyledons and corn seedlings. The recent work of Schrader *et al.* (1967) has demonstrated that the induction of nitrate reductase and nitrite reductase (which is located inside chloroplasts whereas nitrate reductase is more soluble and is located in the cytoplasm) is quite differently affected by chloramphenicol. Nitrite reductase induction was repressed by chloramphenicol whereas nitrate reductase induction was either not affected or stimulated. These results have prompted Schrader *et al.* (1967) to conclude that nitrate reductase is synthesized by a cytoplasmic ribosomal system and nitrite reductase by a chloroplastic ribosomal system. This parallels and extends to a specific protein those results reported earlier by Clark-Walker and Linnane (1966; see Introduction). This is of considerable interest because it indicates sites of specific protein synthesis in plant

TABLE IX

Effect of inhibitors on amino acid incorporation by
1000-*g* fraction of tobacco leaves.

Experiment	Additions (μg/ml)	[^{14}C] valine incorporation*	
		cts/min	(% inhibition)
1	Nil	879	
	RNase: 0·002	821	7
	0·008	720	18
	0·002	680	23
	0·08	314	64
	0·2	213	74
	8	176	80
	20	184	78
2	Nil	856	
	DNase: 10	733	14
	100	644	25
3	Nil	2028	
	Chloramphenicol: 200	615	70
	Actinomycin D:　20	1670	18
4	Nil	1045	
	Puromycin:　1	624	40
	10	319	69
	100	296	72

* The amino acid incorporation is expressed as the extent of labelling of material insoluble in cold trichloroacetic acid (cts/min/assay).
(From Spencer and Wildman, 1964).

cells. Synthesis of nitrite reductase cannot be restricted to chloroplasts. Nitrite reductase is induced in isolated roots in the dark; more generally plastids and/or mitochondria may be concerned with the synthesis of nitrite reductase.

It appears that the chloroplasts of plants have all the components of a complete genetic system but it seems likely, at least in higher plants, that only some of the messenger RNA is synthesized by the chloroplast DNA; the rest is synthesized by the nuclear DNA. Enucleated cells afford a system for investigating the extent of nuclear control over this synthesis. Anucleate higher plant cells are not readily obtainable but isolated sub-protoplasts may afford a suitable experimental system (cf. Cocking, 1965). At the moment, however, work is largely restricted to the giant unicellular alga *Acetabularia mediterranea* from which it is possible to separate nucleate and anucleate cellular fragments. Brachet and his co-workers (Brachet, 1967) have been able to show that net protein synthesis occurs in anucleate fragments and also net synthesis of RNA. The proteins synthesized by the anucleate fragments include several enzymes the synthesis of which is usually considered to be controlled by nuclear DNA and Brachet has suggested that relatively stable messenger RNA, with a life of about 2–3 weeks, is present in these anucleate fragments as judged by the length of time during which anucleate fragments can synthesize protein. Studies with actinomycin D which is generally accepted as a specific inhibitor of DNA-dependent RNA poly- merase have shown (Table X) that at very high concentrations actinomycin D

TABLE X

Incorporation of amino acids by chloroplasts isolated from anucleate fragments of acetabularia. Influence of high concentrations of actinomycin D on the incorporation into proteins of chloroplasts isolated 11 days after enucleation.

Inhibitor	Cts/min/mg chlorophyll and per hr of incubation
None	775,000 (100%)
Actinomycin D (83 μg/ml)	109,000 (14%)
Actinomycin D (167 μg/ml)	0 (0%)

(Modified from Goffeau and Brachet, 1965).

completely inhibits amino acid incorporation by isolated chloroplasts of *Acetabularia* fragments which have been enucleated for 11 days. This result suggests that chloroplast DNA at this time is directing the synthesis of chloro- plast proteins.

Autoradiographic methods have been applied by Shephard (1965) to the normal and anucleate cells of this alga and he has obtained further evidence for the autonomy of these chloroplasts. Their DNA is apparently replicated *in situ* and this DNA mediates the synthesis of RNA which in turn provides a template for the synthesis of certain plastid proteins. Comparable studies with higher plants are required before general conclusions are drawn from these algal investigations.

As emphasized by Campbell (1965) in his review of protein synthesis in animal cells, the major problem concerning sites of protein synthesis in cells is that associated with cellular differentiation itself. Evidence has been obtained that the cell only makes messenger RNAs for the synthesis of these proteins which it wishes to make and that the gene repressor, which this suggestion necessarily involves, may be a protein. It has also been proposed by Harris (1963) that a whole range of messenger RNAs are made and then broken down. Information obtained about sites of synthesis of plant viruses could help greatly in our appreciation of the factors influencing the ability of a specific protein to be synthesized at a particular site in the cell, since their multiplication is uncomplicated by considerations of DNA involvement (Shapiro and August, 1966). The final assembly of the virus particle provides us with a readily identifiable form of differentiation.

REFERENCES

Attwood, M. M. and Cocking, E. C. (1965). *Biochem. J.* **96**, 616.

Bamji, M. S. and Jagendorf, A. T. (1966). *Pl. Physiol., Lancaster* **41**, 764.

Beevers, L., Schrader, L. E., Flescher, D. and Hageman, R. H. (1965). *Pl. Physiol., Lancaster* **40**, 691.

Boardman, N. K., Francki, R. I. B. and Wildman, S. G. (1966). *J. molec. Biol.* **17**, 470.

Boulter, D. (1965). *In* "Biosynthetic Pathways in Higher Plants". (J. B. Pridham and T. Swain, eds), p. 101. Academic Press, London and New York.

Brachet, J. (1967). *Nature, Lond.* **213**, 650.

Campbell, P. N. (1965). *In* "Progress in Biophysics and Molecular Biology". (J. A. V. Butler and H. E. Huxley, eds), Vol. 15, p. 3. Pergamon Press, Oxford.

Chrispeels, M. J. (1964). Cytoplasmic Differentiation in Seedling Tissues. *Ph. D.* Thesis, University of Illinois.

Clark-Walker, G. D. and Linnane, A. W. (1966). *Biochem. biophys. Res. Commun.* **25**, 8.

Cocking, E. C. (1965). *In* "Viewpoints in Biology". (J. D. Carthy and C. L. Duddington, eds), Vol. 4, p. 170. Butterworth, London.

Davies, J. W. and Cocking, E. C. (1966). *Biochem. J.* **101**, 28, P.

Davies, J. W. and Cocking, E. C. (1967a). *Biochem. J.* **104**, 23.

Davies, J. W. and Cocking, E. C. (1967b). *Planta* **76**, 285.

Eisenstadt, J. M. (1967). *In* "Biochemistry of Chloroplasts". (T. W. Goodwin, ed.), Vol. 2, p. 341. Academic Press, London and New York.

Eisenstadt, J. M. and Brawerman, G. (1966). *Biochemistry, N.Y.* **5**, 2777.

Fukuhara, H. (1967). *Biochim. biophys. Acta* **134**, 143.

Goffeau, A. and Brachet, J. (1965). *Biochim. biophys. Acta* **95**, 302.

Goodwin, T. W. (1966). "Biochemistry of Chloroplasts". Vol. 1 and Vol. 2 (1967). Academic Press, London and New York.

Graebe, J. E. and Novelli, G. D. (1966). *Expl Cell. Res.* **41**, 521.

Hall, T. C. and Cocking, E. C. (1966a). *Pl. Cell Physiol., Tokyo* **7**, 343.

Hall, T. C. and Cocking, E. C. (1966b). *Biochim. biophys. Acta* **123**, 163.

Hall, T. C. and Cocking, E. C. (1966c). *Pl. Cell Physiol., Tokyo* **7**, 329.

Harris, H. (1963). *In* "Progress in Nucleic Acid Research". (J. N. Davidson and W. E. Cohn, eds), Vol. 2, p. 19. Academic Press, London and New York.

Heber, U. (1962). *Nature, Lond.* **195**, 91.

James, W. O. and Richens, A. M. (1962). *Proc. R. Soc.* B **157**, 149.

Kirk, J. T. O. and Tilney-Bassett, R. A. E. (1967). "The Plastids; Their Chemistry, Structure, Growth and Inheritance". W. H. Freeman and Co., London.

Leech, R. M. (1964). *Biochim. biophys. Acta* **79**, 637.

Lett, J. T. and Takahashi, W. N. (1962). *Archs Biochem. Biophys.* **96**, 569.

Loomis, W. D. and Battaile, J. (1966). *Phytochem.* **5**, 423.

Lowry, O. H., Rosebrough, N. J., Farr, A. L. and Randall, R. J. (1951). *J. biol. Chem.* **193**, 265.

Lucas, J. M., Schuurs, A. H. W. M. and Simpson, M. V. (1964). *Biochemistry, N.Y.* **3**, 959.

Macdonald, I. R., Bacon, J. S. D., Vaughan, D. and Ellis, R. J. (1966). *J. expl Bot.* **17**, 822.

Mans, R. J. (1967). *In* "Biochemistry of Chloroplasts". (T. W. Goodwin, ed.), Vol. 2, p. 351. Academic Press, London and New York.

Margulies, M. M. (1964). *Pl. Physiol., Lancaster* **39**, 579.

Nisman, B. and Pelmont, J. (1964). *In* "Progress in Nucleic Acid Research and Molecular Biology". (J. N. Davidson and W. E. Cohn, eds), Vol. 3, p. 235. Academic Press, London and New York.

Parisi, B. and Ciferri, O. (1966). *Biochemistry, N.Y.* **5**, 1638.

Parthier, B. (1964). *Z. Naturf.* **19b**, 235.

Raacke, I. D. (1959). *Biochim. biophys. Acta* **34**, 1.

Rendi, R. and Ochoa, S. (1962). *J. biol. Chem.* **237**, 3711.

Rhodes, M. J. C. and Yemm, E. W. (1966). *New Phytol.* **65**, 331.

Schrader, L. E., Beevers, L. and Hageman, R. H. (1967). *Biochem. biophys. Res. Commun.* **26**, 14.

Schwartz, J. H., Eisenstadt, J. M., Brawerman, G. and Zinder, N. D. (1965). *Proc. natn. Acad. Sci., U.S.A.* **53**, 195.

Shapiro, L. and August, J. T. (1966). *Bact. Rev.* **30**, 279.

Shephard, D. C. (1965). *Biochim. biophys. Acta* **108**, 635.

Siekevitz, P. (1952). *J. biol. Chem.* **195**, 549.

Sissakian, N. M., Fillipovich, I. I., Svetailo, E. N. and Aliyev, K. A. (1965). *Biochim. biophys. Acta* **95**, 474.

Smillie, R. M. (1963). *Can. J. Bot.* **41**, 123.

Spencer, D. (1965). *Archs Biochem. Biophys.* **111**, 381.

Spencer, D. and Wildman, S. G. (1964). *Biochemistry, N.Y.* **3**, 954.

Spencer, D. and Whitfield, P. R. (1966). *Archs Biochem. Biophys.* **117**, 337.

Stanley, W. M., Salas, M., Wahba, A. J. and Ochoa, S. (1966). *Proc. natn. Acad. Sci., U.S.A.* **56**, 290.

Stern, R., de Luca, M., Mehler, A. H. and McElroy, W. D. (1966). *Biochemistry, N.Y.* **5**, 126.

Steward, F. C. and Durzan, D. J. (1965). *In* "Plant Physiology". (F. C. Steward, ed.), Vol. IVA, Chapter 4, Academic Press, New York and London.

Steward, F. C. and Bidwell, R. G. S. (1966). *J. expl Bot.* **17**, 726.

Vanyushin, B. F. and Dunn, D. B. (1967). *Biochim. biophys. Acta* **134**, 91.

Walker, D. A. (1967). *In* "Biochemistry of Chloroplasts". (T. W. Goodwin, ed.), Vol. 2, p. 53. Academic Press, London and New York.

Webster, G. C. (1959). *Archs. Biochem. Biophys.* **85**, 159.

CHAPTER 12

The Occurrence and Properties of Polysomes in Plant Tissues

U. E. LOENING

Department of Botany, The University, Edinburgh, Scotland

The concept of the polysome as an aggregate of ribosomes joined by messenger RNA arose from the necessity of accommodating the long messenger molecule on a ribosome and allowing the ribosome to translate the message into the polypeptide chain (Wettstein *et al.*, 1963; Rich *et al.*, 1963). The existence and functioning of polysomes has been well established in animal tissues; the question here is to determine whether polysomes can be similarly found in plants and what techniques can be used to isolate them.

I. GENERAL PROPERTIES OF POLYSOMES

Strings or clumps of ribosomes can be seen, with the use of the electron microscope, both in whole cells and in cell fractions from homogenates. The isolated polysomes sediment on centrifugation more rapidly than the single ribosomes, in a series of peaks according to the number of ribosomes per polysome. It would be expected that the longer the polypeptide chain being synthesized, the longer is the messenger RNA coding for it and therefore the greater the number of ribosomes in one polysome. Very frequently, the polysomes are attached to endoplasmic reticulum membranes in the cell and this is particularly the case in the more active protein synthesizing tissues such as pancreas and developing plant cells. Similar membrane-bound polysomes have also been found in bacteria, for example in *B. megaterium* by Schlessinger (1963).

Descriptions of polysomes *in situ* in fixed tissues were in fact published several years before their significance was appreciated. The occurrence of rapidly sedimenting ribosomes had also been noted earlier but in most cases these results were ascribed to nonspecific aggregation and remained unpublished. Among the early findings, Watson (1959) had described coils of ribosomes in rat liver, attached to the endoplasmic reticulum or to the nuclear membrane. This was even before messenger RNA had been described and a true interpretation of the pictures could therefore not be given. In these pictures, it appears that the larger ribosomal subunit is to the outside of the coil and the smaller to the inside. More recently, Sabatani *et al.* (1966) suggest, in a biochemical and electron microscopic study of membrane-bound ribosomes, that the larger subunit is the one that is attached to the membrane. The smaller subunit can be dissociated from the whole microsome with EDTA leaving the larger one still attached. The relationship of these biochemical results to the electron microscope studies of the polysome coils remains obscure and requires further study; the nature of the attachment of the coils and whether the coiled arrangement is a property of the membrane or of the messenger connecting the ribosomes is not known.

The structure of isolated polysomes has been investigated with the electron microscope using shadowing, negative staining or positive staining. In the latter, when the ribosomes have been stretched apart from each other, the strand of messenger RNA can be seen (Dass and Bayley, 1965; Slayter *et al.*, 1963). The pictures from Das and Bayley show, apparently, branched messenger RNA in the form of Y rather than X. While it is possible that the polysomes can become entangled during isolation, this is not so likely to lead to the Y type of branch. It is probable therefore that some ribosome interactions causing clumping or stringing are nonspecific and not due to the messenger RNA. Some of the strands which are visible could be dried stain (G. Palade, personal communication).

While there are inconsistencies, as indicated above, in our understanding, we can consider the following five criteria to be characteristic of polysomes:

(1) The polysomes should become labelled with nascent protein after brief *in vivo* incorporation of labelled amino acids by the tissue; i.e., it must be shown that the polysome is the active structure in protein synthesis.

(2) The isolated polysomes should be capable of amino acid incorporation into protein *in vitro*, more so than the free single ribosomes.

(3) Messenger RNA must be a part of the polysome structure.

(4) There should be some correlation between the yield or content of polysomes in the tissue and the protein synthesizing activity of the tissue.

(5) The isolated polysome structure should be fragile to ribonuclease action which will degrade the messenger string and release free ribosomes; similarly shearing forces may break the polysome structure.

We consider below how such structures can be identified and isolated from plant tissues and some of their properties.

II. Detection of Polysomes *In Situ*

There are now many published pictures of fixed plant cells in which the ribosomes occur in clumps or coils. One example can be taken from studies by Bonnet and Newcomb (1965) with radish in which the endoplasmic reticulum is in places dilated to a vesicular structure. In this case one can see the ribosome-covered, "rough" endoplasmic reticulum in every gradation from transverse to tangential section. This gives an opportunity to show that the bulk of the membrane attached ribosomes occur in coiled arrangements containing 10 to 40 ribosomes. Helical arrangements of ribosomes, probably not attached to membranes, have also been observed (Echlin, 1965). In this laboratory, we have found the coiled and helical forms within the same cell in cultured explants of Helianthus tuber (J. Tullet, unpublished). These studies have not demonstrated that the coiled arrays are in fact polysomes in the sense that the ribosomes are necessarily bound to each other by messenger RNA. The cytological study must now be combined with a biochemical one.

III. Methods of Isolation of Polysomes

A. HOMOGENIZATION OF THE TISSUE

In plant cells the tough cell wall leads to homogenization problems which have already been mentioned in this symposium; it is difficult to break the cell wall without disrupting, to some extent, the polysome structure. A number of methods have been tried from mechanical chopping with razor blades (Spencer and Wildman, 1964; used for chloroplasts) to grinding with mortar and pestle or homogenizing gently in teflon-glass homogenizers with carefully controlled clearances. Another technique is to freeze the tissue in dry ice or liquid nitrogen and grind the frozen tissue to a powder; the powder is then broken up into medium in a teflon homogenizer (Lin and Key, 1967). None of these methods is entirely satisfactory and others will be needed.

The homogenizing medium must be constituted so as to stabilize the polysomes as well as other structures which could release ribonucleases. It must contain magnesium ion to maintain the integrity of the ribosomes and sodium or potassium ion or both. The ratio of magnesium to monovalent salts is probably more critical than the absolute concentration (Breillart and Dickman, 1966). Sucrose may be added to preserve other cell particles. The medium will be buffered, usually with Tris, and close control of the pH may be necessary especially when using deoxycholate to dissolve the endoplasmic reticulum membranes (Waters and Dure, 1966). Such detergents should, of course, be added only after the larger cell particles have been removed by centrifugation; it is probably difficult, however, to spin down mitochondria and lysosomes completely without also sedimenting some of the larger membrane-attached polysomal particles.

Throughout these procedures, some nuclease inhibitor will probably be required. There is a range of different nucleases in most plant cells and one cannot expect to find an inhibitor which inhibits all of them and does not interfere with the fractionation procedures. The inhibitor must be chosen to suit the particular tissue. Bentonite is one of the most commonly used nuclease inhibitors; this is a negatively charged earth which binds the positively charged basic proteins, effectively removing them from solution. The method of purification of bentonite described by Singer and Fraenkel-Conrat (1961) for the preparation of Tobacco Mosaic virus RNA involves washing the bentonite with EDTA and then with water or salts. R. Watts (unpublished results) has shown that the amount of EDTA remaining in the gelatinous precipitate is large and would bind much of the magnesium ion added to the homogenizing medium. The washing procedure must therefore be repeated many times. Further, because of its negative charge, bentonite also has a tendency to bind ribosomes and polysomes (Tester and Dure, 1966); this is particularly the case with magnesium rather than sodium bentonite, so much so that magnesium bentonite has been used by Dunn (1965) to remove ribosomal materials from leaf homogenates and to extract t-RNA from the supernatant. There is considerable discrepancy among different workers on the effects of bentonite. We have found in this laboratory that even sodium bentonite binds ribosomes and t-RNA (P. Babos and J. Ingle, unpublished results) whereas Dr. R.Watts considers that only damaged ribosomes attach to bentonite. A quantitative check of yields is advised (Tester and Dure, 1966).

Polyvinyl sulphate has been used as an RNase inhibitor in a number of cases, such as in one of the earliest extractions of polysomes from plant tissues by Clark et al. (1964). They pointed out that it is satisfactory to add PVS in low concentration to the homogenate (Chinese cabbage leaf) in which the whole cell sap is present but that if it is used at a later stage in the preparation for resuspending the polysomal pellet, it causes degradation of the polysomes. This phenomenon has since been studied in another connection by Vanyushin and Dunn (1966) who showed that PVS reversibly dissociates ribosomes to their subunits. The degradation noted by Clark and his colleagues is likely, therefore, to have been a dissociation rather than degradation and the cell sap evidently contained something, such as other basic proteins, which prevented this dissociation.

Magnesium ion itself is an inhibitor of some ribonucleases and some media used have contained no other inhibitor (Lin and Key, 1967). As mentioned above, the magnesium concentration used in relation to that of sodium may be critical (Breillart and Dickman, 1966). Zinc ion is also a strong inhibitor of some plant nucleases in low concentration (Stockse and Vandendriessche, 1961) and was used by Barker and Rieber (1967) in the isolation of polysomes from germinating pea seeds. They used magnesium and zinc together and found that the zinc concentration was critical; 1 mM Zn^{2+} failed to inhibit the nucleases and 10 mM caused aggregation. They therefore used 5 mM Zn^{2+}.

B. ANALYSIS OF POLYSOMES BY CENTRIFUGATION

Two procedures of density gradient centrifugation have been used. The cell homogenate is first cleared by a medium speed centrifugation (up to 20,000 × g) and the supernatant is then either layered immediately on the density gradient or centrifuged to pellet the polysomal fraction, perhaps through sucrose layers as described by Wettstein *et al.* (1963). The pellet is resuspended and analysed on a sucrose gradient. The former method has the advantage of speed, minimizing the time of nuclease action, but suffers because frequently not sufficient of the dilute homogenate can be layered on the gradient and uv absorbing materials frequently interfere with the final scanning of the gradient. In the latter method, the polysomes are concentrated and purified but more time is allowed for nuclease action and there may be considerable breakdown in resuspending the pellet by shearing action. Analytical centrifugation in the Spinco model E has also been used with schlieren optics. A high concentration of polysomes is required to give the schlieren pattern but uv absorbing materials do not, of course, interfere.

IV. PROPERTIES OF PLANT POLYSOMES

A. EXAMPLES FROM SEVERAL SPECIES

Phillips *et al.* (1964) described the density gradient analysis of polysomes from slime moulds. These show the monomer ribosome and the expected regular series of peaks of increasing sedimentation constant. The bulk of the ribosome content of the homogenate was present as polysomes and the pentamer peak was the most frequent of these. They found that short incubation *in vivo* of the mould in labelled leucine resulted in preferential labelling of the polysomes over the free ribosomes and ribonuclease treatment caused the polysomes to break down leaving only the "monosomes". The term "monosome" is conveniently used to refer to such ribosomes as are obtained by breakdown of polysomes by ribonuclease action or other means such as shearing. The term ribosome is then confined to the naturally occurring monomer; its properties are usually different from the monosome since it does not contain fragments of broken messenger RNA nor of nascent protein.

Clark *et al.* (1964) used analytical centrifugation to demonstrate the presence of polysomes in Chinese cabbage leaves. Small amounts of polysomes were seen in the schlieren pictures up to the pentamer. Again low concentrations of ribonuclease caused degradation of the polysomes. That the concentration of ribonuclease may be important if it is to be used diagnostically for polysomes was suggested by the work of Henney and Stork (1964) on *Neurospora* polysomes. Their schlieren patterns show the ribosomal sub-units, the 80S monomer and a number of polysome sizes. Ribonuclease, at a concentration of 1 μg/ml, degraded the polysomes to monosomes as expected but 25 μg/ml caused aggregation of the ribosomes and gave spurious patterns.

Watts and Mathias (1965 and unpublished results) extracted polysomes from germinating barley seeds. In the absence of bentonite, polysomes were obtained in low yield and were unstable; extended centrifugation caused breakdown. In the presence of bentonite, prepared by extensive washing as mentioned above, the polysomes accounted for 70 to 80% of the total ribosome population and the authors consider this ratio to be closely similar to that *in vivo*. These preparations could be incubated at 37° for 5 min with very little breakdown. Incubation with ribonuclease 10^{-3} or 10^{-1} μg/ml resulted in a considerable breakdown of the polysomes as shown by an increase in the proportions of the monomer and smaller polysomes. The degradation was not complete, however, and the density gradient patterns were still similar to many normal polysome extracts described in the literature. The concentrations of ribonuclease used were 10 and 1000 times smaller than those usually employed for this purpose and the experiments show the extreme sensitivity of polysomes to nuclease action. In the presence of bentonite, however, these polysome preparations were stable at 5° for several days.

Lin *et al.* (1966) have described the isolation of polysomes from soya bean roots using the technique of grinding the frozen tissue followed by gentle homogenization in a medium containing Tris, KCL and Mg^{2+} ion but no other inhibitor of nucleases. No deocycholate was used since the bulk of the ribosomes of this tissue are free of membranes. They were able to show, by labelling *in vivo* with ^{32}P or with labelled adenosine and uridine, that isotope was very rapidly incorporated into these polysomes and that the base composition of the labelled RNA was similar to the "D-RNA" which is considered to be messenger RNA. The specific activity of RNA prepared from the polysomes was higher than that from the ribosomes. The density gradient patterus did not show as high a proportion of the larger polysomes as those of Watts and Mathias (1965) but they were perfectly adequate to show that the D-RNA was specifically associated with the polysomes. Electron microscope pictures of negatively stained preparations of these polysomes showed that they occur in clumps whereas after nuclease treatment they appear singly or in dimers. Lin *et al.* (1966) further showed that the polysomes were several times more active in incorporating leucine or phenylalanine into protein *in vitro* than were the free ribosomes or preparations which had been degraded into monosomes.

The above experiments are examples which demonstrate that the polysomes isolated from plants do have the characteristics outlined in the five points above.

B. THE EFFECTS OF INHIBITION OF PROTEIN SYNTHESIS

The influence of the physiological state of the tissue on the properties and content of polysomes can now be considered; first the influence of metabolic inhibitors and conditions of shock and then changes during growth and cell development.

Several experiments with plants and animals have shown that the extent to which the ribosomes occur as polysomes varies continuously according to the physiological state of the cell. Clark *et al.* (1964) found that they were unable to extract polysomes from Chinese cabbage leaves after even momentary wilting. Similarly, Lin and Key (1966) found that anaerobiosis caused the complete disappearance of polysomes from soya bean roots. Merely harvesting the tissue from the growing medium and incubation in aerated water with shaking resulted in some loss. It is probable that the shock of the move caused a large loss of polysomes and that the proportion found after 1 hr shaking in water represents a late stage in recovery. When the roots were incubated in still water, there was a greater loss than in stirred water. Bubbling nitrogen, or incubation in DNP, resulted in a complete loss. This suggests that energy is continuously required for the maintenance of the polysome population. On the other hand, incubation for 1 hr in actinomycin D, which was shown to inhibit RNA synthesis almost completely, had little effect on the proportion of polysomes. In all these conditions, the activity of the isolated ribosome preparations in the incorporation of leucine *in vitro* was directly related to the proportion of polysomes. Waters and Dure (1966) similarly showed that during the first 16 hr germination of cotton seeds, actinomycin D almost entirely inhibited the synthesis of RNA (measured by ^{32}P incorporation) but the proportion of polysomes was maintained, protein synthesis continued and the germination of the seed at this stage was not affected. It is clear that continuous synthesis of RNA is not necessarily required for the maintenance of polysomes and we can conclude that these tissues contain a high proportion of stable, active messenger RNA. The immediate control of the amount of polysomes and of protein synthesis seems to depend more on the state of the tissue, including the degree of shock provided by the experimentalist, than on the short-term rate of RNA synthesis.

The recovery from shock provides some clues concerning the fate of the messenger RNA in the absence of polysomes. Lin and Key (1967) followed the time course of recovery of the soya bean root during aeration after anoxia. At 30 min after the start of aeration, a proportion of polysomes had reformed; thereafter the recovery continued more slowly. The rapid recovery over the first 30 min was only slightly inhibited by actinomycin D, while the continued slower recovery was strongly inhibited. There are clearly two phases in the recovery, the first of which is independent of RNA synthesis. It appears, therefore, that the loss of polysomes due to anoxia does not destroy all of the messenger RNA but dissociates it from the ribosome. A proportion of the messenger RNA survives in the cytoplasm and can be used for the formation of polysomes as soon as energy is again provided.

Similar conclusions were reached by Conconi et al. (1966) with reticulocyte cells synthesizing haemoglobin. They found that fluoride ion rapidly resulted in a loss of polysomes but that protein synthesis recommenced and polysomes were formed on the removal of the fluoride. This was in the absence of RNA synthesis since these cells have no nuclei. Ninety per cent of the protein synthetic activity was recovered when only 10 to 20% of the polysomes had re-formed. In this case, therefore, the proportion of polysomes was not directly related to the rate of protein synthesis. The limiting factor appeared to be the supply of some form of energy for the peptide bond formation; faster chain growth on a smaller number of polysomes led to similar rates of protein synthesis.

These findings taken together suggest that the breakdown of polysomes under anoxic or other unfavourable conditions is due to the inhibition of the attachment of ribosomes to messenger RNA and perhaps to reduction of the initial rate of travel of ribosomes along the messenger but that those polypeptide chains which were in the course of being synthesized are completed. Thus ribosomes leave the polysomes at the end of the read-out process but under unfavourable conditions chain initiation is inhibited and polysomes disappear. It is also seen that messenger RNA can exist in stable form in the cytoplasm free of ribosomes. This interpretation predicts that the ribosomes formed under anoxic conditions are free of nascent protein and of messenger fragments. Lin and Key (1967) showed that after incubation in vivo with radioactive leucine, the ribosomes which accumulate during anoxic conditions are not labelled. This is in contrast to the monosomes which are formed by degradation of polysomes by nucleases. One can also predict that if protein synthesis is inhibited by a substance which prevents the read-out process, the polysomes should remain intact under anoxic conditions. Cycloheximide is an inhibitor of this type (Wettstein *et al.* 1964) in contrast to puromycin which acts as an analogue of t-RNA. Lin and Key found that, in fact, in the presence of cycloheximide, polysomes were maintained under anoxic conditions for at least 2 hr and protein synthesis was inhibited. On the other hand, Waters and Dure (1966) found that 16 hr treatment of the cotton seeds with cycloheximide inhibited both protein and RNA synthesis and the polysomes were lost. However, this treatment is very much longer than the experiments on the soya beans and other physiological factors presumably become important.

These experiments show that the presence of messenger RNA in the cytoplasm does not necessarily result in the formation of polysomes; the messenger can exist in the cytoplasm free of ribosomes. There is thus some precedent for the possibility that protein synthesis can be controlled at the level of translation in the cytoplasm by metabolic conditions. It becomes of interest therefore to enquire whether in other systems in which protein synthesis is controlled the mechanism is through the control of messenger RNA synthesis or at translation.

C. THE CONTROL OF POLYSOMES DURING GROWTH

A few changes in the levels of polysomes in tissues under different conditions of growth or metabolism have been observed. These must be regarded as preliminary experiments in the search for suitable systems in which the genetic or translational control of protein synthesis can be studied.

Thus Clark *et al.* (1964) in their experiments with Chinese cabbage leaves noted that there was a diurnal variation in the amount of polysomes obtained. In the dark, polysomes were gradually lost and light stimulated a production of polysomes within 30 min. This required RNA synthesis so that it would appear that at least a part of this control is at the genetic level.

The onset of protein synthesis during the germination of seeds or spores is being investigated in a number of laboratories.

Henney and Stork (1964) found that the ascospores of *Neurospora* did not contain polysomes but that polysomes are formed over several hours during germination. Growing tissue lost its polysomes during periods of starvation.

In the seeds of higher plants there is considerable controversy about whether polysomes exist in the dry seed, at what stage protein synthesis begins and whether RNA synthesis is necessary for this. Waters and Dure (1966) suggested that in cotton seed, polysomes are present throughout and that while RNA synthesis can be detected during the first 16 hr of germination, it was not essential for the maintenance of the polysomes, for protein synthesis or for the immediate process of germination. The RNA synthesis could be inhibited with actinomycin D without inhibiting protein synthesis. At a later stage in germination, however, up to 72 hr, it is probable that RNA synthesis is essential. Barker and Hollinshead (1964) were unable to detect RNA synthesis in the pea seeds and actinomycin D had no effect; this does not necessarily mean that there is no RNA synthesis during the early germination of the pea seed—the results could have been due to the impermeability of the seedling at this stage. Barker and Rieber (1967), however, suggested that polysomes are synthesized during the first 17 hr germination of *Pisum arvense*. They failed to extract polysomes from the dry seed and electron microscopy of fixed, sectioned dry seeds suggested that polysomes do not exist at that stage. They found that the newly formed polysomes at 17 hr can be isolated only if zinc ion is used as a nuclease inhibitor in the grinding medium. After two or more days' germination, polysomes were obtained even without zinc ions. This is more probably due to some change in the nuclease sensitivity of the polysomes, than to a change in the nuclease content of the cells. The yields of polysomes they obtained were small in all cases. R. L. Watts and A. P. Matthias (unpublished results) found that barley seed, germinated for one day, also contained polysomes which were more sensitive to nucleases than those obtained after long periods of germination.

Marcus and Feeley (1964) found that the ability of the isolated ribosomes to incorporate amino acids into protein increased during germination; in this case, and that of Barker and Rieber (1967), the ribosomes from the dry seed could be stimulated to incorporate phenylalanine with added polyuridylic acid, suggesting that they were functional but lacked only messenger RNA. The absolute levels of incorporation obtained by the two groups were very different, however. This, and the possible over-riding effect of poly U over natural messengers, makes the interpretation of their experiments tentative.

There are clearly three simple possibilities for the mechanism of the onset of protein synthesis during germination: either polysomes are present at all times, even in the dry seed, and protein synthesis starts with the general increase of metabolism in the cell; or polysomes are formed using pre-existing messenger RNA in the cytoplasm; or there is a requirement for new messenger and/or other RNA synthesis. I would like to suggest that these alternatives are not mutually exclusive but that more than one mechanism can operate at one time. It is also possible that different mechanisms operate either in different species of plant or even in different batches of the same species depending on physiological differences during ripening and storage of the seed. Perhaps a clue to this view is provided by the experiments of Waters and Dure (1966) in which RNA synthesis could be detected in the germinating seed but could be inhibited without apparently affecting other processes. The extent to which messenger is stored in the cytoplasm, and the form in which it is stored, may thus vary. This would explain the somewhat conflicting preliminary results reported above.

V. Polysomes in Chloroplasts

The above discussion has been about polysomes in the cytoplasm of plant cells with the assumption that the RNA of these polysomes is synthesized in the nucleus. It is clear now that chloroplasts contain another class of ribosomes (Eisenstadt and Brawerman, 1964; Sissakian et al., 1965) and a few recent papers have shown that these also can occur as polysomes. The stability of isolated chloroplast polysomes is probably even lower than those from the cytoplasm and there is likely to be considerable variation between species in this respect as judged by the stability of the RNA (Loening and Ingle, 1967). Clark (1964) found evidence for the existence of chloroplast ribosomes and showed that their presence was dependent on light. Chen and Wildman (1967) have shown that isolated chloroplast polysomes are active in amino acid incorporation *in vitro* into protein. The most exacting density gradient analysis of chloroplast ribosomes, in comparison to cytoplasmic polysomes, has been carried out by Stutz and Noll (1967). They showed clearly for the bean leaf that the chloroplast polysomes are polymers of the 70S ribosome and that the cytoplasmic polysomes are polymers of the 80S ribosomes. The superb gradients of mixtures of the two show unequal spacing and irregular heights of the peaks due to overlap of the narrower chloroplast polysome spacing with the wider cytoplasmic particles. The yields they obtained were small and the time of preparation of the extracts was long (about 4 hr) and no special nuclease inhibitors were used. It is remarkable that the polysomes survived for so long which suggests that the bean (Pinto) is a suitable species for further study.

These experiments and those on the isolated RNA (Loening and Ingle, 1967; Stutz and Noll, 1967) show that the protein synthesizing system of the chloroplasts is distinct from that of the cytoplasm. It should now be possible to investigate the separate control of the two systems and determine, for example, whether the chloroplast ribosomes can use nuclear messenger RNA.

REFERENCES

Barker, G. R. and Hollinshead, J. A. (1964). *Biochem. J.* **93**, 78.
Barker, G. R. and Rieber, M. (1967). *Biochem. J.* **105**, 1195.
Bonnet, H. T. and Newcomb, E. H. (1965). *J. Cell Biol.* **27**, 423.
Breillart, J. and Dickman, S. R. (1966). *J. molec. Biol.* **19**, 227.
Chen, J. L. and Wildman, S. G. (1967). *Science, N.Y.* **155**, 1271.
Clark, M. F. (1964). *Biochim. biophys. Acta* **91**, 671.
Clark, M. F., Matthews, R. E. F. and Ralph, R. K. (1964). *Biochim. biophys. Acta* **91**, 289.
Conconi, F. M., Bank, A. and Marks, P. A. (1966). *J. molec. Biol.* **19**, 525.
Dass, C. M. S. and Bayley, S. T. (1965). *J. Cell Biol.* **25**, 9.

Dunn, D. B. (1965). *2nd Meeting, Fed. Europ. Biochem. Soc. Vienna, Abstracts.*
Echlin, P. (1965). *J. Cell Biol. Cytol.* **24**, 150.
Eisenstadt, J. M. and Brawermen, G. (1964). *J. molec. Biol.* **10**, 392.
Henney, H. R. and Stork, R. (1964). *Proc. natn. Acad. Sci., U.S.A.* **51**, 1050.
Lin, C. Y. and Key, J. L. (1967). *J. molec. Biol.* **26**, 237.
Lin, C. Y., Key, J. L. and Bracker, C. E. (1966). *Pl. Physiol., Lancaster* **41**, 976.
Loening, U. E. and Ingle, J. (1967). *Nature, Lond.*
Marcus, A. and Feeley, J. (1964). *Proc. natn. Acad. Sci., U.S.A.* **51**, 1075.
Marcus, A. and Feeley, J. (1965). *J. biol. Chem.* **240**, 1675.
Phillips, W. D., Rich, A. and Sussman, R. R. (1964). *Biochim. biophys. Acta* **80**, 508.
Rich, A., Warner, J. R. and Goodman, H. M. (1963). *Cold Spring Harb. Symp. quant. Biol.* **28**, 269.
Sabatani, D. D., Tashiro, Y. and Palade, G. (1966). *J. molec. Biol.* **19**, 503.
Schlessinger, D. (1963). *J. molec. Biol.* **7**, 585.
Singer, B. and Fraenkel-Conrat, H. (1961). *Virology* **14**, 59.
Sissakian, N. M., Filipovich, I. I., Svetailo, E. N. and Aliyev, K. A. (1965). *Biochim. biophys. Acta* **95**, 474.
Slayter, H. S., Warner, J. R., Rich, A. and Hall, C. E. (1963). *J. molec. Biol.* **7**, 652.
Spencer, D. and Wildman, S. G. (1964). *Biochemistry, N.Y.* **3**, 954.
Stockse, J. and Vandendriessche, L. (1961). *Archs int. Physiol.* **69**, 545.
Stutz, E. and Noll, H. (1967). *Proc. natn. Acad. Sci., U.S.A.* **57**, 774.
Tester C. F. and Dure, L. S. (1966). *Biochem. biophys. Res. Commun.* **23**, 287.
Vanyushin, B. F. and Dunn, D. B. (1966). *Biochem. J.,* **100**, 62P.
Waters, L. C. and Dure, L. S. (1966). *J. molec. Biol.* **19**, 1.
Watson, M. L. (1959). *J. biochem. biophys. Cytol.* **6**, 147.
Watts, R. L. and Mathias, A. P. (1965). *2nd Meeting Fed. Europ. Biochem. Soc. Vienna, Abstracts, 9.*
Wettstein, F. O., Staehelin, T., and Noll, H. (1963). *Nature, Lond.* **197**, 430.
Wettstein, F. O., Noll, H. and Penman, S. (1964). *Biochim. biophys. Acta* **87**, 525.

CHAPTER 13

Lysosomes

P. B. GAHAN

Department of Biology and Cell Science,
The Woolwich Polytechnic, London, England

I. THE LYSOSOME CONCEPT

During the early studies on the hydrolases uricase and acid phosphatase, some workers (Palade, 1951; Berthet and de Duve, 1951; Schein *et al.*, 1951; Schneider and Hogeboom, 1952) found that if tissues were homogenized and the homogenates were subjected to differential centrifugation, then these enzymes appeared in the mitochondrial fractions. Equally, when similar experiments were performed by other workers (Tsuboi, 1952; Novikoff *et al.*, 1953) these two enzymes appeared to be associated with the microsomal fraction. It was the discrepancy between the various groups of results that enabled de Duve and his collaborators (de Duve *et al.*, 1953; Appelmans *et al.*, 1955) ultimately to define the lysosomes. By adjusting the methods of centrifugation, it was possible to show that the mitochondrial fraction from rat liver consisted of two sub-fractions which were termed heavy and light mitochondria. The light mitochondrial fraction was found to contain the highest concentration of acid phosphatase and yet corresponded to only approximately 4% of the total homogenate nitrogen. Further investigations showed the light mitochondrial fraction to contain also high concentrations of cathepsin, acid ribonuclease, acid deoxyribonuclease and β-glucuronidase. This list has now been extended to include lipase, phospholipase c, α-glucosidase, arylsulphatases A and B, α-manosidase, β-galactosidase and β-N-acetyl-glucosaminidase. When these particles were isolated in 0·25M sucrose, they

appeared from biochemical evidence to be intact since relatively little hydrolase activity could be found in the supernatant fraction. However, if the
particles were treated in a number of ways (Table I) then the enzymes appeared
in the supernatant fraction and were no longer bound to the particles.

TABLE I

Treatments affecting the structure of lysosomes

Sonication	CCl_4
Inadequate osmotic protection	Waring blender
Lecithinase	Freezing and thawing
Detergents	Fat solvents
Protease	Autolysis (acid pH and high temperature)

Towards the end of the initial studies, there emerged some particular
features concerning this group of particles. Firstly, the particular hydrolases
studied appeared to be associated with the same group of particles. Secondly,
these hydrolases all had an optimum activity at about pH 5. When initially
isolated, there was virtually no soluble enzyme activity, a feature termed
"latency". This enzyme activity, however, could be made available by suit-

TABLE II

Morphological variation in lysosomes.

Term	Synonym	Structure
1. Autophagic vacuole	Cytolysome	Single or double membrane; contains morphologically recognizable cytoplasmic components, e.g. mitochondria
2. Cytosome	Primary lysosome "Virgin" lysosome	Almost any cytoplasmic organelle limited by a single unit membrane and of dubious identity
3. Multivesicular body		Single limiting membrane; contains inner vesicles similar morphologically to Golgi vesicles
4. Residual body	Telolysosomes "Post-lysosomes" Dense body	Membrane-lined inclusions probably of undigested residues appearing as whorls, myelin figures, membrane-fragments, etc.

able treatment of the particles and this was termed "breaking the latency". All of the treatments which were used to break the latency were known to affect the binding of lipid to protein and so could be expected to affect lipid-protein membranes. It appeared to de Duve and his colleagues that since all of the enzymes were hydrolytic enzymes, their containment in a sac might afford

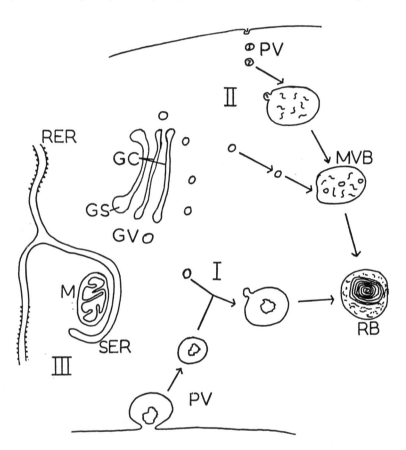

FIG. 1 I. Golgi vesicules (GV) or cytosomes are formed by Golgi saccules (GS) budding off Golgi cisternae (GC). These fuse with pinocytic vacuoles (PV) to form secondary lysosomes and then residual bodies (RB).

II. Alternatively, pinocytic vacuoles may fuse to form a larger vacuole which then incorporates cytosomes to form a multivesicular body (MVB). These can also give rise to residual bodies.

III. Autophagic vacuoles may arise by the enclosure of, for instance, a mitochondrion (M) within the smooth endoplasmic reticulum (SER), the whole then moving away. Enzymes within these vacuoles are thought to arise from the rough endoplasmic reticulum (RER) via the smooth endoplasmic reticulum. (After Novikoff et al., 1964).

some protection to the cell itself and that the release of these enzymes into the cell might cause the death of the cell. He then coined the rather picturesque misnomer "suicide particles" to describe these light mitochondria or lysosomes (de Duve, 1959). Examination of isolated lysosomes in the electron microscope shows that they possess a single limiting membrane (and not the double membrane which is so typical of the cell in general) and have no detailed internal structure (Novikoff *et al.*, 1956). Optical and electron microscope cytochemical investigations on tissue sections of a wide range of animal tissues have also yielded confirmation of the presence of particles containing acid hydrolases (reviewed by Gahan, 1967).

Further studies at the electron microscope level in animal tissues have shown that "lysosomes" are not, in fact, a single series of particles each with a single limiting membrane as was originally thought but that there are a number of sub-cellular particles which contain hydrolase activities (Table II). These details have been unified to give a functional classification of lysosomes and lysosome-like particles in animal cells (Fig. 1).

II. LYSOSOMES IN PLANT CELLS

A. BIOCHEMICAL STUDIES

In the early biochemical studies most plant biochemists attempted to apply directly the methods of analysis used by animal biochemists. The results of such experiments tended to discourage the majority of plant biochemists and a number of workers were unable to obtain any evidence for the presence of lysosomes. Of such experiments, few were published. However, Douglas *et al.* (1963) attempted to isolate lysosomes from tissues of cauliflower and bean. Rat liver was also used to allow assessment of the isolation procedure. They obtained a lysosomal fraction only from the rat liver and were completely unable to find anything resembling lysosome-like particles in the plant material. More encouraging were the results of Harrington and Altschul (1963) who attempted to isolate lysosomes from germinating onions. They obtained a light mitochondrial fraction which contained acid phosphatase activity, this activity being released into the supernatant fraction after treatment of the particles with Triton X-100. Little comment is needed to stress the differences in preparing sub-cellular fractions from plant tissues as opposed to preparing them from animal tissues. In consequence, the early negative biochemical results in attempts to identify lysosomes could have been due to the absence of such particles from plant tissues but could equally have been due to the need to modify quite severely the preparation techniques employed. Matile *et al.* (1965) used 48-hr-old seedlings of *Zea mays* or tobacco seedlings which were ground in the presence of sand in ice cold 7% sucrose buffered at pH 7·1. After filtration of the homogenates through cheese cloth, they were centrifuged to remove sand, cell debris, nuclei and starch and the resulting cell-free extract was layered onto a linear density gradient ranging from 20% to 50% sucrose. The preparations were then centrifuged at 40,000 rev/min for $2\frac{1}{2}$ hr (*Zea mays*) or $4\frac{1}{2}$ hr (tobacco) and the contents of the tubes were collected in either 15 or 19 fractions, respectively. The fractions were analysed for acid protease, acid phosphatase, esterase and acid ribonuclease. In fraction 6 of the corn seedlings there were peaks of acid protease and esterase activity and part of the acid phosphatase activity. The relative density of the particles in this fraction was calculated to be $1\cdot138$ g cm^{-3} and they were comparatively rich in protein. There was a similar culmination of peaks of acid hydrolase activities in fraction 10 of the tobacco, corresponding to particulate material and appearing to be rich in protein. A second set of peaks of hydrolase activity for each of the seedlings occurred at about fraction 9 for corn and fraction 13 for tobacco. The density of the second peak for corn corresponded to approximately $1\cdot105$ g cm^{-3}. Again the second bands were also found to be rich in protein. In addition to the demonstration of banding of activities corresponding to certain groups of particles, it was also clear that portions of the total hydrolase activities were not attached to particles and upon centrifugation these enzymes remained among the soluble proteins of the cell-free extracts. Matile and his associates were not able to decide from these results whether the free enzyme molecules were normally free in the cell or whether they represented a fraction of the hydrolases which were originally bound to particles which had been somewhat damaged during the preparation procedure, especially since the relative amounts of free and particulate hydrolases varied considerably from one preparation to another. Semadeni (1967) has studied similar fractions and has found that acid hydrolases which include protease, phosphatase, non-specific esterase, ribonuclease, arylsulphatases A and B and amylase are also sedimentable from cell-free extracts of corn seedlings. After differential centrifugation of the extracts, the sedimentable hydrolysates recovered were mainly in the mitochondrial and microsomal fractions. It could be demonstrated that protease, phosphatase, ribonuclease and esterase of the mitochondrial fractions were contained in membrane-bound particles and isopicnic centrifugation of cell-free extracts in sucrose gradients revealed the presence of three particulate fractions carrying hydrolases. The heaviest of these had a relative density of $1\cdot138$ g cm^{-3} and contained the acid protease, acid phosphatase, acid ribonuclease and esterases. A lighter fraction with a relative density of $1\cdot105$ g cm^{-3} contained the same acid hydrolases. The specifically lightest cell fraction with a density of the order of $1\cdot070$ g cm^{-3} contained the acid hydrolases glucose-6-phosphatase, arylsulphatase C and small amounts of α- and β-amylase activities. This latter fraction also contained the NADH-diaphorase activity. β-Glucuronidase, phospholipase C, lipase and arylsulphatases A and B, all of which are typical animal lysosomal enzymes, were completely absent from the cell-free extracts of corn seedlings. Matile (1966) also claims to have isolated vacuoles from the rootlets of corn seedlings, the vacuoles having densities higher than $1 \cdot 029$ g cm^{-3} and containing protease, acid ribonuclease, acid deoxyribonuclease, acid phosphatase and two different nonspecific esterases. The vacuoles from higher plant cells have been equated with organelles in which the processes of intracellular digestion can take place; in other words, they have been equated with the lysosomes of animal cells.

B. CYTOCHEMICAL STUDIES

Owing to the lack of positive biochemical data, some workers applied a cytochemical approach to assess if lysosomes were present in plant tissues. Jensen (1956) reported that acid phosphatase activity in root-tip cells was associated with particulate structures in the cytoplasm which he identified as mitochondria. These observations were later confirmed by Avers (1961) who found acid phosphatase activity at particulate sites in the root tips of *Phleum pratense* and *Panicum virginatum*.

Walek-Czernecka (1962) studied onion scale epidermal cells and showed that acid phosphatase and nonspecific esterase activities were associated with cytoplasmic particles. She further demonstrated (1965) that aryl-sulphatase, lipase, β-glucuronidase, β-galactosidase and acid deoxyribo-nuclease were also present at particulate sites in the cells of the onion scale epidermis.

Gorska-Brylass (1965) performed a similar series of studies but this time on pollen grains and pollen tubes of some 34 plant species and found acid phosphatase, β-glucuronidase, acid deoxyribonuclease and nonspecific esterase activities to be localized at particulate sites.

Gahan (1965) studied lysosome-like particles in plant tissues by attempting firstly to define the localization of the acid hydrolases in the cell and secondly to determine if the sites of localization responded in a manner expected of lysosomes as considered by the definition of the animal lysosomes. By using frozen sections of roots of *Vicia faba*, it was possible to prepare serial sections of tissue which appeared to be preserved in a manner approaching that of living tissue (Gahan *et al.*, 1967). Incubation of such cells for acid phosphatase activity using β-glycerophosphate as substrate showed that in the root meristem cells the hydrolase activity first appeared after 20 min of incubation and, furthermore, was at particulate sites in the cytoplasm (Gahan, 1965).

In order to test that the delay in observing a reaction was due to a true "latency" of the particles and not to the need to incubate the sections long enough to obtain a sufficient end-product of the enzyme reaction to be seen

N

with the light microscope, sections were pre-incubated in a pH 5 buffer alone for 10 min and then were transferred to the test medium. It was found that only 10 min of incubation was required in the test medium to obtain a reaction normally seen after the full 20 min incubation. As a further test of latency, sections were treated by freezing-and-thawing six times prior to incubation in the full reaction medium when it was found that only 2 min of incubation was required to demonstrate the presence of the particulate sites of activity which were normally seen after only 20 min of incubation in the untreated frozen sections. It would appear from these data that particles termed "lysosomes" by the animal biochemists could be demonstrated cytochemically. However, it was also required that more than one acid hydrolase should be present at these particulate sites if the fuller meaning of the term lysosome were to be possibly applied to plant cells. It was not possible to demonstrate arylsulphatase and β-glucuronidase in root cells of *V. faba* although β-glucuronidase was demonstrable in shoots of germinating pea seeds (P. B. Gahan and J. McLean, unpublished results). Esterase activity was demonstrable in roots of *V. faba* using either 5-bromo-indoxyl acetate (Holt, 1958) or naphthol AS D acetate (Burstone, 1962) as substrate. Moreover, it was shown (P. B. Gahan and J. McLean, unpublished results) that when acid phosphatase and esterase activities were present in the same cell, then these two hydrolases could be associated with the same particle (Fig. 2A, B, C).

If one observes the general distribution of acid hydrolases throughout a range of plant tissues at the light microscope level then, in addition to these sub-cellular particles or particulate sites, one can also observe that, when using β-glycerophosphate as substrate, acid phosphatase activity appears also in association with the chloroplasts and naphthol AS phosphatase with the plasmodesmata (J. McLean and P. B. Gahan, unpublished results). Furthermore, esterase activity in certain regions of the root-cap cells can be clearly seen in and between the cell walls (J. McLean and P. B. Gahan, unpublished results).

Electron microscope cytochemical studies have shown further that acid glycerophosphatase activity is present in the Golgi cisternae and that aryl-

---

Fig. 2 Frozen, longitudinal section through the stele of root of *V. faba*.
A. Naphthol AS phosphatase activity (blue) at particulate sites in the cells. Incubation for 30 min at 37°C in 0·05M-acetate buffer pH 5 containing naphthol AS Bl phosphate as substrate and Fast Dark Blue R as coupling agent.
B. Napthol AS esterase activity (red) at particulate sites in the cells. Incubation for 5 min at 37°C in 0·05M-acetate buffer pH 5 containing naphthol AS D acetate as substrate and Fast Red Violet LB as coupling agent.
C. Incubation for 5 min for esterase activity followed by 30 min incubation for phosphatase activity. The deposition of both red and blue end-product at the same site causes particles to appear purple, indicating the presence of the two enzymes at the same site. A, B and C × 320 (on diapositives).

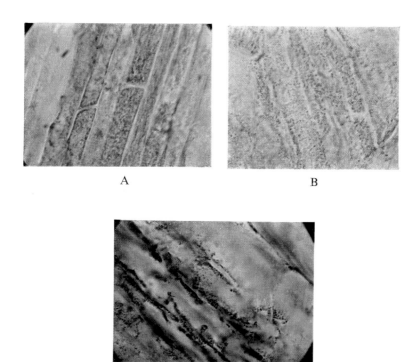

A

B

C

Fig. 2

Facing p. 234.

sulphatase activity, as demonstrated with *p*-nitro-catechol sulphate, is present in the endoplasmic reticulum (Poux, 1967). Thus, while lysosome-like particles appear to be present from optical microscope studies, all localized reactions do not appear to resolve themselves as sub-cellular particles when viewed in the electron microscope.

III. LYSOSOMES AND SPHEROSOMES

In the early cytochemical studies of hydrolase activities in plant cells, Walek-Czernecka (1965) and Gorska-Brylass (1965) both attempted to determine the type of particle with which the hydrolase activity was associated, either by means of phase-contrast observation or by staining the particles with intra-vital dyes. The particles were readily differentiated from proplastids which did not appear black when observed with phase-contrast and were also readily distinguished from filamentous mitochondria, although some difficulty apparently was found in distinguishing between spherical mitochondria and these particles. However, if the preparations were stained with Janus green then the mitochondria took up the colour and appeared blue-green while the hydrolase-containing particles remained colourless. Similar studies by J. McLean and P. B. Gahan (unpublished results) have shown that either in tissue sections or in cell-cultures from crown gall tumours it was possible to obtain a Janus green reaction at mitochondrial sites and an esterase activity associated with a second group of highly refractile particles in the same cell.

Observations on particles of diameter $0.3–0.8\mu$ in pollen tubes showed that they had peculiar optical properties and somewhat variable shapes; they appeared to be present as ". . . swollen rings, or sickles, or crescents, or oglomerated nubs inside a delicate capsule" whereby the density varied (Gorska-Brylass, 1965). The particles were also distinguished from simple fat droplets by means of cytochemical reactions. Moreover, in the growing pollen tubes, the fat droplets tended to coalesce at frequent intervals to form larger drops while the hydrolase-containing particles tended to remain apart.

The general characteristics of these hydrolase-containing particles, as described by Walek-Czernecka (1962), Olszewska *et al.* (1965) and Gorska-Brylass (1965), corresponded closely to the previously recorded description of the spherosomes in plant cells (Dangeard, 1919; Sorokin and Sorokin, 1966). Moreover, the two hydrolase-containing fractions from corn seedlings isolated by Semadeni (1966) also gave responses characteristic of spherosomes when studied with fluorochromes.

Spherosomes have been characterized in plant cells by electron microscope studies (Frey-Wyssling *et al.*, 1963; Mühlethaler, 1955; Perner, 1957; Hohl, 1960; Paleg and Hyde, 1964; Sorokin and Sorokin, 1966). Electron microscope

observations on the hydrolase-containing particles isolated from corn seedlings (as well as on the intact seeds and seedlings) by Matile *et al.* (1965)
showed the particles to correspond to spherosomes which, in general, appear
as an electron-dense stroma surrounded by a single membrane.

Very little is known of the chemical composition of spherosomes due to
the difficulties encountered in isolating them from plant tissues. Cytochemical
methods have revealed them to react freely with lipid stains (Drawert and
Mix, 1962; Ziegler, 1953) as well as with phospholipid indicators (Sorokin
and Sorokin, 1966) and with specific reagents for proteins (Perner, 1952;
Jarosch, 1961). From the nature of the enzyme cytochemical studies it is
possible that at least part of this protein is enzymic. Sorokin and
Sorokin (1966) were unable to identify carbohydrate material by the PAS
reaction.

IV. FORMATION AND FUNCTION OF SPHEROSOMES

Electron microscope studies of spherosomes do not show such a wide range
of particles containing hydrolases as are found in animal cells and it would
be difficult initially to form an equivalent intra-cellular digestion pathway to
that occurring in animal cells. Frey-Wyssling *et al.* (1963) have suggested
that the spherosomes form by budding from the endoplasmic reticulum,
much in the same way as some workers have considered for primary lysosomes (Brandes, 1965). However, there is no clear-cut evidence for the occurrence of pinocytosis within cells of the intact plant organ and, until contrary
evidence is produced, it is difficult to envisage an identical intra-cellular
digestive system operating in plant cells.

Biochemical and cytochemical studies clearly indicate the formation of
lipid droplets within spherosomes and it appears that on ageing, spherosomes
become transformed into lipid droplets (Dangeard, 1919; Frey-Wyssling
et al., 1963). What is not evident is whether the contents of the original
spherosome are transformed into lipids or whether lipid synthesized elsewhere is accumulated within the spherosomes or whether the spherosomes
are themselves the sites of lipid synthesis. It is known from biochemical
studies that fatty acid synthesis can occur in mitochondrial fractions of plant
tissues (reviewed by Mead, 1963). Thus, the third suggestion seems initially
the most interesting especially since Semadeni (1966) was also able to demonstrate the incorporation of ^{3}H-acetate into lipids of isolated spherosomes
from which he concluded that lipid synthesizing enzymes were present on
the spherosomes.

This function alone, however, does not completely account for the presence
of acid hydrolases in spherosomes and further studies are required to elucidate
this point.

V. CONCLUSIONS

From the foregoing studies, it would appear that there are gross differences between the hydrolase-containing particles in plant and animal cells. Further differences can be seen in a study of the mitotic cycle. Robbins and Marcus (1963), Allison (1965) and Maggi (1966) have presented evidence that during mitosis in animal cells, there is an increased permeability of the lysosomal membrane. Similar studies on plant cells have shown that there is no such behaviour in mitotic cells from root and shoot meristems of *V. faba* or shoot meristems of *Solanum lycopersicum* (P. B. Gahan and J. McLean, unpublished results). The hydrolase-containing particles behave similarly in both mitotic and interphase cells. In mitotic cells in differentiation regions, however, there is a much higher esterase activity which appears to be correlated to differentiation rather than with division.

Since there are such marked differences between the hydrolase-containing particles of plant and animal cells, it would seem that the term "lysosome" should be reserved for the particles present in animal cells and "spherosome" for the particles present in plant cells.

ACKNOWLEDGEMENTS

Financial assistance by the Science Research Council for support of some of the work described in this article is gratefully acknowledged.

REFERENCES

Allison, A. C. (1965). *Nature, Lond.* **205**, 141.
Appelmans, F., Wattiaux, R. and de Duve, C. (1955). *Biochem. J.* **59**, 438.
Avers, C. J. (1961). *Am. J. Bot.* **49**, 996.
Berthet, J. and de Duve, C. (1951). *Biochem. J.* **50**, 174.
Brandes, D. (1965). *J. Ultrastruct. Res.* **12**, 63.
Burstone, M. S. (1962). "Enzyme Histochemistry and its Application in the Study of Neoplasms". Academic Press, New York.
Dangeard, P. A. (1919). *C. r. hebd Séanc. Acad. Sci., Paris* **169**, 1005.
de Duve, C. (1959). Subcellular Particles Symposium, Woods Hole, Mass. (1958). (T. Hayashi, ed.), p. 23.
de Duve, C., Gianetto, R., Appelmans, F. and Wattiaux, R. (1953). *Nature, Lond.* **172**, 1143.
Douglas, H. W., Laycock, M. V. and Boulter, D. (1963). *J. expl Bot.* **14**, 198.
Drawert, H. and Mix, M. (1962). *Ber. dt. bot. Ges.* **75**, 128.
Frey-Wyssling, A., Grieshaber, E. and Mühlethaler, K. (1963). *J. Ultrastruct. Res.* **8**, 506.
Gahan, P. B. (1965). *J. expl Bot.* **16**, 350.
Gahan, P. B. (1967). *Int. Rev. Cytol* **21**, 1.
Gahan, P. B., McLean, J., Kalina, M. and Sharma, W. (1967). *J. expl Bot.* **18**, 151.
Gorska-Brylass, A. (1965). *Acta. Soc. Bot. Pol.* **34**, 589.

Harrington, J. F. and Altschul, A. M. (1963). *Fedn Proc. Fedn Am. Socs exp. Biol.* **22**, 475.

Hohl, H. R. (1960). *Ber. schweiz. bot. Ges.* **70**, 395.

Holt, S. J. (1958). *In* "General Cytochemical Methods". (J. F. Danielli, ed.), Vol. 1, p. 375. Academic Press, New York.

Jarosch, R. (1961). *Protoplasma* **53**, 34.

Jensen, W. A. (1956). *Am. J. Bot.* **43**, 50.

Maggi, V. (1966). *J. R. microsc. Soc.* **85**, 291.

Matile, Ph. (1966). *Z. Naturf.* **21**, 871.

Matile, Ph., Balz, J. P., Semadeni, E. G. and Jost, M. (1965). *Z. Naturf.* **20**, 693.

Mead, J. F. (1963). *A. Rev. Biochem.* **32**, 241.

Mülethaler, K. (1955). *Protoplasma* **45**, 264.

Novikoff, A. B., Beaufay, H. and de Duve, C. (1956). *J. biophys. biochem. Cytol.* **2**, Suppl. 179.

Novikoff, A. B., Essner, E. and Quintana, N. (1964). *Fedn Proc. Fedn Am. Socs exp. Biol.* **23**, 1010.

Olszewska, M. J., Walek-Czernecka, A., Kwiatkowska, M. and Gabara, B. (1965). *Acta Soc. Bot. Pol.* **34**, 399.

Palade, G. E. (1951). *Archs Biochem. Biophys.* **30**, 144.

Paleg, L. and Hyde, B. (1964). *Physiologia Pl.* **39**, 673.

Perner, E. S. (1952). *Biol. Zbl.* **71**, 43.

Perner, E. S. (1957). *Naturw. Rdsch., Braunschw.* **1**, 6.

Poux, N. (1967). *J. Histochem. Cytochem.* **14**, 932.

Robbins, E. and Marcus, P. I. (1963). *J. Cell Biol.* **18**, 237.

Schein, A. H., Podber, E. and Novikoff, A. B. (1951). *J. biol. Chem.* **190**, 331.

Schneider, W. C. and Hogeboom, G. H. (1952). *J. biol. Chem.* **195**, 161.

Semadeni, E. G. (1967). *Planta* **72**, 91.

Sorokin, H. P. and Sorokin, S. (1966). *Protoplasma* **62**, 216.

Tsuboi, K. K. (1952). *Biochim. biophys. Acta* **8**, 173.

Walek-Czernecka, A. (1962). *Acta Soc. Bot. Pol.* **32**, 405.

Walek-Czernecka, A. (1965). *Acta Soc. Bot. Pol.* **43**, 573.

Ziegler, H. (1953). *Z. Naturf.* **86**, 662.

Author Index

The numbers in italics refer to the pages on which the references are listed in full.

Subject Index

A

Acer pseudoplatanus, 53
Acetabularia sp, 30, 155, 156–7, 158, 208
Acetabularia mediterranea, 213
Acetate, 104, 111, 113
Acetoacetyl ACP, 106
Acetoacetyl-CoA, 109
Acetyl ACP, 106
Acetyl-CoA, 101, 103, 104, 105, 106, 107, 109, 111, 116, 121, 171
β-N-Acetylglucosaminidase, 228
Acetyl-S-ACP, 171
Aconitase condensing enzyme, 68
Aconitate, 103
cis-Aconitate, 111
Acridines, 89, 91–2
Acriflavin, 91, 94
Actinomycin, 94, 208, 213, 222, 223, 224, 225
Acyl carrier protein (ACP), 106, 107, 108, 175
lipids, 163–78
Adenosine, 221
diphosphate, ADP, 65, 111, 124, 125, 126, 129
monophosphate, AMP, 111, 126
triphosphate, ATP, 11, 67, 76, 84, 101, 110, 111, 114, 119, 120, 122, 124–35, 151, 155, 171, 172
Adenylate kinase, 67
ADPG-starch transglucosylase, 11
L-Alanine, 20, 108, 203
Alcohol dehydrogenase, 67
Aldolase, 67
Algae, 80, 140, 155, 156, 163, 168, 169, 206
blue-green, 164, 165, 169, 174, 175
chloroplasts, 139, 141
green, 175
marine, 165
Allium cepa, 51 (*see also* Onion)

Amino acids metabolism, 108–9, 112
Amoeba, 82
Amphibia, 35
Amphibian egg, 17, 21
Amylase, 232
Anaerobiosis, 90, 222
Angiosperms, 48, 187
Annulus, 17
Anthocerotales, 140
Antibiotics, 9, 10
Apple, 62, 64, 104, 106
mitochondria, 101, 103, 105, 106, 112–16
tissue, 57
Arabinan, 190
Arabinose, 189
Arachidonic acid, 165
Arachis hypogaea, 64, 66 (*see also* Peanut)
Arginine, 20, 26, 108
Argininosuccinic acid, 108
Aroids, floral parts, 63, 74
Arsenate, 125
Arum maculatum, 49, 62, 64, 66, 70, 71, 73, 75
Aryl sulphatase, 228, 232, 233, 234, 235
Ascorbate-tetramethyl phenylene-diamine system, 131
Ascorbic acid, 57, 58, 63
oxidase, 11, 67, 73, 74
Ascospores, 91
Aspartate, 113, 115, 116
Aspartic acid, 108, 110
Aspidistra, 143
ATPase, 66, 127, 129, 202
Atractyloside, 126
Autoradiography, 81
Auxin, 196
Avena sativa, 139
Avocado, 62, 65, 70, 107, 115, 116
Azide, 73

253